THE ROCKS REMAIN

'Beautifully written, full of wit and charm. . . . A marvellous piece of work.' Gerald Durrell

'There are good things besides the otters. But the otters are the real business, that's where the quality lies.' *Sunday Times*

'Vivid and completely absorbing.' *Yorkshire Post*

'The otters are described in the loving detail that only a man who understood them so well could achieve and which only a writer of Mr Maxwell's eminence could convey. . . . Will certainly be as great a success as its predecessor.' *Sphere*

'Another hard-to-put-down book.' *Woman's Journal*

'Moving and humane, comic and tragic.' *Spectator*

THE ROCKS REMAIN

Ring of Bright Water, one of the most famous books to have been published since the war, described the pioneering days at Gavin Maxwell's lonely cottage on the West Highland seaboard with the otters Mijbil and Edal. *The Rocks Remain*, with the arrival of new otters – Teko, Mossy, Monday and others – with the installation of electricity at Camusfeàrna, with extensions to the buildings and additions to the transport facilities, with the acquisition of the motor vessel *Polar Star*, with the sometimes unwelcome spotlight of publicity on the author's private life, is a book written from a deeper and wider experience.

The story of the succeeding years, though of fresh delights, is not without episodes of danger and even disaster. Both Edal and Teko, with all their endearing qualities, cannot always be trusted. The wreck of the *Polar Star* in which the author all but lost his life, an explosion in the kitchen at Camusfeàrna, an invasion of rats, the total and spectacular destruction in Majorca of the author's new Mercedes, are transmuted from chapters of calamity to chapters of breath-taking suspense and high comedy. The scenes in North Africa, mysterious, strange, sometimes farcical, throw into vivid focus the life at Camusfeàrna to which the author always returns as though to spring water from the desert.

The Rocks Remain is a further superbly-written revelation of a personality, a place and a way of life that have captured the imagination of readers the world over.

By the same author in PAN Books

RING OF BRIGHT WATER
LORDS OF THE ATLAS
RAVEN SEEK THY BROTHER

THE ROCKS REMAIN

GAVIN MAXWELL

UNABRIDGED

PAN BOOKS LTD : LONDON

First published 1963 by Longmans Green & Co. Ltd.
This edition published 1966 by Pan Books Ltd.,
33 Tothill Street, London, S.W.1

ISBN 0 330 21025 5

2rd Printing 1968
3rd Printing 1970

Printed in Great Britain by
Cox & Wyman Ltd, London,
Reading and Fakenham

Contents

Acknowledgements

WE ARE GRATEFUL to the following for permission to include copyright material:

John Calder Ltd for an extract from *The Naked Lunch* by William S. Burroughs; the *New Statesman* for the poem 'The Scapegoat' by Gavin Maxwell, an earlier version of which appeared in the issue of 28 June 1952; Oxford University Press, Bombay, for an extract from *Twin Rivers* by Seton Lloyd, and Putnam & Co. Ltd for 'The Circulation of Light' from *The Smell of Burning* by Thomas Blackburn.

The following photographs were taken by James Millar Watt: the indoor picture, *Edal; Teko and Dirk; Monday on the day she arrived; Monday's experiments in water; Mossy and Monday;* the beach scene facing page 161.

We are grateful to Garage Auto-Freno, Palma, for permission to reproduce the photograph of the damaged Mercedes.

All other photographs were taken by the author.

ILLUSTRATIONS
IN PHOTOGRAVURE

*This book is for
those who Remain my Rocks*

1

Portrait of an Earthquake

TO THE MOST turbulent of lives come unforeseen periods of calm and tranquillity, as though some river running perpetually over rapids broadened suddenly into a deep, still pool of silence. Such a season of fair weather, an idyll belonging more properly to childhood or to old age, I described in *Ring of Bright Water*, the story of the West Highland cottage that I have called Camusfeàrna and of the otters that shared it with me. The time that this narrative covered represented perhaps the most placid period of my adult life; but without knowing it I had drifted nearer and nearer to the tail of the pool (for, I think, I had been in no backwater but in one of the main stream's many and various reaches), nearer to the rock lip where the water falls in cascade and spume before rushing on towards the sea. I was caught again in the full strength of a shallower current, whirled as a *bateau ivre* back into its familiar confusion, striking greater and lesser boulders as I had done before, and more closely aware of the other human beings who were swept along with me.

Thus this book, though a true sequel to its precursor, will have little of its flavour; it is the partial story of the succeeding years, their difficulties, disasters and delights; and if disaster either so minor as to be comic or so major as to appear tragic seems to predominate, it is, like the rocks that remain, in the eye of the beholder.

The title represents not so much the residuum as the

remembered catalyst of a long preoccupation. I first heard the song during the early years of the war, and then it was the nostalgia of the words and tune that made me consciously remember them. The words were clumsy – almost, in places, McGonagall – and I remember trying to rewrite them, trying to transmute their clichés, so that now I am uncertain whether the first verse, from which I have taken my title, is the original old Scottish version or a relic of some attempt of mine at improvement.

> Age on age the rocks remain,
> And the tides return again;
> Only we poor mourners, sinners,
> Weavers, toilers, fishers, spinners,
> Pass away like visions vain.

In either case it was, as I have said, the superficial appeal of the nostalgic theme that engrossed me then, a theme recurrent in so much northern folksong. Later, I became engrossed with the image of the rock not as a single symbol of permanence but in the dual role of saviour and destroyer; the rock, in whose lee one ship may shelter from storm, will destroy another that lies to windward; the reef that forms a harbour is in itself the greatest possible peril until it has been successfully negotiated. This theme I tried to express in several poems – or rather one poem in several parts – published in the *New Statesman* not long after the war; none of them is worthy of repetition, but I quote the concluding verses with all their imperfections as at least clarifying the title of this book.

> Whatever arm can stem the sea
> Can claw the shrinking planks apart,
> The rocks that pierce the carvelled tree
> Are strong to harbour and to hurt,
> O, shield and spear unite in me.
> One with the island now my hull

Is clenched within the creviced rock;
One with the sea when tide's at full
She holds the power of shield and shock,
The sheltering arm, the hidden skull.

I had never seen this theme developed in any medium until recently I saw, and acquired, a painting by Michael Ayrton, in which sombre forms possessing the quintessential qualities both of boat and of rock stood as the foreground to a ferocious yet strangely remote sea. This painting now hangs in my sitting-room at Camusfeàrna, and is the subject of much vexed speculation by the average visitor who wants to know whether these are in fact 'meant' to be rocks or boats, and exactly where the sealine is 'supposed' to join the sky.

In the same way there will no doubt be those who expected from this book a second *Ring of Bright Water* and who will want to know exactly where events abroad are 'supposed' to join those at Camusfeàrna, and whether certain incidents are 'meant' to be disastrous or farcical. Like the demarcation line between sea and sky, and like the application of realism to the boat-rocks on the shore, these questions have no relevance to my theme.

I finished the manuscript of *Ring of Bright Water* at Camusfeàrna on 16 October 1959. I was then, and at the time of writing still am, engaged upon lengthy but not always leisurely research into certain aspects of twentieth-century Moroccan history, and at about eleven-thirty on the evening of March 1 the following year I was writing in a small and exceedingly shabby room in the *medina*, or old Arab town, of Marrakesh. It was the eve of Independence Day. It was also the end of the second day of Ramadan, the annual Muslim month of fast during the daylight hours, and the near-by Place Djemma El Fna was loud with drums, tambourines, pipes, and the brass-bells of water-sellers – the whole babel of a people for whom, during this season, the night becomes the only time of activity. It was a warm, breathless night, and the air was heavy with the smell of spices and cooking.

The single electric light bulb dangling from the high ceiling gave a light inadequate for writing, and I was bent low over the table. 'Hadj Abdullah ou Bihi, grand caid of the Haha', I wrote carefully, 'was sent for to the Sultan's palace, where he was given the choice of a cup of poisoned tea or starvation to death while publicly exhibited in an iron ...' The word I was writing trailed off into a meaningless hieroglyphic. It seemed as though someone had shaken my chair violently from behind; automatically I looked over my shoulder, and as I did so a long shudder shook the room and the tiles of the floor seemed to slope towards me. My pen and some small change clattered down from the table. The house was of the flimsy construction common to most of the *medina*, and my first thought was that someone was moving heavy furniture in a contiguous part of the building. A second later the shudder was repeated, the same sensation of vibration and tilting as when a ship's screws are lifted clear of the water as she pitches in a heavy sea. The explanation of furniture moving seemed inadequate; after a few moments I began to believe that I had been the victim of an hallucination, and then as there was no repetition I thought no more of it.

The following morning I paid one of my very rare visits to the Mamounia Hotel, known to the British public largely through the patronage of Sir Winston Churchill. I went there to meet some English acquaintances who were holidaying in Morocco and who did not share my preference for the *medina*. The conversation was desultory when, after a few minutes, we were joined by a fellow hotel guest of theirs, a well-groomed and monosyllabic colonel whose manner suggested that he found both thought and speech to be irksome.

'Worried about John,' he said at length. 'Went to Agadir – there's been an earthquake there.'

'Surely you must mean Dakar, dear?' said a vague feminine voice. 'Agadir's quite near here, you know.'

'What would John be doing in Dakar?' asked the colonel testily. 'He went to Agadir and there's been an earthquake there. Worried, don't you know.'

'Oh, I expect he's all right,' said the female voice. 'It can't have been much, can it?' The ice tinkled in glasses that held long, soothing drinks; silent servants in extravagant Moorish liveries passed to and fro over rich carpets; outside in the sunny tropical garden exotic birds fluted and trilled as they flitted between fruit-laden trees.

Agadir N Irir (usually abbreviated to Agadir, which means only fortress or escarpment, of which there are many in Morocco) had become in a few years the great tourist resort of Southern Morocco; from an insignificant Moorish fishing village there had shot up, during the later years of the French occupation that ended in 1956, an Atlantic riviera of five-star hotels and international bars that drew a certain type of tourist from all over the world. The speed of this development had brought an enormous increase in Moorish and European population, from some five thousand odd in 1936 to nearly 50,000 in 1953. Although the figure was officially no more than 35,000 by 1960, this was probably a considerable underestimate.

An hour after the colonel's laconic (and wholly justified) preoccupation with the fate of John, the wildest rumours were circulating in the streets of Marrakesh, temporarily silenced only by the first official announcements that seemed, even in their pathetic underestimate, to be those of a major disaster. Eight hundred killed and many wounded; the great luxury Hotel Saada gone down like a card castle, burying its full complement of expensive holidaymakers who would have spoken, I thought to myself, as had my acquaintances at the Mamounia.

The truth came very slowly. The next morning the newspapers reported that it was now feared that the dead might number 1,200 and the wounded 2,000; by the following day the speculative figures had risen to 3,000 and 2,500 respectively. That evening I met a friend, a resident French photographer, who had lived for twenty-five years in Marrakesh and who had spent the day in Agadir. He was exhausted, explosive, and seemingly on the edge of nervous collapse. His hands trembled.

'*Je m'excuse,*' he said, '*mais que voulez-vous?* I am suffering from shock – I who in the war was blown up by a mine and am no stranger to death and the dead. This is worse than war – Agadir is a place of horror, you understand? – horror. The press is mad, mad, I tell you! Three thousand dead? – they mock us! *Selon moi* there cannot be less than eight thousand, and that is a minimum. Whole quarters in which not one soul can have lived – just dust – dust that smells of death, so that you must wear a mask or be sick, or both. The limbs of the dead stick up out of the ground as if they were waving to you. It is a place of horror, I tell you, horror.'

Slowly, day by day, the published figures mounted, until they reached and finally passed his estimate; 10,000 dead and 5,000 wounded. The temperature rose to abnormal heights for the season of the year, reading 104 degrees in the shade at Agadir and 97 degrees at Marrakesh. The rapid putrescence of 10,000 corpses made the work of the rescue teams intolerable; it was Ramadan, and while special dispensation was given to the workers by King Mohammed V in his role of Imam or spiritual leader, many refused to accept it, and carried on their dreadful work without food or water. In Marrakesh the strain of daylight fasting that includes all liquid stretched the nerves of a population many of whom had relations in Agadir, and as the true facts filtered through there were scenes of hysterical grief in every street of the town. Loud-speaking cars toured hour by hour, giving names of known survivors, but the information was slender, because a vast number of Gadiri (people of Agadir) had taken refuge in the plains surrounding the town and were camping under the *argan* trees with what possessions they had been able to salvage in their flight. The government put out an appeal for all refugees to report their names to the nearest authority, cheikh, caid, pasha, or governor; but among this new race of nomads there would be many whom the message would not reach for weeks or even months. Sometimes, too, the loudspeakers would announce that no further survivors might be expected from this or that quarter of the town; the car would pass on leaving scattered figures prostrate and weeping in the dust.

Tales of strange portents preceding the earthquake came from many sources. A few minutes before the first tremors all the dogs of the town had begun to howl in unison, cats wailed and prowled, mules and donkeys struggled with their tethers. An English couple at the cinema had a premonition of some cataclysm and left the building for the beach, where, as the first tremors shook the ground beneath them, they saw a column of fire shoot up out of the sea. A man returning from a café saw a great flight of ravens alight for a moment upon the houses and then take off in commotion and calling.

The survivors remembered the noise more than the movement of the ground; the roar of toppling buildings and the screams of human beings who fell with them. All lighting was extinguished with the first quake, and those who were able to struggle free and to search among rubble and ruin for their children worked in the confusion of total darkness and the noise of all hell. The first rescuers on the scene, the

French Marines, brought only pinpoints of light, so that for long sound predominated over sight.

It is a point of enormous significance that the vast majority of those who survived the first two seismic tremors believed unquestioningly that the disaster must be universal; it was not to them the end of Agadir but the end of the world, or even of the universe. The darkness and the din, the pain, the pressure of the fallen stone were illimitable; outside that world there could not exist elsewhere any other that they had known before. Thus the historians of biblical times recorded that strictly local flooding of the Tigris–Euphrates basin as the Great Flood, world-wide because it went beyond the limit of their physical vision; and wove round Noah a myth as the saviour of every animal species, unknowing that the continuation of all life, animal and human, went on un-hindered and unhelped, helpless and hopeful, outside the puddle of his flood.

There is lapidary evidence for the historical truth of what in biblical civilization came to be known as The Flood; even its date can be estimated with some accuracy at 3000 BC. Between the Hebrew and the Sumerian versions of this story there are only minor divergencies, and if it is a surprise to realize that there was more than one ark afloat, it must be remembered that greater or lesser floods were certainly common in Mesopotamia, and some technique for saving the lives and livestock of a family or tribe had probably been standardized, as had also the technique of releasing birds to search for land. 'The' Flood was, plainly, the greatest that had been known, and thus its chroniclers crammed the whole world into the narrow confines of the lowlands lying to the north-west of the Persian Gulf.

Seton Lloyd in his *Twin Rivers* describes the discovery, in the mid-nineteenth century, of 25,073 inscribed clay tablets in the palaces of King Sennacherib and King Ashur-bani-pal at Nineveh, the better part of two royal libraries, which when deciphered some fifteen years later at the British Museum, yielded the Chaldean account of the flood.

The account of the flood which emerged from all this was every bit as dramatic as the Biblical version. It concerned a patriarch called Utu-nipishtim, whose home was at Shuruppak on the Euphrates. Like Noah, he was approached by the god Ea, who told him of the impending doom of the earth and commanded him to build a boat, giving some details about its size and construction. This done, he complied with Ea's further wish that he should load it with 'all that he possessed and all the seed of life'. Utu-nipishtim continues the story: 'I made to go up into the ship and my family and kinsfolk, the cattle of the field, the beasts of the field, all handicraftsmen, I made them go up into it.' As the appointed time of the deluge drew near, he watched the aspect of the approaching storm. 'Terror possessed me to look upon it. I went into the ship and shut my door. . . . The water attacked the people like a battle. Brother saw not brother. Men could not be recognized from heaven. Even the gods were terrified at the cyclone. They shrank back and went up into the heaven of Anu. The gods crouched like a dog and cowered by the wall. . . .' For six days the wind and the storm raged and the cyclone overwhelmed the land. 'When the seventh day came the cyclone ceased, the storm and the battle which had fought like an army.' At the same time the ship 'grounded on the mountain of Nizir' and after 'opening the air hole' Utu-nipishtim began the same sort of investigation as Noah made, 'brought out a dove and let her go free, but because she had no place to alight on she came back. I brought out a swallow and let her go free, but because she had no place to alight on she came back. I brought out a raven and let her go free; the raven flew away, she saw the sinking water. She ate. She waded and splashed but came not back.' Again like Noah he now emerged from his ship and sacrificed to the gods and 'the gods gathered together like flies over him that sacrificed'.

These situations in which local cataclysm is assumed to be universal would seem to be at the opposite pole to animistic beliefs in which every disaster is assumed to be aimed specifically at the individual or the tribe; but there is in fact a meeting-point in the conception that 'we have *all* offended the gods'.

It was only when daylight came, and the survivors could see, not only that beyond Agadir the face of land and sea looked as before, but also that there were undamaged buildings and living human beings in the town itself, that the truth became plain to them.

The extent of the damage in different quarters varied not only with the type of building construction, but also with the altitude above sea-level, so that the houses built upon the rock cliff on the northern side stood better than those at a lower level; in many cases, as in that of the Mauretania Hotel, from which many Austrian, Dutch and Danish holidaymakers escaped alive, their façades crashed but left the main internal structure intact. The Hotel Saada, in contrast, built almost upon the beach, collapsed totally, but in slow motion, the roof sliding out from the walls until the unbalance crumbled them too. From the Saada, one of the great luxury hotels of the town, there were very few survivors from the eighty-odd tourist residents who had dined in the hotel. One of these was Robin Maugham, whom I had met in Rabat a few weeks before. He had come to Morocco in search of a story, not background material for a novel but something sensational that would stand being written up by itself. When I had met him he had been in the country for some weeks and found nothing to his taste; as a newspaper had given him a considerable sum of money for his journey he felt that his position was becoming embarrassing. I was fortunately able to redeem him from his predicament by giving him the outline and references of a story that was the apotheosis of all that he could wish, the then inadequately and ill-reported story of the Hillal Oil. The manufacturers of this poor quality olive-oil had adulterated their product with engine-oil bought from American bases, thereby causing in one day the paralysis of thousands of people in the city of Meknes. The dogged attempts of one doctor to diagnose the new disease; his search, at first in vain, for any common dietetic factor among his patients; his sudden realization that the material in which the varying foods had been cooked might be the key; his flying of a sample to Europe for analysis; the call-out of the army to round up every bottle of Hillal Oil in the country, and the doctor's triumphant arrest of the whole epidemic in an almost unbelievably short space of time – all these made high drama, and Robin Maugham was well satisfied. I had met him again in Marrakesh a few days before the earthquake; he had finished his research and now felt justified in taking a few days' holiday at the Saada Hotel in Agadir. On the morning after the earthquake, I said to a mutual acquaintance, 'I'm afraid Robin Maugham must have been killed; there's something oddly pathetic about his dying in an episode he would so much have wanted to report.' My companion hesitated, and then said almost diffidently, as if he were indulging too extravagant a flight of fantasy, 'Doesn't he somehow strike you as being someone who will always fall on his feet? He was looking for a "story" in Morocco – do you know I could almost believe that he was in that hotel and somehow survived and got a unique story?' The next morning I read among the slender list of survivors '*Rollin viscomte Morgan, diplomate Anglais*'. He had been imprisoned under a fallen beam, with just enough room for his body and no more, for many hours; eventually he was extricated, by great skill and luck, unharmed but noticeably garrulous, and packed off to England to write his scoop.

Opposite to the Saada the Prefecture, built according to seismic-resisting principles, stood completely intact. All houses built of *pisé* (mud walls packed wet between shaping-boards and then allowed to bake dry in the sun) were demolished, not so much into rubble as into dust, so that the bodies of the dead and their erstwhile household possessions were the only solid things remaining. The old Kasbah, built on the summit overlooking the town, fell as a tree falls and out of its 800 inhabitants only fifty survived. The main *medina*, Talbourdjt, built of *pisé* in the typical Moorish way, collapsed with all its *souq*, mosques, schools, and warrens of small dwellings; from its 5,000 inhabitants the survivors were counted on the fingers of two hands. Too long a task, surely, for Mr Thornton Wilder. Because of this total destruction, rescue work in Talbourdjt was impossible. Here were no fallen blocks of masonry under or between which unseen survivors might have been trapped as Robin Maugham had been; there could be nothing but the dead. So these areas were ignored until the great heat and the terrible stench made impossible even the recovery of bodies. The rescue workers concentrated upon the areas of heavy fallen masonry where life still might, however improbably, linger. By Saturday 5 March, when I left Marrakesh to spend two nights in Rabat before returning to London on Monday, the information was more exact. Apart from the great mass of Moroccan dead, 850 of the Spanish community of 2,000 had been killed and as many wounded; the old fishing village of Founti had been utterly razed; there had been almost total casualties among the women workers of the great sardine canneries; 100 Italians were missing, 37 British. Of Moroccan official bodies the heaviest casualties had been among the 8th Battalion of the Royal Armed Forces in barracks, and among the *gendarmerie* or country police. The headquarters of the police proper had not been damaged significantly, but because it was the season of Ramadan its members had leave of absence during the night, and they died in the cafés, cinemas, private houses or unofficial brothels where they were relaxing from their second day of fast.

The occurrence of the disaster during the season of Ramadan had still further repercussions among the survivors. Although the rule that nothing may pass the lips between sunrise and sunset does not, according to orthodoxy, apply to the sick or those who are journeying, there were many who believed that the fast would have been broken if they received medicine, and a considerable number of the wounded even refused blood transfusion on that score.

The Crown Prince Moulay Hassan, now King Hassan II, had taken charge at his father's orders, and from a temporary headquarters at Inezgane, a few kilometres from the ruined city, he acted with speed and decision, decision that to those who did not fully understand the situation he was facing seemed callous and brutal.

By sunrise on Friday conditions in what was left of Agadir were so terrible as to demand ruthless measures against the growing probability of epidemic. Prince Hassan had no reasonable choice. The temperature at mid-morning had reached 105 degrees, and the smell of putrescence extended to a radius of three miles outside the town. The workers in the ruins now wore gas-masks or breathing pads, and their hands were gloved. Those areas where rescue was considered impossible were treated with quick-lime to destroy the bodies; if it destroyed living bodies as well as the dead there was no alternative. Rats, driven upwards by the blocking and drying of the sewers in which they lived, were everywhere among the rubble and ruins; dogs and innumerable stray cats fed upon every exposed corpse; over all hung a humming pall of flies. Even in this place of horror furtive looters skulked among the ruins and took rings and bracelets from the dead; some of these, when challenged, claimed that they had lingered on in the town searching in despair for a lost child.

By order of Moulay Hassan the last inhabitants were removed from the city and its confines were sealed by military barricades. Looters were shot at sight and their bodies thrown among those endless ranks awaiting a common grave. All livestock loose among the ruins were killed. Great quantities of rat poison were laid throughout the whole ruined city; DDT and disinfectants were sprayed constantly from lorries and hovering helicopters. Fifty bulldozers continued inch by inch to work wherever there remained a remote chance of life.

On arrival at Rabat on Saturday evening I met, in the house of a mutual friend, Moulay Ahmed El Alaoui, a cousin of the king and then Chief of Press Services at the Royal Palace. The king, he told me, was paying his third visit to Agadir the next morning, this time in company with all the diplomatic representatives and press attachés; there were two aircraft leaving Rabat at eight am, and he would secure me a seat in one of these if I wished. He arrived in a palace car at seven-twenty the next morning to carry my host and myself to the airport.

Moulay Ahmed, of whom I shall have more to say in a later chapter, is one of the many phenomena of the new independent Morocco. He is a dynamo working at such incredible pressure that one feels he must blow up; he is everywhere at once, doing a hundred jobs at once, with the same sort of furious impatience. He was very close to the king and had his ear, so that his work always extended far beyond its official designation. Because of his tireless energy and apparent ability to work without sleep (he may arrive for a chat at a friend's house, unannounced, at any hour between midnight and six am, and he was popularly believed to sleep from six am until seven am, though there is no positive evidence of this), because of this energy it devolved upon him, for example, to plan the innumerable details of King Mohammed V's 1960 tour of the whole Middle East and the Holy Cities, and to supervise the entire daily routine of the unwieldy touring court. With this background knowledge of his exalted position it was at first a shock to me to realize that it was he himself who carried out much of the petty administration of his own decisions, with a complete and characteristic disregard of formalities. One of the happier anecdotes, of which a volume might be collected, as could also a volume of the less fortunate, concerns his office as Minister of Tourism. Motoring between Rabat and Casablanca, he encountered a party of Swedish tourists whose car towed a caravan, and who were proceeding in the opposite direction, that is, towards Rabat. He immediately ordered his chauffeur to turn the car and to pursue and overtake the Swedes. This accomplished, he dismounted and stopped the tourists as a traffic policeman would. He then asked them if they were going to Rabat and if they had anywhere to camp. Moulay Ahmed is not always of ministerial appearance, and it was with some astonishment and apprehension that the visitors replied that they had not yet made any definite arrangements. 'Then,' said Moulay Ahmed, with all the great charm of which he is capable, 'let me introduce myself. I am the Minister of Tourism, and you shall camp in the forecourt of the Ministry itself. I myself shall accompany you there now.' Abandoning whatever project he had been engaged upon he led his prisoners back triumphantly to the capital; for several days thereafter the amazed population of Rabat could observe a party of foreigners camping in the gracious and conspicuously placed forecourt of the Ministry, drying laundry fluttering merrily from a line attached to the caravan. Swedes are notoriously unselfconscious people.

It was only to be expected, therefore, that it was Moulay Ahmed himself who at the airport controlled, manually when necessary, the variegated hordes of press attachés and journalists, shouting out the list of names, pushing back those who were in the wrong stream, pulling forward bodily those who were vague or misunderstanding, alternately a brusque bus conductor and a statesman, an irritable usher and a high administrator. After half an hour or more of this separation of sheep from goats the two aircraft took off for Agadir, the one containing the king, his ministers and the foreign ambassadors, and the other the press attachés and members of the international press.

From Agadir Airport the party left as a long convoy of vehicles; first the military motor-cycle and security police out-riders, then the royal cars boxed-in by further motor-cycles, then a busload of ambassadors and another of the press. The cinematographers had been grouped by Moulay Ahmed's unique combination of force and cajolery into a sort of loose pyramid upon a jeep; near the summit of this pyramid he chose, capriciously, to perch himself. On the roof of the press bus travelled a few hardy photographers who had decided to brave the various odours of which they had been warned.

The procession drove straight to the town, across the flat lands of *argan* trees, round whose trunks and spiny branches were visible everywhere the improvised homes of the destitute – blankets hung or stretched as screens between limb and trunk, a handful of salvaged possessions by a camp-fire at their sides. Men, women and children lined the road-side to see the passage of the king, for, though this was his third visit since the earthquake, his presence was of far greater significance than would be that of a British monarch in parallel circumstances, for since the Sultan of Morocco is the spiritual leader of his people, in him reposes the power of *baraka*, or blessing.

At the road-barrier guarding the dead town's entrance

macabrely masked figures sprayed each vehicle in turn with white clouds of disinfectant. The procession with its outriders began very slowly to tour the streets of what had been Agadir.

The image was not, in effect, greatly different from that presented by any town destroyed by aerial bombardment; here were the same crazily leaning walls, the same mass of broken glass; the same tumbled heaps of masonry and scattered household goods; the same walls torn off to reveal the cascading chaos of furnished rooms; the same houses that stood, arbitrarily, while their neighbours had fallen. Only in one respect did it differ significantly – the great areas that were no more than fine dust, now whitened with quicklime, through which but few solid objects protruded. Some of these objects were extremely unpleasant. Where the rubble was more solid, more capable of containing life – however improbably after six days of blazing heat – masked rescue workers were still moving masonry; elsewhere bulldozers moved among the debris with the infinite slowness of a dream.

The occupants of the bus clamoured that every window should be kept closed; opening mine a little, I found that the air reeked of disinfectant and DDT, with a sour-sickly undertone that made it possible to imagine the unspeakable conditions of the previous day. Behind me I heard an English voice say: 'I don't see any rats and I can't smell much except hospital smells; I think this story's been overwritten.' I wanted to ask him whether the story of one death can be overwritten; this should have been a funeral cortège for 10,000 dead among whose bodies we were even now passing, and the brisk on-the-job attitude of the horde of journalists to whom this was – it appeared – no more than a news item to be covered, seemed harshly jarring.

As the procession drew abreast of the remains of the Hôtel-de-Ville, each car became enveloped in a grey cloud of DDT through which were dimly visible masked riflemen standing grotesquely at the present for the passage of the royal cars; they moved on down the Boulevard Mohammed V, officially opened by the king amid the cheering ranks of Agadir's citizens only a few months before. There was no halt on this weird tour of a city so newly dead; again the cars reached the road-block, were sprayed by dim, masked figures, and moved out into the world of the living. For me the nearest parallel in my experience was emerging from the suffocation of drowning, which not only entails a struggle, as did for me this equivalent proximity to mass death, but contains also a contact with negation, a sharp and shrivelling awareness of the enemy at hand and allies unprepared.

From Agadir the cumbersome cortège took the road for Inezgane and royal inspection of the emergency camps for the destitute. The first of these had been completed less than twenty-four hours before; an accommodation settlement of British Army tents ranged on flat open ground, with a minor clinic at which the injured who came in from their shelters in the surrounding country could, according to the gravity of their condition, be treated or sent on to the new medical camp. Already this settlement held 1,300 of the homeless, and four more similar camps were projected to house the remainder as they could be located and brought in. Some 15,000 people had left the ruins; many were camping in the surrounding countryside, as yet unaware of any arrangements made for them; still others were known to have reached far-off towns and villages.

In this first camp were many children, and these, seemingly unperturbed by terrors now five days old, were playing organized games and doing PT exercises under the leadership of Muslim Boy Scouts. Many others, however, were showing symptoms of delayed shock, and were waiting transfer to one of the hospital camps. The orderly rows of tents, the green turf, the strolling ambassadors (some of whom were taking photographs of each other against suitable backgrounds), the royal presence and the extravagant greeting accorded to him, all combined to impart to this camp an air almost of fête.

The next halting-point of the royal procession was the first of the hospital camps. Here were newly arrived units of British, German, Swiss and Italian Red Cross, with well-equipped surgeries and X-ray plants; but as yet there were very few patients, for many had still to be transferred from the naval base to which they had first been taken, and more than 2,000 had already been flown to the hospitals of the great cities of Morocco. The German unit, for example, had six patients, one of whom had only been dug out the evening before, and had thus survived four days of deep interment.

There was no time to linger here, for in contrast to the leisurely atmosphere at the first settlement, the party now swept along at the heels of the king as he dived into tent after tent before hurrying back to his car, and it required the omnipresence of Moulay Ahmed to ensure that something rather more than a handful of ambassadors and pressmen did not swell the numbers of the displaced at each successive camp visited. Many of the party began to flag in the heat and the dust, but the king seemed tireless, a dignified figure in a grey *djellabah* and white *babuch* that kicked aside the spiny litter of fallen *argan* twigs as though they were as well used to the harsh ground of the *bled* as to red carpets and the marble mosaic of palace floors. On the day of his first visit many had remarked upon the deep despair of his appearance as he walked among the ruins with an oft-repeated gesture of upraised palms; now his expression seemed one of determination, the jaw set and his hands often momentarily clenched.

In the early afternoon, while he rested for a few moments at the Crown Prince's headquarters at Inezgane, fresh tremors shook the ground, no stronger than those I had felt at Marrakesh, but enough to make me wonder whether all this work might not be wasted. Some two hours later, as the two aircraft took off for Rabat and passed over the bay, a strange turmoil of water moved the sea between the shore and the squadron of French warships lying at anchor, as though some great mass were being pushed up from below. It was difficult to judge how this must have appeared from sea-level, but it was alarming enough for the squadron to weigh anchor hurriedly and stand a mile farther out to sea.

There was no general scientific agreement as to the cause of the earthquake; one thing seemed certain, that many years would pass before Agadir again became a recreation ground that tourists would trust. Despite this, the king's gesture of faith was to announce that rebuilding was to begin immediately, and that the new city would be officially inaugurated in a year's time, on 2 March 1961 – the anniversary of Independence Day, whose celebrations were changed so terribly to tears in 1960.

Tragic majesty, Sidi Mohammed Ben Youssef, Mohammed V, King and Sultan of Morocco, eleventh and most enlightened ruler of the long Alaouite dynasty – kidnapped and banished when he aspired for the future of his country against the exploitation of French 'protection'; exiled first to cold Corsica (where he was made to pay even the wages of the numerous police who guarded him); from there transferred, as a potential threat to Mediterranean peace, to pass two years in a ruinous and roof-leaking hotel in Madagascar; tragic majesty, who would never lead the celebrations of another Independence Day. On 26 February 1961, Agadir little changed, Mohammed V was absolved from all earthly necessity for explanation, and Morocco was in mourning for her first national hero. No one has ever announced the inauguration of a new Agadir.

2

Return to Camusfeàrna

I HAD LEARNED, the day before I visited Agadir, of a minor tragedy in my Chelsea house, but the human holocaust in Morocco had deadened the bitter little sting of pain that I feel upon the death of creatures for which I have made myself responsible.

The houses of the Square where I live when in London are of small rooms, in four floors. (They were, I believe, artisans' houses until after the First World War, and upon learning from my late charlady that she remembered the house when its tenant was a police constable, I asked her how he had occupied all the space. 'Well,' she said, 'they used to have a lodger, and then of course there were the servants.' My eyebrows must have shot up. 'Oh yes, they always had a married couple to look after them – never a hand's turn would the missus do, but ring the bell in the sitting-room for tea or whatever it was that she or his nibs wanted.') After Chelsea squares became fashionable the ground-floor back and front of these houses were, in most cases, knocked into one, giving a single long room of some twenty-five feet, with the structural supports of the old division projecting some eighteen inches from each wall. In the garden end of this room I was wont to work when I was in London, and in the other I had accumulated, slowly and almost by chance it seemed, a small collection of brilliant tropical birds, who flew at liberty and fed upon fruit suspended from natural branches. This collection had begun with an unwanted gift

33

of two gem-like mites that I had for a time kept in a large and elaborate Victorian birdcage; eventually, having a dislike for the concept of caged birds, I liberated them in the room, and was so struck by their beauty in flight that I added another pair of a different species. The first had been tanagers, a South American group which contains some of the most brilliantly coloured birds in the world, and soon the addition of new tanager species became a minor, dilettante hobby. Certainly it was one mainly of sensory titillation, for we arranged concealed spotlamps to light the jewels in their wings as they flew, and papered the walls above the bookcases black so that none of the iridescence of the feathers should be lost by silhouette. By the spring of 1960 there were some fourteen of these birds, including one species that had been rarely kept successfully before. Most of them would fly down and take food from the hand.

The necessary temperature in this room was maintained by an oil stove, and one night a week or so before my return to London from Morocco, some irregularity of wick or paraffin feed had started a fire. The circumstances that caused this never became clear, but it was a slow, smouldering fire giving off a dense smoke and covering walls and ceiling with an oily black soot. Jimmy Watt, who had spent the winter in London with Edal the otter (for Camusfeàrna was not yet a place of permanent residence), had not been awoken by the fumes until too late, and all the birds were dead.

Edal, however, was unharmed. She occupied a basement room of her own, with a tunnel through the wall into the garden, and she slept peacefully even through the pandemonium of the fire brigade's arrival; considering, perhaps, that the unseemly din above her was some typically tiresome human prank of no concern to her. So I returned, weighed down by the image of Agadir as few other second-hand experiences had affected me before; sad, but mocking myself for being so, at the death of my birds whose wings seemed to have borne along so many sentences that without their inspiration would have been lumberingly pedestrian; as yet unquestioning that I should find Edal ready to return to Camusfeàrna and renew the idyll, unquestioning that the refuge, the pool of silence, could go on and on for ever.

When we had been separated in the past she had been used to greet me as does a dog after its master's prolonged absence, and when I walked into her room now I expected a demonstrative welcome. She was curled up on the bed, and when I called her name she barely lifted her head. She looked at me vaguely and immediately curled up again. At first I thought she was sleepy and had not recognized me; only slowly did I begin to understand that she was very ill. She had eaten nothing, I was told, for two full days.

It was the beginning of a three weeks' struggle, the first of two in six months, to save her life. Immediate veterinary tests showed the presence of liver fluke; it was not generally suspected then, as it is now, that this parasite with its curious multi-stage life cycle is probably endemic in otters and causes no damage to function unless present in vast numbers, and Edal was therefore treated for liver fluke as being the root cause of her symptoms. Under this treatment, which made her constantly sick, her condition deteriorated rapidly, and she became extremely emaciated. When further tests showed the presence of Shigella dysentery, we decided to abandon interest in the flukes altogether.

Her treatment was not easy. In her own room she would not allow the vet to examine her or to inject her, and he suggested that from the psychological viewpoint her submission would be much more probable in the alien atmosphere of his surgery. In this he proved right, as he did also in suggesting a method of restraint that appeared to me wholly impracticable. It was necessary to give her three separate injections in quick succession every day, besides taking her temperature rectally, and granted that no wild animal could be expected to undergo these painful indignities without protest, we had somehow to restrain her head from turning. Edal wore a harness, not a collar, because an otter's head is so little wider than the neck that a collar can always be slipped; now the vet suggested that if she wore two collars, with the lead attached to the hindmost one, the bunching up of the skin would keep them in position. This idea proved entirely successful, and every day Edal was immobilized on the operating table by three separate leads strained in different directions. It was strange that, as the drive to the surgery and the repetition of this ordeal became a daily routine, she showed no antipathy either to the waiting-room or the surgery; she never shied away from its door and she would sit on one of our laps, among the dogs, cats, parrots and other household pets that form the bulk of a city vet's practice. When the time came for her to be carried down to the surgery and laid upon the operating table she made no protest.

For a fortnight or so there was little change. At best she had an even chance of living, and though we tempted her with every kind of dainty she would eat nothing of her own free will; we had all this time to feed her forcibly with concentrated liquids.

At last one morning I noticed, as we drove down the King's Road on our daily visit to the surgery, that she seemed for the first time to be taking a little of her old interest in the traffic and the passers-by; she even hauled herself up to put her paws against the glass and peer, a little myopically, out of the passengers' window. In the waiting-room she was restless, and in the surgery she eyed the vet with distinct disfavour. He looked at her and said: 'I do believe we've done the trick. This morning she looks for the first time like a truly viable animal.' The same afternoon I opened her door quietly and looked round it, half expecting to find her inert upon the bed as she had been for so long, but she was engaged in guzzling a plate of scrambled eggs, stuffing her mouth full with those curious little simian hands just as she used to do. It was the first solid food, indeed the only food that she had eaten voluntarily, for sixteen days.

From then on she made a steady recovery; by 14 April she was her usual high-spirited and inquisitive self, and greeted a TV unit with all her old enthusiasm for novelties. She was, moreover, extremely patient with the constant retakes requisite to the threadbare story scripted for her by the BBC. (Mr Macdonald Hastings, the viewing public were asked to believe, had been astonished to see in the King's Road an otter at the heels of Jimmy Watt and myself. Fortunately, having a whole television unit with him, he and it followed us home unobserved and noted the number on our door. By what disembodiment he was then assumed to have passed through that door it is difficult to imagine, for the next scene showed him peering, unannounced, round the door of my sitting-room and registering delighted surprise at the sight of Edal sitting on my lap.)

A few days later she travelled up to Camusfeàrna by train with Jimmy. As in the past with other otters, I contrived that she should share his first-class sleeper, but as before she required a dog ticket. This time, instead of leaving blank the space for description of the dog, I indulged a flight of fantasy, and wrote 'Illyrian Poodle'. This breed is not of my invention but of Mr William Burroughs, and figures briefly in *The Naked Lunch*.

Manhattan Serenade: A. J. and entourage start into New York nightclub. A.J. is leading a purple-assed baboon on a gold chain. A.J. is dressed in checked linen plus-fours with a cashmere jacket.
Manager: *Wait* a minute. Wait a *minute*. What's that?
A.J.: It's an Illyrian poodle. Chicest beast a man can latch onto. It'll raise the tone of your trap.

Manager: I suspect it to be a purple-assed baboon and it stands outside.

Stooge: Don't you know who this is? It's A.J., last of the big-time spenders.

Manager: Leave him take his purple-assed bastard and big time spend some place else.

... A.J. drives a gold stake into the floor and pickets the baboon.

I cannot leave A.J. without even introducing him. He is:

actually of obscure Near East extraction – had at one time come on like an English gentleman. His English accent waned with the British Empire, and after World War II he became an American by Act of Congress. ... It is rumoured that he represents a trust of giant insects from another galaxy ... A.J.'s cover story? An international playboy and harmless practical joker. It was A.J. who put the pirhana fish in Lady Sutton-Smith's swimming-pool, and dosed the punch with a mixture of Yage, Hashish and Yohimbine during a Fourth of July reception at the U S Embassy, precipitating an orgy. Ten prominent citizens – American, of course – subsequently died of shame.

The ticket-puncher looked at Edal without great curiosity. 'What's that?' he asked. 'Illyrian poodle.' 'Huh? Never saw one of them before. Sort of a dog, is it?' 'Sort of,' I said. The joke had fallen a little flat.

Before Edal and Jimmy had left for Scotland there had taken place a further one of those coincidences that make my experiences with otters read like fiction rather than fact. To appreciate the extent of the coincidence it should be understood that the West African species of otter to which Edal belongs has very rarely been brought to this country at all, and never, so far as I know, had there been a specimen bottle-reared from blind helplessness as Edal had been by Dr Malcolm Macdonald. Now a Mr and Mrs Davin, on short leave from Sierra Leone, telephoned to me to say that they had brought to England with them a male otter cub that they had acquired unweaned in Africa and had reared on a bottle. The cub had already been promised to a country gentleman whom they had met on the boat, but they would like me at least to see it.

Presently their car was at the door. I did not want to bring the cub into the house, for fear that some trace of Edal's infection might linger there; this was doubly important, as his owners explained to me, for not only did he eat with his fingers as did Edal, but he also had a baby habit of sucking them, especially when confronted with unfamiliar surroundings. Mr Davin reached into a travelling-box in the back of the car, and emerged with a superb ball of dark chocolate-coloured, almost black, plush; this in his arms uncoiled and re-formed as a small, stout otter lying on its back. It put three fingers of its right hand into its mouth and began to suck noisily, looking about it with interest.

This otter seemed more completely domesticated than even Edal had been. It was the hour when the local school empties and the children began to crowd round, screaming and laughing and calling to their distant companions, the bolder ones trying to touch him. To most animals, and more particularly to most wild animals, a surrounding crowd of vocal children and advancing hands would constitute a situation of fear, but this otter seemed in no way disconcerted; indeed it was clear that he considered them as potential playmates from whom he was being unjustly withheld. I coveted this creature; already in my mind's eye I could see him and Edal gambolling together under the waterfall at Camusfeàrna or porpoising after each other in the calm blue waters of the bay below the house; already I was mentally enlarging the size of the otter bed in the cottage kitchen.

Teko (he had been named after an up-country veterinary station in Sierra Leone, without his owners being aware that

'Tek' is in fact an Old English word for otter) was not content in the Surrey home to which, after our meeting, he had been taken, and when I learned that Mr and Mrs Davin intended anyway to visit the West Highlands during their holiday, bringing Teko with them, I felt that the warmth of his welcome would be so great both from humans and from Edal as to leave his owners no room for choice about his future. As in the case of Dr Malcolm Macdonald, they would have somehow to find a home for him before returning to West Africa, and I knew that few households were allowed to revolve round the life of otters as mine did at that date. I reckoned, however, without Edal's highly developed sense of property.

I arrived at Camusfeàrna a few days after Jimmy and Edal; I watched her revel anew in the freedom of stream and sea after her long winter sojourn in the drab confines of her London quarters, and in the fair golden weather that in those days seemed never to desert Camusfeàrna for long – it seemed to be the beginning of just such another summer idyll as the last. But there was to be no idyll, then or thereafter, for I had left the calm reaches of the river.

I had been at Camusfeàrna a fortnight or so when Mr and Mrs Davin arrived in the neighbourhood and found themselves lodgings some twelve miles away. By now they had more or less made up their minds that if Camusfeàrna seemed a suitable home for Teko they would leave him with me. I had provided them with a harness for him, so that his introduction to Edal could be carried out with the greatest caution and both animals under restraint. This policy paid dividends, for without our forethought there would have been little left of the unfortunate Teko. A year before, when Edal first arrived, any other animal was a welcome playmate; then, I am sure, she would have taken Teko to her heart with delight, but by now I entertained a suspicion that jealousy and possessiveness played no small part in her make-up, and I was determined that this first meeting should leave nothing to chance.

On the green sward of the field in which Camusfeàrna stands Mr and Mrs Davin waited with Teko on a lead, while I went upstairs, clipped Edal's lead to her harness and led her out. At first she did not see him, for the group stood among scattered clumps of rushes, but she saw strangers, and stood on her hind legs like a penguin to get a better view, for otters are myopic, and of their five senses trust their eyesight perhaps the least. (So, incidentally, do human beings, or at least place it secondarily to the sense of touch; the idea of a ghost or any other supernatural phenomenon having its root in the principle of intangibility, touch remaining our one final test of 'reality'. For an otter, a ghost would, I presume, consist of some being that could not be smelled, and something that had no smell could not be 'real'.) Then she advanced a few paces and stood up again. She was then no more than ten or fifteen yards from the group, and this time she saw Teko. Her nostrils wiggled frantically, and at last she caught a whiff of his scent. She uttered a shriek of anger, and made a dash for him that almost pulled me off my feet. It was not an encouraging start. For a quarter of an hour we walked the two otters along the beach and about the field, always at a respectful distance from each other, while Edal kept up a running commentary of rage in that high, screaming wail which of all the animal cries I have heard sounds the most vindictive. Then I took her back to her room in the house, and Teko's owners and I conferred, as do generals when they have reluctantly to agree that they are attacking an unassailable position.

It seemed to us that the place of their meeting might affect her attitude, for otters are territorial animals, and that she might be more willing to accept him if the encounter were to take place on neutral ground over which Edal did not feel herself to reign supreme. The following day we made a second attempt, on the road above Camusfeàrna, but there was no noticeable improvement. Then we took Edal to the vicinity of the house where Mr and Mrs Davin were lodging twelve miles away. Here it seemed to me that she had begun to tolerate his presence a little, and her hymn of hate was not quite so continuous. There were, to use a printer's metaphor, more white spaces in the previously unbroken text of vituperation. She was, consciously, I think, lulling us into a sense of false security, hoping all the while for an opportunity which when it came left no doubt of her intentions. We were at the moment in single file, and she was walking beside me quite silently a few paces behind Teko and his owners, when he lagged a little behind them and gave her the chance for which she had been waiting so patiently. With a bound and a scream she had him by the tail and was worrying it like a dog trying to kill a rat. I contrived to haul her off almost in the same instant as it happened, and Teko fled whimpering pathetically to the consoling hands of his foster parents, while Edal's voice rose to a positive paean of hate and triumph.

The following day I watched Teko's departure with profound disappointment; Edal's intransigent attitude to the question of consorts had posed a problem to which I could see no solution. Time was short and Teko's owners were wasting their leave in searching for a home for him; while they did so I offered them the use of my London house with its otter room and tunnel to the garden.

Suitable homes for otters are not, however, easy to find, and it was no very great surprise to me when, little more than a fortnight later, they approached me again to ask how long it would take us to prepare separate quarters for Teko, who, they pointed out, had never been accustomed to freedom, and was conspicuously easy to entertain. I did not yet fully believe in Edal's permanent hostility towards him. Teko seemed to me an infinitely desirable creature, and I disliked the thought of his being placed in hands less tender and experienced than my own. I replied that it would take between a fortnight and three weeks.

In the event, however, no more than a week was available, and though fortunately most of the necessary materials were to hand, Jimmy and I had to work far into every night and begin again at dawn. I had foreseen that after the publication of *Ring of Bright Water* more and more uninvited visitors would find their way to the house, and visualizing that these might be accompanied by dogs unfriendly to otters I had decided to enclose a small piece of land surrounding the house with a continuous five-foot-high wooden paling. The wood for this formidable undertaking had been delivered by sea (the twine tying the planks into bundles of forty had in many cases broken as the cargo was lowered overboard and the whole bay had been bobbing with timber as difficult to round up as had been my Shetland sheep on Soay years before), and now lay above the tide-line on the beach below the house. With this wood we decided to construct for Teko a separate enclosure at one end of the cottage, where was also a small lean-to outhouse that might be converted to his use. Even in the early days storage space at Camusfeàrna had always been a problem, and over the years the contents of this modest building had become an inextricable jumble of lobster pots, ropes, paint tins, tools, boxes of nails and every imaginable form of junk, so that to extract any desired object from it had long since become a major task, necessitating both time and patience. Below this entangled miscellany the floor was covered several inches deep in coal-dust and debris.

Teko was an animal accustomed to living in human houses, and to lodge him in accommodation that did not in some sense resemble a human room would have been as inappropriate as to chain a drawing-room Pekinese to a barrel of straw in the open. In that week, then, we were required to reclaim, repaint and furnish the outhouse; to enclose a piece of land with wooden paling; to sink wire-netting deep into the ground against the possibility of Teko digging his way out; to construct some form of lavatory for him that would be easy to keep clean (the Specialist would have been hard pressed to do better), to dig and cement a pool in which he could play, and to lead running-water to it. With these basic conditions as his background, Teko could then be entertained in the living-room at any time when Edal was confined to her own quarters, and he could accompany us for walks or swims behind the dinghies after she had been exercised. The keeping of these two otters did, it is true, appear likely to become a full-time job; but as a visitor remarked, not without malice, this was perhaps as good a way of earning an anti-social living as any other.

All this work we completed in the week at our disposal, and though the cement was still damp enough to take the imprint of Teko's feet as he entered, and the paint was barely dry upon the walls of his house, he appeared entranced with his new quarters; never once did he whimper or call or behave otherwise than as if the place had always been his home. I put a camp-bed in his house and for the first few nights I slept there myself, for sharing sleeping quarters with an animal is the most certain way of establishing mutual confidence. It was not, in this case, an entirely comfortable procedure, for no sooner had I manoeuvred myself into the sleeping-bag than he would begin to explore my face with his simian fingers, pushing mobile digits between my lips and into my nostrils and ears, uttering the while a curious snuffle that led me to believe he had contracted a cold; only after the first few days did I discover that this was a sound of pleasure and contentment, like the purring of a cat. After some half-hour of this demonstrative affection he would squirm down into the warmth of the sleeping-bag and slumber peacefully through the night. Or so I had thought, but on the third morning I awoke to find myself engulfed in a smother of liberated kapok, blocking my nose, eyes and ears; Teko had spent the greater part of the night happily chewing holes in the lining of the sleeping-bag. I have contended, and continue to do so, that otters have a keen sense of humour, almost in the way that these words are used of human beings; the action equivalent to human laughter is for the otter to lie on its back and wriggle while keeping its mouth wide open. Teko clearly found the result of his handiwork extremely funny.

Teko at that time was a weighty ball of very soft dark brown fur and fat and *bonhomie*; in character he was like neither Mijbil nor Edal, for he was (and still is) basically a clown. It is now nearly three years since he came to Camusfeàrna, and in that time he has grown to be the largest otter that I personally have seen, weighing perhaps fifty pounds. But his character is *au fond* unchanged, despite the two acts of violence with which his record is now stained. He has always been content to play by himself for hours at a time; in those days, when he had only a small pool, he would adapt any floatable object, a stick or an empty tin, for his water games, dragging it under water and pouncing on it as it rose again, and occasionally leaping with it on to terra firma and racing round and round the pool in circles; later, when he had a large and deep fibre-glass swimming-pool of his own, he spurned all other toys in favour of a football, and with this he elaborated techniques to which Edal had never aspired. At the beginning the basic game was to try to keep the football under water; the impossibility of this project fascinated him, and round the original theme he wove a host of variations. He would shoot out of the water like a dolphin and land upon the football, trying to bear it under with him; release it suddenly so that it shot up high in the air; stalk it from the bank and perform a thunderous belly-flopper upon it with clasping arms; dribble it round the grass enclosure using nose, four feet and tail – it was his mascot, his totem, his *alter ego*, and without it he seemed lost. His most surprising feat I should not have believed had I not witnessed it many times. The edges of the fibre-glass pool were on all sides at the top of a small bank, so that from them led down a grass declivity of two or three feet. When, therefore, his antics shot the football out of the pool, it would inevitably roll down this slope; in the early stages he was content to try to push it and manhandle it back by any means he could. This was necessarily a slow and frustrating process, and quite suddenly he discovered that he could just clasp it in his arms and walk upright on his webbed hind feet. Almost always, however, either balance or the ball would begin to slip before he reached the top of the incline, and watching him from the window one morning as this began to happen I was astonished to see him actually throw the ball up into the pool, with a swinging, upward motion of both arms.

His most popular indoor parlour trick, in those days when he was allowed to meet visitors freely, was to play with the dancing beam of a torch shone upon the floor. Finding this to be elusive, intangible to nose or paws, he seemed to conceive of his tail as possessing some magic power for the capture of will-o'-the-wisps; thus he would reverse towards the spot of light, trying to scoop at it with his tail, executing the while a quick jig step to keep pace with its movement, a highly individual step that came to be known as the *pas de loutre*.

Like Edal when she first arrived, Teko was at the outset an indifferent, barely adequate swimmer, but he lost his fears more quickly than she had done, and soon he was at home in the deepest of waters or the wildest of waves. His first day with bathers appeared utterly fascinating to him; it had not apparently crossed his mind that this curious upright foster-race who tended him could upon occasion be aquatic too. When Raef Payne, who had restored and occupied the old croft opposite to mine, accompanied him to the sea with schnorkel and flippers, Teko was wild with delighted amusement. At first he was content to dive when Raef dived, and perform intricate aquabatics around him deep under water; then he discovered that he could ride the swimmer's back and go down with him; lastly, he found that he could embarrass the human considerably by removing the schnorkel mask when it was least expected. After such a joke he would porpoise round and round the swimmer with the rhythmic grace of a ballet dancer; he seemed to laugh at his own antics and at those of all the world around him. I am glad that one coloured film was made of Teko that summer, before anyone had any cause to fear him.

Alas, Edal's only reaction to this splendid beast remained one of violent jealousy against an interloper. Like the Marquis of Montrose, her heart did evermore disdain a rival to her throne, as it was plainly as such rather than a consort that she viewed him.

Exercising the two animals separately occupied much time, and I found my writing falling sadly behind. I decided to engage a second otter keeper, and in July Terry Nutkins arrived by way, so to speak, of the London Zoo. He was not employed there, but spent much of his free time about the Elephant House; his ambition was to be a *mahout*. This project presenting patent difficulties, he was inclined to accept any employment involving the care of animals outside an urban area. He came to Camusfeàrna as Teko's keeper, and the two established immediate *rapport*.

3

Peace Dropping Slow

IN THE AUTUMN of 1959, soon after the narrative of *Ring of Bright Water* had been brought to a close, my mother had undergone a serious operation in London, and it was clear that the timelessness of Camusfeàrna, its isolation from the outside world, must be regarded as an essentially egotistical aspect of my life. Camusfeàrna was a haven and a refuge, but with the necessity of spending an ever-increasing part of each year so far from responsibility came, too, the necessity for communication. I had expected the telephone to be beyond my means, brought, as it would have to be, by a separate line of posts all the weary distance from the road at Druimfiaclach; I was unfamiliar with the whimsical vagaries of the Postmaster-General's office, and the quotation of a mere five pounds installation fee I took at first sight for an unusually crass clerical error. In this I was wrong, and beyond a slightly increased rent for the instrument, the miracle was unqualified.

For some time before the installation of the actual telephone itself the effect was that of being under siege from a slowly approaching army. The advance began out of sight, far away up the hill, with a series of muffled but menacing explosions that grew daily heavier; the attackers themselves remained as yet invisible, though after the fourth day their hoarse and seemingly ferocious cries drifted down to us on the wind between distant detonations. Then one morning they were upon us; a mighty bang and a patter of falling rock-chips brought us bounding from our beds early one morning to see their heads upon the horizon three hundred yards away. They stood motionless in a group, regarding our defencelessness; one of them held before him a small up-rooted birch tree.

'Birnam Wood,' I said.

'Don't worry, these people only attack at dusk.'

How often I have wished that were true of the telephone itself. The large outside bell above the door of the house jangles arrogantly at all hours, and often at what Terry Nutkins might, with unusual aptness, have termed 'the most undignified moment of the day'. Terry, never of an academic or scholastic turn of mind, had when he first arrived a limited but highly experimental vocabulary; one day I found in my typewriter the beginning of a practice business letter which read: 'Dear Sir, I received your letter on Monday at a very undignified moment of the day. I can't say that I liked the tone of your voice.' Such undignified moments were even less convenient for telephone calls at Camusfeàrna than they are in civilization, for at that time we still had no sanitation; Moab was our washpot, and over Edom we cast out our shoes. As a factor replied to a former Duke of Argyll, visiting an outlying island of his property, 'Is it a *toilet* you're wanting, your Grace? The whole bloody *island* is a toilet!'

The first incoming telephone call was received at Camusfeàrna on 11 April 1960, and in retrospect the bell seems seldom to have been silent since. While the presence of the telephone has removed from Camusfeàrna a little of our sense of security, it has substituted another, for as a place of permanent residence it is a house of crisis, particularly in the winter; and in the frequent emergencies of human and animal health, of shipwreck and the accidents of fire and flood, there is the knowledge that help, however remote, can be summoned. Now, too, we could telephone for the household food supplies, as opposed to ordering them by letter two days in advance; it brought, in however small a quantity, relief from the exigence of a routine that left ever less time either to write or to enjoy Camusfeàrna. The next logical step towards buying back a little of the leisure I had lost by treating the house as a permanent home rather than a temporary haven, seemed the installation of electricity to take over at least a few of the endless chores which kept us house-bound during long days of summer, or cold and comfortless in the twilight of winter. Like the telephone line, the power-wires also followed the roadside at Druimfiaclach; the distance was the same, and in my innocence it even appeared to me possible that the same poles might carry both lines. I knew little of departmentalism. Not only was it impossible for the North of Scotland Hydro-Electric Board to use the same poles but even to use the same route of approach. The telephone line branches to Camusfeàrna from Druimfiaclach – now I received a plan showing the proposed electrical supply starting from a full half-mile farther to the southward, and an estimate for installation into which that for the telephone would have divided nearly two hundred times. But I was determined upon it, determined to avoid the transport of ponderous calor-gas containers and paraffin drums through the winter hurricanes; in my mind, too, were shining, ill-defined images of labour-saving devices; visions of placid hours of writing uninterrupted by the recurrent oppression of household tasks undone. So there came again the distant din of an advancing army, and at length a new group reached the southern horizon and stood looking down upon us with, it seemed, a wild surmise. On 4 July a party of the raiders approached the house itself, staggering across the green field under the weight of what appeared to be an enormous battering-ram; to complete the illusion of warfare they began immediately and feverishly to dig slit-trenches. At length the battering-ram was hoisted upright and revealed itself as the feed-post to stand beside the house, the slit-trenches as recipients of vast baulks of timber to anchor its guy-wires.

When Teko was plainly settled into his new home we tried again, with all the caution born of experience, to introduce him to Edal. Some part of our difficulty lay in the fact that we did not know whether Edal had a greater affection for her keeper, Jimmy Watt, or for myself; Edal, it was clear, considered herself polyandrously married to both of us, and apparent infidelity by either of us towards another otter could touch off the full fury of a *Lutra cornuta*. The question posed itself simply as to who should lead which animal on these trial walks; nor did her behaviour do much to elucidate the problem, for she was furious if either of us led Teko, and even more furious if he stopped for a second to pick up some shell or other piece of jetsam that struck him as a desirable toy. Habituation by proximity had already proved a failure; we had constructed a small window in the wall of Teko's enclosure, a mere six inches square and formed of two thicknesses of fine-mesh wire netting two inches apart, through which they could see and smell each other but could inflict no damage. But soon we had to close this hatch in order to preserve reason. Daylong Edal would stand at the grille and with all the force contained in her small frame she projected the unearthly, ear-splitting expression of her enmity; no other sub-human sound that I know is so baring to the nerves, unless it be the screaming of a falcon that has been mishandled in transference to its foster-parents. (Falcons taken too young from the eyrie become fixated upon the humans who have removed and fed them, and will scream at the mere proximity of their foster-parents. To overcome this a 'screamer' is fed with tongs from behind a screen of sacking. Presumably, but of this I have no knowledge, the falcon will then scream at any pair of tongs crossing its vision, but there are fewer of these loose in the world than there are human beings.) But while Edal's screaming-window was an unqualified failure as a factor in her acclimatization to Teko, I did, as the weeks passed, begin to entertain some small hope for their future; when exercised together on leashes her attention was not so perpetually concentrated upon him, nor, when Jimmy and I separated and unleashed our respective otters, did she seem so keenly inclined to pursue Teko and put him to rout.

Then, early in August, all experiments stopped together, for it became not a question of whether we could save this situation but, for the second time that year, whether we could save Edal's life. Edal, who had for so long played marbles on the kitchen floor, slept on our pillows, and displayed all the intense affection of which an otter is capable, developed an infection of the brain arising from a septic tooth. In twenty-four hours she became a mad, savage, half-paralysed but unapproachable creature, recognizing no one, as dangerous as a wounded leopard yet to me as pathetic as a child mortally sick. I can still see her crazed head weaving in search of something to attack, her useless hindquarters dragging behind her before she would collapse in a twitching rigor. Perhaps I may not be blamed too much for having hoped that each of these might be the end of an animal that now bore no resemblance to Edal.

It had started, as I have said, with a septic tooth, and as soon as we saw that she was in pain we arranged to have the tooth extracted on the following day. This involved taking her by car to a far-distant town, and, as always upon such emergency occasions, the next day was a Sunday. The vet was, however, prepared to perform the operation at any time, and we

arranged by telephone that Edal should be at his surgery by
eleven o'clock in the morning. (A long succession of crises
such as this and worse than this have made me wonder how
Camusfeàrna was ever supportable without the telephone;
Parkinson's Law that expenditure rises to meet income may
evidently be extended to the theorem that crises rise to meet
communication.)

Early in the morning we set off up the hill on foot, for
there is no road to Camusfeàrna. At this stage Edal seemed
normal, though once or twice it struck me fleetingly that
there were moments when she found balance difficult. This
suggested to me a derangement of her cerebellum, the hind
part of the brain responsible for controlling movement, and
with my limited knowledge it appeared no more than
sensible to take some precaution against a similar disturbance of the cerebrum, the fore-brain controlling behaviour.
I insisted, therefore, that Jimmy, in whose charge she would
be while I drove, should wear thick gloves.

The car was a hard-top Land Rover, with a full division
between front and rear. We had not as yet any precise reason
to be afraid of her, and with a sheepskin coat we made for
her a bed on the centre seat of the front cab, so that she was
between us. Trouble started within the first half mile. Without any warning she flew at Jimmy's hands, and had they
not been heavily gloved the damage would have been great.
Again and again she repeated these attacks, and I thought
my own ungloved hands would be her next target, for she
seemed to resent movement, and I had to reach directly in
front of her in order to use the gear lever. But in her confused brain it was Jimmy that she hated at that moment, and
she treated me as if I did not exist. After three miles of acute
nervous tension it became plain that the situation was untenable, and that one or other of us would be seriously hurt
long before we had completed the eighty miles in front of us.

In her present condition it was not easy to see how to transfer her to the rear compartment, much less close the door upon her. We had to dangle her down out of the front cab on the end of her lead, taking care all the while that she could not come within range of us, and then to hoist her over the rear drop-board, a very much more difficult procedure. When, after some ten minutes of effort, we had at last completed the task and closed the door upon her, we argued that her behaviour might in fact be no more than the effect of the tranquillizers we had given her before we started; they had, it is true, been of a variety that we had not tried before, but in all my previous experience tranquillizers administered to otters had produced the reverse of the desired and expected effect. They seemed to act much as alcohol affects the majority of human beings, leading to breakdown of all inhibitions and the collapse of learned behaviour; a wild animal in acute pain and without inhibitions could hardly be expected to display tranquillity and good humour.

At the surgery, two hours later, we were confronted with fresh difficulties, for there was no anaesthetic chamber, and we were forced to improvise with a large tea-chest. Into this we lowered her as we had lowered her into the rear compartment of the Land Rover, and then air-sealed the top with heavy towels before pumping in the anaesthetic. Edal took what was for me an almost intolerable time to lose consciousness, for all the while she wailed like a wounded hare, a sound so utterly piteous and abandoned that I found my hands unsteady and a cold sweat coming out on my forehead. Jimmy was unable to bear it, and took refuge in the Land Rover outside.

When at last these dreadful cries had ceased we removed the towels and lifted her limp body out of the box and on to the operating table. Two vets worked upon her, but found it impossible to shift the molar. No ordinary practitioner could be expected to know the precise jaw and skull structure of an otter, much less of a foreign species; this tooth resisted every normal means of extraction, and, not knowing how high the roots were planted in the skull, they were afraid of inflicting fatal damage if they used greater force. Seeing Edal lying there limp upon the operating table, her mouth full of blood and her fur foul with her own excreta, I did not believe in her recovery. The one slender chance was that the mauling the tooth had received might have provided some drainage for the septic fluids.

We carried her back into the Land Rover no more than seconds before she came round from the anaesthetic; through the rear window I could see her, dazed and bloodstained, walking round and round the narrow floor space in stumbling circles. The part of me that remains a child was very near to tears.

At the end of the two-hour journey home I felt a small spark of hope, for she was able to walk down the hill, and though she was noticeably off balance I supposed this to be the after-effects of the anaesthetic. She would not eat, but in the circumstances this seemed no great cause for surprise. We contrived, again by dangling her from the end of a lead, to hoist her upstairs into her own quarters; there she appeared to go to sleep in her bed, and we left her for the night.

Early the next morning Mr Donald MacLennan, the local vet, came – I use the word local for want of a better, for he lives at Broadford in Skye, more than fifty miles away by road and sea-ferry. I was totally unprepared for the rapid overnight deterioration in Edal's condition, and I opened her door to bring her downstairs. She was partially paralysed and wholly mad. She fell rather than walked down the stairs, and stumbled out into the garden, where she toppled over on her side, kicking and twitching. I took this first convulsion for a death-agony, but after perhaps a minute she recovered from it, raised herself unsteadily, and looked around her with mad eyes for something to attack. Finally, for despite the paralysis she seemed enormously strong, she struggled into the living-room and dragged herself up into a low wooden armchair with a slot back. Here she was unapproachable, screaming and literally gnashing her teeth at the least sign of movement in the room.

The vet looked at her and said nothing; I was unused then to the painstaking deliberation of his diagnoses, and I took his silence for a death-warrant. Yet I did not want him to shoulder the responsibility; I knew that in a month's time, when *Ring of Bright Water* was to be published, Edal would become a famous animal, more famous, perhaps, than Elsa the Lioness, and I felt it unfair to this young man to leave the decision to him alone. I telephoned to London, and the advice I received was unequivocal. Had I got a gun in the house? I had a pistol and only one remaining round; I searched for it and found it before returning to the living-room. It seemed to me now only a question of how Edal's execution could be carried out with the least possible distress to herself and to the humans who had made a pet of her. But the young vet, with his soft, deliberate Highland speech, said: 'It is not fair to consult a practitioner six hundred miles from the patient; he is not on the spot, and he has no opportunity to form an opinion as he would like. A bullet will prove nothing, and also it would spoil the body for postmortem. I think there is a very faint chance, and if you are willing to try I am. We shall have to give her very massive injections of antibiotics daily for five days, and if there is no improvement then she will go into a coma and die quietly.' I felt, and I expect looked, helpless; I could not see how we might approach Edal closely enough to touch her, let alone restrain and inject her.

We had one small help – the slotted back to the chair on which she was sitting. While I distracted her attention from the front, Jimmy contrived somehow to clip a lead on to her harness through the gaps in the woodwork. Then, by using a shepherd's crook, I managed to lift the lead through until it was on the same side of the chair-back as she was. Down this lead we slipped the hand loop of another, so that she could be held from two different directions; in this way we moved her slowly off the chair until we could take a turn of one lead round a table leg. Then we drew the other lead tight too, from a direction at right-angles to the first, and I took hold of her tail. Even when she was held from three points and could not turn her head she managed to lash her body like a wounded snake. It must have been little easier than injecting a flying bird, but that vet did it, as I was to see him do it so often in the future. Then we put on rubber thigh-boots, and half hoisted, half dangled her back upstairs and into her own room, leaving attached to her the two leads that would make further injections possible.

For the following four days we repeated the same procedure, and each day Donald MacLennan showed the same extraordinary legerdemain in injecting his moving target. We entered that room only in thigh-boots – we did not know then how little protection these would have offered had Edal reached and attacked us with purpose – and always as we went about the daily routine of cleaning the floor and changing her water she would drag her paralysed hindquarters after her in pathetic attempts to attack.

Then at last came a day when as I entered the room I seemed to sense something different in her appearance. She was curled up in her bed in the corner, so that only her head protruded from the blankets, and she seemed to look at me questioningly, as though I had been away for a long time and she was not sure whether it could be me. I came nearer to her, and suddenly she gave a little whimper of recognition as she had been used to when she was pleased to see Jimmy or myself. With great hesitation I gave her the back of my bare hand to sniff, and the greeting sounds redoubled. I knew then that, however long her physical paralysis might remain, she was now mentally normal. I knelt down on the floor beside her and put my face down to her and stroked her, and she rubbed her whiskers over my cheeks and pushed her nose into my neck while all the time she whimpered her welcome and affection for someone who had been away for so long.

Physically, her convalescence and recovery were protracted, but they progressed in precisely the sequence that the vet had hoped for; a returning power in her fore-quarters, then her hind limbs and, last of all, the ability to move her tail. It was early October before I was able to take her out of the house for the first time; that she had locomotive power was all that could be said, for her movements were awkward and ill-coordinated, each front foot raised high on the forward pace as if she were striking at something, and even in the hundred yards or so that I took her she lay down several times with a look of bewilderment and despair on her face. Very slowly, over a period of months, she regained the full use of all her muscles, began to play again, and to gallop and swim and dive. One day early in November I found her playing on the floor with a new toy that she had somewhere discovered; it was the single round of pistol ammunition with which I had been about to end her life on 8 August 1960.

The little seaside village four miles from Camusfeàrna had its own disciple of McGonagall, a small, sandy-haired man, at that time still under thirty. He is known as the Bard, and few local events of any significance escape celebration by his pen.

It was therefore to be expected that the death at the hands of Big Angus of my first otter Mijbil, with its many repercussions in the neighbourhood, would have drawn from him some prolonged utterance. I did, in fact, know of the existence of this ballad, but I had never heard it nor read it. The Bard was, indeed, only the barest of acquaintances.

Late one dark Saturday evening he and a friend of his own age, Duncan from the Isle of Skye, knocked at Camusfeàrna door. They explained that they had been mackerel fishing with an outboard dinghy, and had found themselves so near to Camusfeàrna Lighthouse that the Bard had decided to call upon us and recite his ballad. He was profusely and repetitively apologetic for his friend who, he said, had taken just a very little too much to drink in the pub before they had set out – not much too much, you will understand, but just enough to make the sensitive Bard feel apologies to be required. We brushed these to one side and led the two to the living-room; there it was clear that the friend was indeed lightly and happily inebriated, not in such a degree as to affect his always excellent manners, but enough to dim his consonants. The Bard's eye was but slightly glassy and his speech was perfect; only the insistence of his repeated apologies for Duncan's lapse of taste in visiting me in his present condition might have led one to suspect that Duncan had not been drinking alone.

With characteristic generosity of spirit they had brought their own whisky with them, and insisted upon providing the first round before they would drink any of my own. This is an excellent and well-tried Highland device for the production of a long and convivial session; the host must always offer one for the road, or in this case the sea, and the guest will always be offended if the host does not accept one in return. It is the perfect formula for oblivion, and quite early on in the evening I began to feel the probability that the Bard and his friend would pass the night at Camus-feàrna. After an hour or so I thought it might be as well to hear the ballad while the going was good, but the Bard turned suddenly coy, and boisterous bullying from Duncan only produced from him further earnest and insistent apologies for his friend's deplorable state. The Bard was still making interesting and intelligent conversation, and it seemed to me that he was perhaps insufficiently primed for public recitation; I filled their glasses again. As the evening wore on a subtle and curious shift of balance began to take place between Duncan and the Bard; the more Duncan drank the more sober he appeared to become, and the more the Bard drank the more he became patently drunk. By midnight the roles had become completely reversed; now it was Duncan, apparently as sober as a judge, who repeatedly apologized for the Bard and rebuked him for his gross behaviour, while the Bard's speech thickened to the point of inarticulacy and he became increasingly unsteady on his feet.

It was at about this point that he considered the time ripe for recitation of the ballad. Calling for total silence he climbed precariously to his feet and stood swaying like a tree in a high wind. Had he allowed himself support even with one hand on chimney-piece or chair-back, the occasion might still have been carried off, but it was the Bard's habit to deliver himself of his verses while standing rigidly to attention, and this position is notoriously difficult at any time after the first dozen whiskies. In the circumstances he did quite creditably to get through the first few lines, though my attention was distracted from them by the obvious imminence of disaster.

A wilder sway than any before canted the Bard backward at an angle from which there could be no recovery, and he toppled over with a tremendous crash into the wood basket, his music still within him. There he lay sprawling, replete, all interest in recitation gone, resisting any effort to set him upright again, clearly completely content where he was. We conferred with Duncan, who the while drank another glass of whisky to complete his sobering-up.

He was brisk and competent. We decided that we should have to carry the Bard to the dinghy in which he had arrived, which was not in the bay below the house but several hundred yards away at the mouth of the river. Outside, it proved to be one of those pitch-black nights without a single star visible in the sky, a night when even the calm surface of the sea gave back no reflection from above. Carrying electric torches, we transported the Bard stumblingly through the sand-dunes and over the steep shingle to the dinghy, the entire floorboards of which were covered in a layer of mackerel some six inches deep. With care and difficulty we sat him upon the front thwart; it was solicitude wasted, for he immediately slithered down among the fish and lay slimily at full length upon them and among them. Hauled into a sitting position again he at once collapsed anew by simple force of gravity; eventually Duncan decided to leave him in his prone position and concentrate upon starting the outboard engine. This took some considerable time, and when at length it did start Duncan remembered that he was unfamiliar with the reefs and the islands, and stopped it again in order to ask me for directions. The whole situation appearing to me precarious, and the Bard plainly unable to be of service to himself or others in the case of shipwreck, I played for safety, telling him to keep straight on down the bay until Camusfeàrna Lighthouse was on his starboard quarter before turning north to pass the light. This time the engine was more refractory, and it was another quarter of an hour before the dinghy finally chugged off into the darkness.

We stood listening to the direction of the engine sound,

anxious to be certain that he was following a safe course. After some minutes I had just said to Jimmy: 'I had no idea he had to go that far to get Camusfeàrna Lighthouse on his starboard quarter', when the engine suddenly stopped. It was a night so still that the least sound came from far across the water almost as though amplified; we listened for a long time to the recurrent stutter of the pull-starter, punctuated by an occasional oath, while the engine remained lifeless. Then Duncan seemed to abandon the attempt and turn his attention to the Bard unconscious among the mackerel. '*Wake* up, Johnnie! Wake *up*, Johnnie, can't you!' *Slap.* '*Wake up, Johnnie!*' *Slap.* ('Do you know, I believe he's slapping him with a fish?') 'For f—'s sake WAKE UP!' *Slap, slap.* No answering voice, not even a groan, and presently the whirring stutter of the starter began again. Jimmy and I were debating whether in all humanity we should not take a dinghy out and bring them back to Camusfeàrna ('the Bard will be pretty fishy by now') when quite suddenly the engine was away with a roar. We listened until the direction of the sound showed that the boat was past all immediate hazards, and we went home to bed.

Somewhere among all those fish there must have been concealed another bottle of whisky; either that or some curious chemical constituent of Duncan's blood caused alcohol to have upon him a long delayed and violent action, for next morning, the rigidly Calvinistic Sabbath morning of a West Highland village, a terrible sight was revealed to the scandalized eyes of the population. Tied up to the end of the village pier was a dinghy and prostrate and pillowed deep among the mackerel it contained were the blissfully unconscious forms of Duncan and the Bard.

It was not until long after this that I learned from the Bard that the text of the ballad that had been so tantalizingly cut short in recitation was lost for ever.

Not all Saturday evening visitors were as unproductive of recitation or of anecdote as was the Bard. My nearest neighbour, Calum Murdo MacKinnon, would often spend an evening at Camusfeàrna, and he is a talented raconteur of considerable repertoire, knowing any tale ancient and modern, sacred and profane, of the scattered local communities. One such evening, I remember, he devoted with much relish to the saga of a certain Dugalt, a bygone hero who in character and activity resembled nothing so much as an aboriginal Basil Seal, tormenting his fellows not only for his own needs and diversion, but almost with a sense of dedication. This archetypal trickster coloured his mischievous and predatory pranks with a rich hue of mockery, and an aura of success, for allied to his hare-brained approach to existence were a keen mind and a rumbustious sense of farce. He was, needless to say, without profession, travelling widely in Northern Scotland and living by his wits and his ever-increasing local knowledge.

He entered, and immediately monopolized the conversation at Camusfeàrna that evening, because we had been discussing a subject of perennial importance to an otter-keeping household, the prices of fish. The current cost of cod in our small local ports reminded Calum Murdo of a record figure once obtained by Dugalt for a medium-sized cod. Dugalt's peripatetic existence had at the time in question led him to Portree in the Isle of Skye and tied up to the pier there, he noticed a fishing boat in whose hold was a heavy catch of cod. He went aboard and began to examine these fish with an expert eye, rummaging about among them and turning them over busily; the crew, who knew his reputation for violence and invincibility too well to interfere, looked on in silence. At length he selected the largest of all the fish, and asked the boat's skipper if he might borrow it for an hour. The value of this cod would have been, say, five or six shillings, but fear of some such reprisal as had earned Dugalt's fame made the skipper accept the curious proposition without demur.

Armed with the cod, Dugalt set off into the township and knocked on the door of the first prosperous-looking house he found. Here he offered the obviously fresh and prime fish to the housewife for one shilling. She accepted with alacrity, supposing, perhaps, that the ridiculously low figure was due either to Dugalt's urgent need for alcohol or to dubious ownership of the wares he offered. Handing him the coin, she was about to take the fish from his hands when Dugalt remarked that a fine lady like her would not be wanting to soil her hands with gutting and scraping out the creature, and that as she hadn't argued about the price he would take it down to the sea and do the job for her. The delighted housewife gave him another sixpence out of the goodness of her heart and he made off towards the beach. As soon as he was out of sight of the house he turned briskly up another street that led away from the sea. Halfway up it he found another likely-looking house and sold the cod again on the same terms and with the same result. At the end of an hour, when he had sold the borrowed fish fourteen times, and collected a little over £1, he returned to the fishing boat. Throwing the cod contemptuously among the crew he called out: 'If the rest of your cod catch make the price this bugger did you've got a gold-mine down there.'

This tale whetted my appetite to learn more of the exploits of Dugalt, and soon Calum Murdo was in full swing. Dugalt, he explained, not only never paid for anything, he never even exposed himself to the risk of doing so, and to this unswerving lifelong purpose he called into play every scrap of local knowledge he could amass. He would listen seemingly without interest to local gossip in the villages he passed through, storing away for future use any scrap of in-

Agadir—Moulay Ahmed Alaoui, King Mohammed V of Morocco, and Crown Prince Hassan

'In bright oases of the desert South'

Edal in her new quarters

Teko demonstrates the use of his fingers

Edal

Above: Teko by his new pool

Right: Teko soon after his arrival at Camusfeàrna

Below: Teko and Dirk

formation that might be of use to him in some outrage as yet unplanned. Calum Murdo went on to provide an example of how he would use a combination of brains and knowledge for ends no more ambitious than the achievement of a free meal.

Dugalt called at a lonely, outlying moorland croft, about whose occupants he had mentally filed away some fact overheard, and asked for a meal. The woman of the house was not unkindly, but she was clearly harassed and distressed, explaining that with a sick husband to nurse and all the work of the croft to do single-handed she had no time to cook for anyone else. Her man was not old, she said, but for some time past he had appeared to be ailing and unfit for heavy work; now he was unable to do a hand's turn, and for much of the time was unable even to rise from his bed. 'It's worse than having a baby to look after,' she summed up, 'because poor John keeps me on the run for something or other the day long.'

'Give me a good square meal,' said Dugalt, 'and I'll cure John for you. I know more than a little of medicine.'

'Well,' she replied, 'that would be worth a lot more than the price of any meal, so I'll cook you what I've got, if you'll do what you can for the poor soul.'

John lay in a box-bed at the other side of the small room, glaring malevolently at Dugalt as he ate largely and at length of all that the house could provide. At length he sat back replete, wiped his lips, and announced that it was time he moved on. 'But,' cried the housewife in dismay, 'you promised to cure my husband!' 'Did I now?' said Dugalt blandly. 'So I did, so I did. Oh dear yes, so I did, and I must keep my word. Now would you be having such a beast as a cow about the place at all?' Yes, replied the housewife, she had a cow, the best cow in all the country. 'Well,' said Dugalt, 'I know fine just to look at John what it is that ails him, and there is only one cure for it. We must kill that cow at once, skin her, and wrap John up in the bloody hide while it's still warm. Then we make a kind of paste out of whatever dung is in the gut and apply it thickly to his neck and head, and then—'

Dugalt's prescription was cut short as John sprang from the bed with a roar of rage. 'You son of the devil! You *picht*!' he yelled, and seizing up a poker he rushed at Dugalt. Dugalt dodged him nimbly, and as he skipped lightly through the door he called back over his shoulder: 'Now you've got him going, keep him on the move! I told you I knew what ailed him, and I cured him like I said I would!'

Not a few of Dugalt's efforts to keep himself at the expense of others and in the comfort to which he felt himself entitled led to minor vendettas; in these he was, of course, the invariable victor. One such war he carried on for years against a minister of the Church of Scotland, and it had as its origin nothing more momentous than Dugalt's attempt to secure himself a comfortable bed for the night. It all began one frosty winter's night when Dugalt came knocking at the manse door at 2 am. The minister heard the knocking, but, hoping that his housekeeper would hear and answer, he pulled the bedclothes over his head and paid no heed. The knocking persisted. At length, reflecting that it would be unseemly to go to the housekeeper's room at that hour of night, and determined to be rid of this nuisance at any cost, the minister descended and opened the door himself. It was the first of his many meetings with Dugalt, and he acted as he would have done to any other tramp, with no suspicions of his visitor's special attributes. Dugalt asked for a bed, and the minister replied that he was welcome to sleep in the loft, where there was plenty of hay to provide a soft mattress. He even went further in his Christian spirit, and brought Dugalt a ladder, placing it for him against the entrance to the loft. It was very dark. Dugalt commented upon this, adding that as his eyesight was poor at the best of times the minister would be doing him a great service if he would ascend first and stretch down a reassuring hand to guide him into the loft. Longing to be rid of his visitor and to return to his warm bed, the minister acquiesced and began to climb the ladder. 'Be sure and call down to me when you're in the loft, Minister,' said Dugalt, 'and then I'll know you're steadying the top of the ladder for me before I start going up.' Presently the minister announced that he was kneeling on the loft floor and holding the ladder steady. With a quick wrench Dugalt twisted it fom his hands and lowered it carefully to the ground. 'If the bed up there's so comfortable, Minister, I'll let you be taking it yourself and I'll use your hard one in-by the house.' Entering the manse by the still open front door, he had little difficulty in locating the minister's bedroom and there he curled up comfortably between good linen sheets.

When the housekeeper got up in the morning she found Dugalt sitting demurely in the kitchen. He had, he said, a message from the minister – she would please cook Dugalt breakfast, and not just porridge or suchlike but a proper breakfast with bacon and eggs. The housekeeper, never of even temper, said she would take no such messages. 'Then,' retorted Dugalt, 'just you go and ask him yourself if what I say's not true.' 'I will that,' she said, and stumped up to the minister's bedroom. She returned in puzzlement some minutes later, to inquire when and where Dugalt had last seen the minister. 'Well,' said Dugalt, 'seeing you're his own housekeeper and will wish him no ill, I'll tell you the truth. He had me bring him Bessie Allison [the local tart] a bit after midnight and they spent the night in the hayloft together. Well, I'm sure you'll not blame the poor body, and I must be on my way now.' By midday he was plotting fresh mischief in a village ten miles away.

This was the first skirmish of what became a prolonged persecution by Dugalt of the minister, who was not, in fact, an unworthy adversary. In the days before his ordination he had been far from holy; he had been a boozer and a fighter, and because he was a man of huge stature and violent nature he had been a figure of fear. His conversion when it had come had been complete and uncompromising. Upon his ordination he had become a veritable tower of Calvinism, and a hell-fire preacher. At first, in the rough highland parish which had been his first charge, there had been few to listen to his ferocious sermons, for his predecessor was a weak man who had lost his congregation, and the rougher element of the district was determined that the new minister should not regain it. They were, however, unfamiliar with his history. On the second Sunday that he preached to the small handful of faithful, he found as he left the church that his way was barred by a crowd of young hooligans. Their leader, a massive youth with cold blue eyes and tow-coloured hair, came forward until he was within touching distance of the minister. 'Minister,' he said, 'it is written that if a man smite thee on the cheek thou shalt turn the other,' and with all his strength he swung his fist at the minister's cheek. He might as well have struck the solid rock of Scotland. The minister neither moved nor flinched. 'It is also written,' he remarked calmly, 'that such measure as is meted out to you shall ye mete out again,' and his fist swung up in a long slicing upper-cut that lifted the young man clean off his feet and laid him unconscious on the grass. The minister looked round at the others. 'And that's what you'll all get if you try that game with me,' he added as he bent and hauled their leader to his feet with a hand twisting his collar. He did more than haul him to his feet, for within an hour he had him and all his gang inside the church, and within a month had secured them, either by fear or by admiration, as permanent members of his congregation.

Now in due course Dugalt heard that it was none other than this formidable man of God upon whom he had played his prank in the hayloft, and curiosity drew him back to the village to hear one of the sulphurous sermons that were so widely talked of. It was thus that one Sabbath morning the minister perceived with some alarm the presence of Dugalt in one of the hinder pews of his church. For a short time Dugalt, to whom a church service held all the attraction of novelty, found himself almost interested by it all, and almost impressed despite himself by the fire of the minister's voice. But gradually his attention began to wander, and as it wandered he became bored, a condition which he was never prepared to tolerate for long. He looked around him in search of diversion.

In those days it was customary for the hill shepherds to bring their collie dogs to church; the shepherds would occupy the rear pews, and it was among them and some twenty or more dogs, that Dugalt now found himself. The dogs, he decided, were the possible raw material of pandemonium. He had some bread and cheese in his pocket, and this he began furtively to toss to the dogs, singling out for his favours those that seemed most thrawn in appearance. At the end of no more than a couple of minutes he had started a dog-fight, and the minister's words were drowned in a demoniac babel of yelping, snarling canine voices. Under the pretext of trying to separate the snapping mass of combatants Dugalt waded into them, kicking and throwing into the fight any who had so far escaped involvement. The mighty voice of the minister rose above the din in a great Gaelic bellow of anguish and despair, 'PUT OUT THAT FOOL! PUT OUT THAT FOOL!' to which Dugalt roared back above the sounds of battle, 'FHIRNACRANNAIG CHEID MI FHEINAMACH!' (literally, 'I'll go out myself, fellow of the churn!' – a reference to the resemblance between the pulpits and the milk churns of olden times.) He flounced out, slamming the door behind him, and when, after some painful minutes, order had been restored in the body of the church the ruffled and fuming minister addressed himself to his sermon. He still underestimated his opponent.

Once outside the church Dugalt looked round him in search of further entertainment. The first thing he noticed was that the key of the church door was in its lock, so as a preliminary to any further activity he turned it securely and put it in his pocket. He was now thoroughly enjoying himself, and beginning once again to bubble over with inventive mischief. Outside the church he noted a gig, the horse grazing on tether; he also noted the convenient placement of the church bellrope used for summoning the faithful to prayer. He connected horse and slack bellrope firmly together, tied the key of the church door to the horse's halter, and retired to a concealed vantage point to await developments. The horse grazed peacefully away until it reached a point at which the bellrope tightened and the bell began to toll; the horse started and flung up his head, and the bell jangled louder and more wildly. The horse sensed the connection between his own movements and these sounds that seemed directed at him, and began to back and to plunge and to rear, and the more he did so the louder and more feverishly the bell clanged. Above its din came the sound of shouting and hammering within the church door. It was a door built sturdily and uncompromisingly, as befitted the God worshipped beyond it; there was no possible way out but the window high in the wall beyond the pulpit. One by one the whole congregation, young and old, lean and stout, sylphlike maidens and balloon-like matrons, shepherds and dogs, made their painful and undignified exit to land sprawling in the grass. Dugalt is said to have rated this exploit high in his annals of outrage, considering that he had made the best possible use of all materials and opportunities to hand.

The incident had, however, in no way satiated his appetite for baiting this aggressive man of God; it served, on the contrary, as a stimulus to further planning, for the minister had preached against Dugalt from the pulpit. His opportunity came later that summer. The minister had a large glebe (the piece of land that is attached to the manse or residence of a minister of the Church of Scotland), and in the year in question he had grown upon the glebe a particularly fine crop of corn. There had long been a disputed right of way across this patch of ground, and as the corn began to ripen the congregation of a rival church began, not unprompted by Dugalt, to exert their supposed right of passage across it. Fearful of the minister's reputation with his fists, they confined their activities to the dark hours or to such times as he was known to be absent, and he had not been able to lay his hands upon a single one of his opponents. Frustrated from physical and satisfying methods of deterrence, he had erected *Trespassers Will Be Prosecuted* notices, and now made it his custom to patrol the property from dusk until a full hour after dark. A lesser man than Dugalt would have considered that his plan to make the minister's life a misery had already succeeded admirably, but Dugalt was an artist, and insisted always upon a full dramatic climax to every episode. The presence of the minister in the cornfield after dark gave him opportunity to display his full virtuosity of technique.

Choosing a night that was neither too light nor too dark for his purpose, he armed himself with a heavy stick and set off stealthily for the glebe. Prospecting carefully from its perimeter, he could just make out the figure of the minister standing in a line of corn flattened by the feet of his rival congregation. Dugalt watched him patrol up and down this strip, and manoeuvred himself into a position at which the outermost point of the minister's beat would bring him to within a few yards of the watcher. Here he waited. At the next approach of the sentry, Dugalt leapt out upon him with a roar, beating him with his stick and yelling, 'Caught you at last, you bugger! You good for nothing trespasser! you *evil* person – trampling the corn of the man of God! How dare you spoil the minister's crop! I'll teach you to set yourself up against a holy man! If he was here himself he'd give you worse than this!' Through the yells and the whacks came the minister's distraught and pleading voice as he tried to ward off the rain of blows. 'It's *me*! I *am* the minister! I'm on my own ground!' but Dugalt affected to hear nothing, and the minister, caught totally unprepared, had no option but to take to his heels. As he ran for the house Dugalt pursued at his tail, beating him about the back and buttocks and screeching his denunciation. Only when the minister reached the manse and slammed the door in his face did he stop, and said in a loud, reflective stage-voice: 'This is the manse. I wonder if that could have been the minister himself, poor soul.'

THE CIRCULATION OF LIGHT

Child after child, as time disposes,
Comes crying down to the blind mazes,
And, with this world, puts on a pelt,
The wolfskin of ancestral guilt.
As if for clarity was needed
A creature on all fours and blinded,
And prerequisite, such a night,
For the beatitudes of light.

Some catch no gleam though; doom, it jars
Their wincing ghost, the manias
Hedged round about them are too thick
For the slim verities of shock
To pierce. Transfixed, till time erases
The beating life of its gross mazes,
Wait they, bereft of wrong and right,
The circulation of the light.

By energies foregone and banished,
By just so much are we diminished,
And yet it is by shades out-thrown
From what we are we can be known,
If we take back from the dark mirror
Of someone else, both love and terror;
Initiate so, by second sight,
The circulation of the light.

Here and today, past time it glosses
With a bad cloud the human faces,
And men, their real need and hunger,
Are blurred for me by some past anger,
Dreams that still colour and work on
My time, long past their origin
In those whose life my life possessed;
Rid me, I say, of this foul taste!
But still it breaks through day and night,
The circulation of the light.

THOMAS BLACKBURN

4

Some Past Anger

A LITTLE BEFORE Christmas 1960 I left Camusfeàrna for North Africa. Jimmy and Terry were in charge of the otters, and a friend who wanted sanctuary in which to write of an expedition from which he had recently returned had undertaken to run the household and deal with any emergency that might arise. I knew that I should not see Camusfeàrna again for several months.

I passed the winter and the spring in Morocco, Tunisia and Algeria; as week succeeded week my curiosity in the strange, dark unfolding of North African Arab destiny crumbled. Yet I could not leave. I became as a sleepwalker or as one in a hypnotic state, in a state of mental and physical confusion, living in an evil dream from which I found it impossible to awake. I grew weak with dysentery, and towards the end it was only with the greatest of effort that I could stir myself to complete the necessary routine of the day. Clinically, I recognized symptoms I had seen in others; they were those of multiple division of aim, for I no longer knew why I was there. Once I thought that I should write a book about those months, and I even knew the title, *The Haywire Winter*. But now I think that I never shall, and this chapter will, mercifully, be all that remains of it. The images that come back to me now are those of March and April, when my ill-health, lethargy and depression were at their greatest, and they are for the most part of two rooms several hundred miles apart.

One of them is, I suppose, within spitting distance of a real street, a shoddy street, but complete with all the properties of an intermediate civilization. There are shops selling ironmongery, radios and bicycles. There is nothing exotic about the street but for the people who promenade its length; Berbers from the mountains, in coarse woollen *djellebahs* with the silver dagger slung under the left armpit; turbaned Negroes from an ancient race of slaves; bearded and black-capped Jews from the Mellah; a host of tattered beggars. That was my street; even then I do not think I knew its name, for it is nowhere written unless on some town plan. From it lead alleys, perhaps six foot wide, of beaten earth with high solid-seeming mud walls, the infinite, bewildering alleys of an Arab town. In them are the smells of spice, ordure, charcoal-cooking, human beings and impregnated dust. In daylight the narrow view of the sky above is blank and blue, anonymous; at night the stars show as a studded belt of diamonds on dark velvet.

The room in which I lived belonged to, but was not part of, an Arab hotel; its entrance a few yards down a dust alley, a few hundred years away from the street outside. At the entrance to the alley, a stone bollard blocks entrance to wheeled vehicles; small children play leap-frog on the bollard but not over the dividing years. The hotel has a door of faded, once-gaudy paintwork and wrought-iron tracery. Beyond the door lies a square, tiled courtyard and a wealth of heavy vegetation. More precisely, there were four banana trees, growing from the four corners of a pool made sinister either by association or by its inmates. When I first knew the courtyard the trees, whose giant leaves, withered brown at their edges, invade the whole rectangle of the gallery above, grew from concrete containers painted in a brilliant shade of blue; but the roots pressed outward and split them, and the paint has flaked away from the concrete.

One tree stands, unclothed, so to speak, from the waist down, and the soil has fallen from between the naked roots. At another corner a tree has gone while its concrete container remains; there is a little bed of earth there, and some small, hesitant verdure competes, unsuccessfully, with rusty razor blades and the butt-ends of cigarettes. Razor blades lie, too, at the floor of the pool, which has lost its splendour. I do not know the species of the fish that inhabit it; there are perhaps two dozen of them, some muddy brown and some red. Like the hotel, they are sickly: one is encrusted with erupting boils, white and diseased upon the red scales. Perhaps this disfigurement was caused by the cat (there were two, but one died of typhus, vomiting out all that was left of its digestive system from the gallery into the patio below) who crouches on the crumbling concrete and swipes with clumsy, amateurish zeal at any fish within reach. As far as I knew, the cat had never actually caught a fish, just as no one had actually destroyed the hotel, but everything was dying of a mortal sickness.

I lived in the hotel's *garçonnière* which was not, by any standards, an ideal residence, and for which I paid five shillings a day. A vast but uncomplicated key turns three times to open its door, beyond which mounts a steep and ruinous stairway in total darkness, for the lights do not work. My room itself is high, bleak and decaying; there is never enough light by which to read, for only a single weak bulb dangles from the remote ceiling. There is a damaged wardrobe, a table with one leg missing, a chair and a bed; there is no covering to the floor, and on the walls are obscene grafitti. At moments this room appeared the limit of my world.

From this room led another containing a wash-basin, a lavatory and a bath, but the water system had been long defunct. A trickle of cold water could be extracted from the bath tap; this would eject from the waste-pipe a scurrying mass of big brown cockroaches, then a greenish slime would rise slowly and remain, for no water could escape from the bath.

As the image of that place returns to me now it is at evening towards the close of Ramadan. The voices of the beggars reach crescendo, for they must collect enough coins with which to eat before, at sundown, the siren sounds the close of the fast for the day. Directly under my window, at one side of the alley entrance, stands a blind beggar in a tattered *djellebah*. His right hand is outstretched, his left cupping his elbow; his head is laid slightly to one side, and he wears what one might take at first sight to be a self-deprecatory grin, as though he were an important person in fancy dress, doing this to accede to the whim of someone else. Twenty-five times a minute, for hours on end by day and by night, he calls at lung-pitch '*Allah*!' Five paces from him, at the other side of the alley entrance, squats another, the hood of his *djellebah* fallen forward over his face (mercifully, for he has neither eyes nor nose). He is not content with so simple a supplication; he shouts a whole sentence of five complex words that are meaningless to me. There is an interval of five seconds between each repetition, an interval so precise that he must count. There can be little else to do inside that dark, muffled world where the only reality is the touch of coin on palm.

A few paces again from him squats a woman, still young and veiled despite the humiliation of her condition. On and around her lap crouch at least three (sometimes it seemed to me to be many more) small children, all, one would have said, below the age of three. They move and squirm and whimper among the folds of her clothing like a litter of blind puppies; their mother, if it is she, rocks from side to side as though in anguish, and her continual plaint is wild and high as the keening of jackals. The little ones are learning to speak; they are being taught the beggar's whine and the imploring gesture. At the sight of a likely looking passer-by the woman will nudge one of them, and, as if by doing so she sets in motion some ill-regulated clockwork machine, some one of her litter will disentangle its little limbs to stretch out a hand as small as a monkey's and set up a ready wail in imitation of her own. If the child does not respond she will pinch it until it cries in earnest.

There are other beggars whose voices reach me, none the less insistent for their greater distance, and beyond their continuous plaint comes the steady rhythm of drums and cymbals. The tops of the snow-covered mountains catch the last of the sun as it slants down into the Atlantic; above the palms and the minarets the homing flights of white egrets are at first still pale against the sky, then they become darker and the late stragglers change to silhouette. Two hooded figures squat in the dust of the alley outside my door, slitting the throats of chickens over a small drain; there is a terrible commotion from the dying wings as the knife cuts through each neck. The dust soaks up the blood slowly, cats paw at it petulantly and lick their toes. One evening at the close of Ramadan . . .

The siren shrills high and thin, a violin-bow of sound arched over the wide confines of the fantastic city, and suddenly there is everywhere the smell of food where before the air held only the dry tang of spice. The voices of the beggars are silent; the predominant sound now is of dancers' drums. Turbaned figures eating bowls of thick *harrissa* soup sit huddled on my doorstep, for it is the only free seat above ground-level. The light goes altogether, and I linger on because I have become one of the alley's ghosts.

One night I woke from a dream to hear the blind beggar's invocation from the street outside mingled with my own voice saying: 'Give me back my eyes.' But to whomever these words were addressed they were no more heeded than the beggar's, who asked so little while I asked so much. At dawn I would wake, or half-wake, from the tension of my dreams; I remember, objectively, that I would slip my feet out of bed and remain sitting there for long, with my eyes resting unfocused upon some ancient obscene scrawl or upon some crevice in the crumbling plaster of my cell. An Arab friend said to me: 'You must go – otherwise you never will. People can die like this, without reason; they turn inward and they are against themselves.'

Again, I dream that I am following the footprints of somebody who is lost. They are plain at first, for I walk in the red dust of a desert, and I pass the bones of a camel. Somewhere close at hand there is a palm oasis, but I skirt it as though by intention. Presently the sky seems to become lower above my head; I realize that I have left the desert and begun to climb. I am in the dry bed of a river filled with shale and stones, and at my flanks are low brick-coloured cliffs of dry earth. (Curious stones are embedded in this bank, like raisins in a cake.) The footprints have become very difficult to follow, and all the time the sky is getting lower and darker. Then I see where someone has scrambled up the mud wall at one side of the river. I try to struggle up, but the loose grit gives beneath my fingers and my feet, and my mouth is choked with dust so that I gasp for breath. I seem always to be slipping further and further downward, but I never regain the river bed I have left. A hand that I can feel but cannot see grips my right wrist and pulls me upward with enormous strength. It relinquishes me upon the lip of the drop, and I lie there with the feeling of the thick red dust packed under my finger-nails. My throat is dry and hurts terribly, but I am filled with a feeling of urgency, and I rise and begin to climb again. I am sure of the trail, and yet I cannot see it, for I am climbing through harsh knee-high aromatic shrubs that rasp against my clothing, and it is almost dusk. Then I understand that I am following a blood trail; even in the dimness the drops glow like rubies on the small hard leaves. The slope becomes always steeper and steeper; it rises to meet the sky, and then suddenly I am beyond the line of verdure and out on the clean mountain snow. Now the footprints are clear once more, but there is blood in the centre of each. I am labouring and far gone in exhaustion, and to make sure of following the trail I place my own naked feet in the naked prints before me. Then the sky closes in upon me and I stop, for I know that the trail I am following is my own.

> All through the night I watched the ruined door,
> Intent, as gamblers watch the fall of dice;
> Awaiting verdict, prisoner at the bar.
> Shadows crossed it, once I heard a voice.
>
> At dawn a mountain hind emerged alone,
> Quick step and sure as with some purpose known,
> Some will that animates the unmarrowed bone,
> For through her ribs I saw the lichened stone.
>
> At noon a naked form was there;
> A watcher, indistinct, began
> To follow as it turned and ran
> Seaward over the shore.
>
> At dusk a broken wheel appeared
> Held by a hand I could not see,
> And I knew that someone whom I feared
> Had discovered an empty room in me.

His Excellency Moulay Ahmed El Alaoui, scion of the ruling royal Alaouite dynasty of Morocco, cousin of the Sultan who had returned from exile as His Majesty King Mohammed V, and intimate of the heir apparent, Moulay

Hassan, combined, at that time, the multiple appointments of Minister of Information, Minister of Tourism, and Minister of Fine Arts; in one of these roles I have already mentioned his activities at Agadir. We had for some time been acquaintances, but each awaited, I think, a nearer intellectual contact than was forthcoming on either side. We shared, I now perceive, common and paradoxical qualities of extreme shyness and extreme arrogance, drawing from each of us a sidelong glance of mutual recognition.

Moulay Ahmed, like many less exalted Moors brought up under the colonial regime of France, had suffered from eye disease and was blind in one eye; the other was roving, observant, mistrustful and xenophobe, but essentially *sympathique*. My habit of wearing dark glasses, due to chronic conjunctivitis following a dust storm in the desert two years before, had excited his adverse criticism, though it was not without precedent at court. (Mohammed V had virtually started a fashion that French 'councillors' were quick to seize upon as an example of ill manners.) This, together with a typically British reluctance to commit myself to foreign languages, had earned me from Moulay Ahmed the name of *Gavin le taciturne*, a noteworthy example of elevation from the timid to the sinister. At one time and another I had called Moulay Ahmed by many different and not always complimentary names, according to the mercurial flow of his temperament and its effects, adverse or otherwise, upon my own activities.

In late February 1961, Moulay Ahmed had for some time been intermittently preoccupied with the impending visit of two British notables whose true status had remained an enigma to me. According to Moulay Ahmed, their names were Monsieur Blanchehead and the Duc de Blitz, and they were two *grands chasseurs* for whom he was issuing special permits to shoot moufflon (the great wild Barbary sheep of

Morocco) in the Atlas Mountains. In vain I protested that among the British ducal houses there was no such alarming title as the Duke of Blitz, apt though it might appear for a famous big-game hunter, and that Blanchehead was at the least an improbable English name. This last misnomer resolved itself into 'Kenneth Whitehead', a name as then unfamiliar to me, but on the authenticity of His Grace of Blitz Moulay Ahmed remained unshakeable. These two were to arrive at Casablanca on the 26th, and as honoured guests of the government, Moulay Ahmed deemed it fitting that he should meet them in person.

Now despite the eminence of his several offices Moulay Ahmed possessed no car, and on more than one previous occasion he had availed himself of my own Sahara Land Rover, whose many modifications made it a moderately dignified and not uncomfortable form of transport. (In fact he was so charmed by this car that he had considered, for at least fifteen seconds, ordering an exactly similar one for his own use.) It was therefore no great surprise to me when he suggested that I should drive him to Casablanca from Rabat to meet Mr Whitehead and the mysteriously explosive nobleman. He wished to leave Rabat at six o'clock in the morning, and urged me to be waiting him punctually at that time. This arrangement was made two days before the arrival of the British party. I did not expect to see Moulay Ahmed in the intervening period, more especially as I knew that the following day the king was to undergo some minor operation and that this would inevitably throw the whole palace government into a state of confusion.

On the afternoon in question I had just finished lunch and was drinking a cup of coffee on the terrace of the Tour Hassan Hotel when a page brought me a message that His Excellency the Minister of Information was in a car below and wished to speak to me at once. It did not occur to me that I should be away for more than a minute or two, so I left my coffee unfinished and my cigarette burning in the ashtray. Outside I found Moulay Ahmed in a handsome car driven by a resident Frenchman whom I knew slightly, an amateur of Berber folklore; his photographs and tape recordings were well known in modern Moroccan cultural circles. Moulay Ahmed beckoned me to the back seat. '*Monte, mon cher,*' he said, 'we are going for a little drive.' I excused myself on the grounds of an engagement in a quarter of an hour, but he would take no refusal. '*Monte, mon cher,*' he repeated, 'we shall be back in ten minutes, and you can keep your appointment.' There seemed no answer to this, so I got in. 'But where are we going?' I asked. 'Just for a little drive – it's such a beautiful day – just for ten minutes.' We left the town, and went northwards along the cliff-line; soon we had left the roads and tracks altogether and we were driving on smooth, hard, green pasture. I had never seen Moulay Ahmed in this mood before; he picked flowers and rhapsodizèd over their beauty, exulted in the smell of fennel crushed in his hand, and explained to me exactly how it should be used in cooking fish. He was like a child on a holiday in the country, finding delight in all around him. By the time I was half an hour late for my appointment I decided that it was best forgotten.

Some two hours after we had set out Moulay Ahmed looked at his watch, and gave a sudden exclamation. 'Quick! I must be at the airport at four o'clock to meet the king's surgeon from Switzerland, and we have only just enough time. Drive straight to that road over there.' He indicated a row of houses some half a mile or more away, where a single parked car suggested the presence of at least a track connecting with civilization.

When we reached the road we were separated from it by a ditch some six feet wide and six feet deep. There was no bridge. The owner of the little parked car had emerged from his house and was preparing to drive away. Yelling at this unfortunate to stop in the name of the government, Moulay Ahmed jumped out, cleared the ditch with a flying leap, and in a matter of seconds was under way in his commandeered transport. His voice came back on the wind: 'Follow me to the airport.'

'That's all very well,' remarked the Frenchman, with the faintest ruffling of his normally suave demeanour, 'but exactly how are we supposed to follow him to the airport, *hein*?'

We cruised up the ditch and down the ditch, but there was no way across it. Finally, we had to return the way we had come, and take the conventional route from the town to the airport. There everything was in confusion. The reception committee was vast, and at its heart was Moulay Ahmed, talking vehemently. Some said the surgeon had lost his instruments en route (I never learned whether there was any truth in this widely circulated rumour). At the end of half an hour or so there was a general movement towards the cars, and I seized a fleeting opportunity to pluck at the harassed Moulay Ahmed's sleeve. 'You won't need us any more now?' His single sound eye looked at me distractedly and irritably. 'Yes, yes, follow in the procession to the hotel.'

Once arrived there it was even more difficult to secure his much-divided attention, but I was determined that there should be no further misunderstanding. I had the audacity to stand between him and the door so that he could not enter without somehow clarifying the situation. I said: 'Is that all now, until six o'clock in the morning?' 'Yes, you may go now – but please be punctual in the morning, six o'clock here without fail.'

I got up at a quarter past five, and I was waiting in the car at six. I was still waiting in the car at eight. By then I thought

I might as well breakfast in the hotel. I did so, and then telephoned to Moulay Ahmed's private number, but there was no reply. The hotel informed me that they had called him by telephone at five am – it was his habit, since he lived in a small flat without servants, to have himself awoken every morning in this manner so out of keeping with his status. I tried him at the Ministry, for, being of largely nocturnal habit, there was no hour in the twenty-four at which he might not sometimes be found there (many a distant *caid* or *khalifa* had reason to resent this idiosyncracy, finding himself dragged from a deep provincial sleep at three am to answer by telephone how many Danish tourists had visited his area in 1959, or the exact species of fish available to sportsmen in some remote lake of the Atlas Mountains), but the Ministry was closed. I telephoned to both numbers every half hour throughout the morning, and by one o'clock I was beginning to become fretful. At half past one I explained the situation to a government official of my acquaintance, but not of my approval, who had sauntered into the hotel. 'No doubt he has his reasons,' he replied, eyeing me with detestation. And I had mine, I said, and began to expatiate on the theme that if the Minister of Tourism wanted help from a foreigner it would be fitting to display more courtesy. He looked at me with profound malevolence. 'If you don't like this country, why don't you get out of it and stay out?' That, I replied, was precisely what I intended to do. It was not a happy encounter.

I remained in the hotel until four o'clock in the afternoon, when this same official brought me a message from Moulay Ahmed. He was unable to go to Casablanca; would I therefore go there at once myself and find the Duke of Blitz's party at such and such a hotel. There I would please take charge. 'And do what?' I asked. 'That's all he said.'

I was going south anyway, so I would, I thought, call at

the hotel and explain to the unfortunate duke what had happened. I arrived in Casablanca at half past five.

The Duke and Duchess of Blitz were more intelligible as Mr and Mrs Ian Biggs; with them was Mr Kenneth Whitehead and a young French *pied noir* who kept an inn in the mountains. On Moulay Ahmed's instructions he had driven two hundred miles to meet the party; he was to arrange their hunting trip, but Moulay Ahmed had issued no permits, and like myself this unfortunate had received no further instruction of any sort; he had expected to be briefed by Moulay Ahmed in Casablanca. We sat in a circle, glumly discussing what to do. Eventually we reached the conclusion that it would be better for the party to spend the night in the hotel and telephone to the Ministry in the morning. We were halfway through dinner, when I became aware of a curious sound in the street outside. It was unmistakably wailing, and it grew in volume every second.

Mrs Biggs went out into the hall and asked one of the hotel staff what had happened. He looked terrified, and stammered as he replied. 'They say the king is dead.'

The implications of this news took little time to sink in; to anyone having even the smallest knowledge of Morocco the situation was grave in the extreme. The heir, now King Hassan II, was not, at that time, popular in the country; there were strong undercurrents of political and personal feelings; more than one party aspired to seize power, and Morocco has never enjoyed a reputation for pacific persuasion. In fact, a revolution appeared, at the least, very probable. One thing, anyway, seemed obvious – this put paid to the Duke of Blitz's hunting trip, and would probably have done so even if the Ministries of Tourism and of Information had not been combined. Morocco would become a nation in mourning for its first hero of independence; a nation in fear, too, and probably under military rule; there would be no time for frivolities such as big-game hunting. The Frenchman, André Deschaseaux (who later became a close friend of mine), would know all this much better than I, but I was doubtful of our capacity to convey it to the single-minded Blitz party. André, being a Frenchman among four Englishmen, left it to me, and I was not wholly successful. I tried to explain by stages; the fact, the political implications, finally the probable effect upon the personal plans of any foreign visitor. One could not blame them for taking it hardly; they had planned this journey – not, incidentally, an inexpensive one – a long time before; they had received assurances and promises, and now the whole card-castle was falling to the ground. But as the sounds from the street grew more and more violent, these considerations began to appear to me increasingly minor.

When there is trouble in Morocco its centre has usually been, during this century, in Casablanca; here (and among Berber tribesmen who have often been ill-informed as to the issues involved) is the heart of violence. It seemed to me eminently desirable that the Blitz party should leave Casablanca for the south, where in many districts of the mountains a Europophile attitude still existed among the Berber tribespeople. I put forward this suggestion; that the whole party should leave now for Asni, André's inn in the foothills of the Atlas. André agreed; he anyway, he said, must return there at once, for his young wife and child were all alone. The party could be divided between the two cars, and we could travel in convoy.

But both André and myself were unknown to the visitors, and they were understandably anxious to consult higher authority before committing themselves to any immediate plan of action. The duchess telephoned to the British Embassy in Rabat, and received unequivocal counsel. There had been serious rioting in Rabat, rumours of even greater violence in certain districts of Casablanca, and the British party were strongly advised not to leave the hotel until the Embassy considered the situation restored to normal. This official recommendation they accepted; no doubt my description of my car as a Land Rover did little to convey a picture of the heavy closed vehicle it was, and was not reassuring. The ducal party decided to remain in Casablanca; André and I decided to leave for the south in convoy. Frankly, I did not expect to see the Blitzes again.

André, knowing the by-ways of the town intimately, preceded me. In some sense our survival value was divided, for while he had all the local knowledge, and was fluent both in Berber and Arabic, my car had all the appearance of officialdom, and carried the word 'Britannia' in Arab characters fore and aft and on both sides. It would also be an extremely difficult car to overturn. We had arranged that should André run into trouble he should abandon his own car and board the Land Rover.

The psychological climate of the populace seemed to vary between one quarter of the town and another. Everywhere the streets were packed; it seemed that of Casablanca's million inhabitants no human being was indoors that night. They formed a densely pressed throng right across the streets, chanting in unison, swaying, a potentially murderous mass, but as yet insufficiently organized for concerted violence. Nearer to the suburbs there were a few broken shop windows, a few overturned cars, but we were never seriously molested. A few stones, or lighter missiles, struck the body and wheels of the Land Rover, but despite the extreme scarcity of wheeled traffic on the streets there was no real attempt to arrest our snail's pace progress. The crowds gave way reluctantly to André's headlamps and horn, and immediately closed in again behind him, so that to avoid isolation I had to keep my front bumpers within inches of his rear.

Once clear of the town and out upon the deserted country roads a new alarm seized me. I had noted André's extreme exhaustion, and now, following him at the prearranged speed of 110 kph that was the Land Rover's maximum, I was horrified to see that every few minutes he would give a wild swerve that took the car to within centimetres of the road's edge. I imagined that on each of these occasions he had momentarily fallen asleep; and it was with enormous effort that I overtook him and persuaded him to stop. I explained my fears. He grinned. 'Don't worry; when I am very tired, very sleepy, this is my way of keeping myself awake; I should have told you. As long as I do that I never fall asleep.'

The first of the road-blocks was out by the time we reached Settat; there had been serious rioting and many dead, but the army were now in control. We reached Marrakesh at one thirty, and there André and I parted company, he to Asni, and I to the single room I rented in the *medina*.

Morocco during the following week was ominous; the explosion seemed imminent. I awoke early in the morning to the sound of children's voices chanting in a short, staccato, uncompromising rhythm. From my window I could see the procession marching down the street in step to the words of their chant: '*Bas, bas Moulay Hassan! Bas, bas Moulay Hassan!*' (down with Moulay Hassan). One glance at the demonstrators showed that this was an organized programme; there were perhaps two hundred of them, and they were all of the same age group, say between eight and twelve years old. They passed on their way, and all was quiet again, the streets deserted.

An hour later the sound of the same refrain came near, but this time the voices were tenor rather than treble, for this was a different group, some five hundred boys of between twelve and fifteen years. After a further hour came an older group of adolescents; then at about mid-morning came a thousand men marching to the same hymn of hate, '*Bas, bas Moulay Hassan!*' It was clear that whether or not there was to be a revolution there was at least going to be a bull-frog show of strength on both sides. I went down to the *Gueliz*, which before independence used to be the French town, to glean what news I could. The central Post Office, an enormous building, presented the most extraordinary spectacle. It was shut, and guarded by something like a battalion of soldiery with fixed bayonets. In front of this closed rank patrolled numerous officers armed with submachine-guns. Nearer, the whole square was a dense mass of Moroccan humanity. They moved slowly, viscously, unnaturally silent; only occasionally, from the heart of the crowd, a single voice, certain of anonymity, called out the words of rebellion, '*Bas Moulay Hassan!*'

Mingling innocently with this menacing press were a few wide-eyed American tourists in the charge of city guides. There are some thirty of these guides in Marrakesh; of these only two, I think, speak any English. One of them is semi-attached to the Mamounia Hotel, and now I overheard fragments of conversation between his clients and himself.

'Say, Abdullah, what are these guys calling out – something about Hassan?'

'They are saying "Long live our new Sultan".'

'And what are the soldiers doing?'

'They parade in honour of our new Sultan.'

'Well, that's swell, but I guess I got to get to that Post Office somehow – I got mail to collect.'

'The Post Office is closed; it is a day of national holiday in honour of the new Sultan.'

'Does this holiday last more than one day?'

'It is not yet known,' the guide answered with aplomb and good humour. 'It may last for some time.'

It did, in fact, last for some time. During it, certain curious documents in my possession came into their own. Some weeks before Moulay Ahmed had, with a characteristically impulsive generosity, furnished me with certain papers whose utility I had not at the time fully appreciated or fore-seen. The first of these was a page-long letter in Arabic characters that I am unable to read: it has been so variously translated to me that it is difficult to choose a rendering. (My mule boy in the mountains pored over it for several minutes, nodding contentedly to himself; when at length he handed it back to me, I asked him what it meant, '*De ne pas vous frapper,*' he summed up succinctly.) The second item, of infinitely greater power in emergency, was a police *coupe file*, a thick rectangle of pasteboard twice the size of a visit-ing card, and bearing across it a diagonal strip of the red and green police colours. Such cards are no rarity in themselves; they are not infrequently issued to the press for strictly limited periods varying from a half an hour to a day. Mine, however, was permanent and without date, and it allowed me to contravene any police regulation or order. Whether in fact it would have excused a murder I never put to the test, but certainly it dealt with every imaginable kind of traffic offence, swept me past police or army road-blocks and, used in conjunction with the letter ordering people not to strike me, bore me merrily through customs and customs police formalities.

In return for such capricious favours bestowed by Moulay Ahmed I had collaborated with him in various egregious projects. The most ignominious of these, as I remember it, was the dubbing with English commentary of a Moroccan documentary film on the first pan-African conference at Casablanca. The film, at the time when I attempted the dubbing, had been joined in random sequence and without cutting; it was only shown during my recording, it was explained to me, in order to clarify the time factor. The result was chaos. At first the screen showed the bows of a large but antiquated yacht cutting through a calm sea. 'Now for the first time,' I began sonorously (I had put much conscientious work into this, and was determined to give value for favours received), 'the white bows of the yacht *Harriyah*, whose name means freedom, carve the calm waters of Casablanca harbour. With renewed hope for the future of Africa' (cut to a long shot of a West African potentate whose dignified white robes are blown above the waist by an airfield hurricane; frenzied attendants try to restore him to decency). I stammer, and continue a little wildly: 'We are here to welcome President Nasser himself, who salutes the flag of Moroccan independence as on this historic occasion he stands upon *Harriyah*'s deck seeing our shores for the first time. . . .' (cut to a close-up of a small fishing boat trying frantically to avoid the *Harriyah*). I choke, but manage to continue with some hesitation: 'At this solemn moment when the eyes of all the world are upon us . . .' (suddenly the screen is filled with a hilarious banqueting scene – zoom in to the preternaturally gigantic face of Nkrumah; the film suddenly speeds up until he is eating chocolates and roaring with silent laughter in a mad, hysteric frenzy), 'when, ahem, the eyes of all the world are upon us . . .' (flicker, flashes, a clapperboard with the legend Take One, then the bows of *Harriyah*, but this time going backwards, followed by Nkrumah spewing out whole chocolates into his hand.) 'For Chrisake,' I said, '*no one* could dub this film' – but I was there for a further hour.

Now with the country in a state of national emergency my papers were more than a luxury toy, they were a *sine qua non*. But for the moment I had forgotten them.

When, some hours later, I tried to return to the *medina* I encountered a road-block at its periphery. Two machine-guns were very much in evidence. An officer carrying a submachine-gun approached my window; I observed with disapproval that this weapon was cocked and that the safety catch was off. 'Where are you going?' he asked. 'To the *medina*.' 'The *medina* is closed – no car may enter or leave.' 'But,' I protested, 'I live there, and I need the car.' 'It is impossible, turn round and go back.' Suddenly I remembered my talismans, and produced from my wallet the letter and the *coupe file*. He glanced quickly at them; then, 'You should have shown me these at once,' he said, and at a rapid order the road-block was opened.

There was an armed sentry at my door. 'Why are you here?' I asked. 'My orders,' he said briefly. I could not tempt him into conversation.

All the afternoon following the death of the king the sound of lamentation came from somewhere behind the mosque of the Koutabia, a chant whose very simplicity and constant repetition evoked some unfathomable ocean of grief. '*Ya Sidna! Ya Sidna! Ya Sidna!*' (Oh our Lord), the note of the middle syllable held for long seconds before falling with a sob to the last.

One evening at the close of Ramadan . . .

After what was, in the circumstances, a surprisingly short delay, the Duke of Blitz's hunting trip was arranged. I accompanied them on the second day. On mule-back we climbed long ridges of the foothills among pungent shrubs and flowering lavender; the rifles took up their positions looking out across a gorge while some fifty Berber beaters swept a few miles of country towards them. Each of us shot a wild boar, and in response to excited urgings from my Berber companion I contributed an unfortunate three-legged jackal.

On the first day the party had set out to shoot moufflon, but I was feeling too ill to accompany them. One moufflon was killed (these giant wild sheep have become rare in Morocco since the massive depredations of the Army of Liberation while living off the country), and the next morning the two Moroccan daily newspapers carried front-page pictures of a moufflon draped over my Land Rover. 'In the presence of the famous English writer, Gavin Maxwell, two superb moufflons weighing respectively . . . and . . . were shot by the noted English sportsmen Mr Biggs and Mr Whitehead.' I was sorry to see the duke thus summarily demoted at his hour of triumph but impressed by the size of the moufflons, which to my certain knowledge had never been weighed.

I had a friend who announced for the English-speaking programme of a North African radio station. Part of her weekly routine was to read the 'Answers to your Questions'; questions that ranged from space travel to pantheism, from spelaeology to politics. The replies that she read were, in fact, those sent in by anonymous experts often from distant countries, but she felt that her public might find irksome the double anonymity of their advisers and her voice. For me, therefore, she conceived the role of a master mind present in the studio, a mysterious Professor Svenski, who knew the answers to all these questions without previous consultation, a miraculous combination of Bronowski, Russell, Huxley, and all the great specialized scientists of the decade. Affecting a stateless middle-European accent perfected by much imitative practice during the war years, I played my part in this mischievous comedy for two successive weeks; a third time, we thought, would tempt exposure, and it was announced that Professor Svenski had left the country for Indonesia.

Thus it was my friend and not I who, the following week, answered a question concerning flying saucers, and to my infinite regret it was she rather than Professor Svenski who received the letter in reply:

'Darling,

'Yesterday when I was listening to the American emission of radio I heard you proclaim with royal assurance that flying saucers existed only in people's imagination though many times photographs of the "flying objects" as you call them officially have been published. Up to now I don't suppose that anybody has discovered that cameras had imagination. If so an official report of the fact should have been made to all academies of science. As a fact, flying saucers do exist and it is a happy thing that they do, because the pilots of these flying machines are former inhabitants of this earth, or at least many of them. They are what the hebrews call angels and what the greeks called the ferry men of the Styx. After your death they will take you on a non-stop flight to another planet, where you will lead your heavenly life. In 1949 began an angel display organized by God to prove once more to modern man who no longer believes in his existence that he is still in life. . . . Today a whole planet is wrapped in idolatry and the celebration of a false God called Jesus Christ whilst the true God to whom public appraise should be given is left in the dark. As a fact, you can speak of him to anyone in the street using his proper name Iaveh and no one will understand you.

'It is he who bygone religions called the Sun God, or more exactly the Shining Monarch, because he irradiates light all about his person.

'The prophet Ezekiel gives a description of him when he saw him for the first time on a flying saucer. Some time ago he appeared in Morocco and Moroccans speak of this apparition as "The Sultan of the Moon".* You can ask your surroundings to check this statement.

'Another fact is that a flying saucer really landed in America, and the pilot of the machine spoke to a polishman called Adamski, now living in America and the visitor gave explanations to Mr Adamski who did not realize the real meaning of it.

1. He told Mr Adamski that he lived a long time ago on this planet but that now he lived on the planet Venus. As men die, Mr Adamski was in the presence of what we call a resurrected man.

2. Mr Adamski believed in the resurrection of man after death. He is a theosopher it seems but so much foolish ideas have been spread with spiritism about ecto-plasmas, etc., that the visitor showed Mr Adamski that his astral body as theosophists call it was made of real matter that you could weigh on a balance and he walked on the ground weighing on his feet and pointed to the depth of his footprints. Mr Adamski did not take the hint, but he made mouldings of the footprints and still wonders at their meaning.

'Of course conversation was difficult because the two persons did not speak the same language, but the acts recorded by Mr Adamski have meanings. Three friends of Mr Adamski witnessed his interview and signed sworn certificates that it was true, so nobody has the right to consider him a liar. One of the witnesses even made a drawing of the man Mr Adamski saw. Who is he?

'The information I have about the saucers was given to me

* A reference to the fact that after the exile in 1954 of Sultan Mohammed V of Morocco, many Moors claimed to discern his profile in the surface contours of the full moon. (Author.)

by God himself. I have written it in a book of which twenty-six volumes were sent to the United Nations in New York to be distributed to leading chiefs of state. Up to now I have never received any answer, and I don't know what they became.

'Anyhow, when God spoke to me for the first time ... he told me his name was Iaveh, and that I would remember it because it resembled my own name; I just had to change the first syllable of my name. If the same thing was done with Mr Adamski you can have Adam-ski, in which case it is probable that Mr Adamski had the honour of speaking to nobody else but *Adam* himself, and looking at the drawing made of him scientists may contemplate the monkey who is responsible for our lives.

'Facts are facts, and if official scientists are pleased at acting like fools we can't help it; as things are there are two messengers of God actually on earth: Mr Adamski and myself. If Mr Adamski enraptured by all the wonders he saw has gone astray in a poetical view of space and creation I am all right in every detail, but nobody wants to listen to me or publish what I write on the subject.

'As for cobwebs, I see many of them but only in the minds of people who deny the existence of saucers.

'After reading my book that I am sending you I hope that you will be convinced, and if afterwards you manage to convince the American nation you will then be a great girl and all America will be at your feet. With regards to me, it is now fifteen years that I am trying to interest somebody to the facts revealed to me by God without success. ... Hoping that you will find pleasure in discovering that fairies do exist and that the King of the fairies is God himself and a great magician, I remain. ...'

The book accompanying this letter was a cyclostyled

manuscript of something like a hundred thousand words, devoted in part to reasoned and clear-thinking destruction of the organized religions of the world – here the author's rapier-thrusts were skilful and deadly – and in part to a rich madness of fantasy, in which God zoomed about through time and space on flying saucers and flying cigars. The book was entitled *God's Orders for all Kings the World Over*, and it opened with a declaration.

I hereby solemnly declare that God ... appeared to me when I was a child ... and gave me explanations which he wanted to be brought to the knowledge of the Pope and to all leaders of nations the world over. ... In December 1939 ... God again appeared to me and reminded me of our meeting. He gave me mission to write his explanations and give them to French authorities. In 1944, with much pains, I managed to get about all together and wrote a document on the subject that I sent to General de Gaulle then in Algiers. ... He never answered my letter.

Nobody wished to see into the matter and it is now eleven years that I am looking for a comprehensive mind. ... Effectively I am the Anti-Christ of Christian prophecy, and my mission is to declare to the face of the world that Christians worship in Jesus Christ a false God. ...

Maybe, I thought, as I read on through the ten long chapters, but his own deity appeared almost wholly pre-occupied by aeronautics.

In ancient days when God went about the world building empires he travelled in a flying machine that we call today a flying cigar ... the spirits who accompanied him were called angels and travelled in flying saucers. ... As a fact, God supervised the hebrew's flight from Egypt on a flying cigar. ... In later years Ezekiel sees him again in his flying cigar accompanied by saucers ... and four other flying machines which he calls 'cherubins' which seem to be aerostatic machines. ... As God explained to me, the Statue of Mercury, messenger of the Gods, represents an angel ... the hat that the sculptor put on the head of his angel is not a hat but the saucer in which he flied. . . . As a fact, a few years ago, God flew over Washington and the States escorted by saucers, unrecognized and unsaluted. . . . I was a child of seven years old when I had the honour of seeing God the Father.

(They got on very well together, and God entrusted to the author the task of explaining to the Pope his mistakes.) Exodus 'tells . . . how the Jews crossed the Red Sea, God leading them always by day and by night in a flying cigar. . . . The following morning God looked out from his cigar on the Egyptian camp and put disorder among them. . . .' (At some points, however, he appears cautious, not to say timorous, for having skilfully landed his flying cigar on Mount Sinai, he gave Moses instructions to keep his people at a distance 'because he feared a rush'. But 'he did no harm to them and gave them refreshments'.)

This extraordinary document, a racy reinterpretation of the Bible followed by an appraisal and critique of the major religions of the world, lacking neither inspiration nor intelligence (except when its author rode a hobby horse or a flying saucer) ended with letters to the heads of all states giving God's instructions. They were nothing if not precise. The general letter prefacing those to individuals gives God's basic requirements for successful administration:

In the temple, there must be a private room furnished like the office of a modern business man at God's disposition where he can write his instructions for the king if he has any to give. [A ruler must] await God's appearance with his officials and ask him his instructions . . . if God is sulking and does not appear then he must order burnt sacrifices as they were accomplished in the past. . . . If God wishes to come he can do so as he did in ancient days in a saucer and land on an aerodrome but we cannot oblige him in this case.

To the Pope:

Vous êtes prié, en tant que chef de L'Eglise du Christ, de convoquer un concile au plus tôt et faire reconnaitre par celui-ci que le Christianisme est une heresie et mettre fin ensuite a l'activité de L'Eglise. . . . En terminant, je vous prie d'agréer, Signor, l'expression de mes condoléances pour vos idées perdues.

To the Queen of England:

Graceful Queen, . . . with regard to the Christian faith, everything in it is false and it is God's will that you put an end to it all over your empire. He appears as a distinguished gentleman and has no wish to harm a distinguished lady like you. . . . I beg you on my knees to believe in me and accordingly show the nations on earth that you are a great girl. . . . Through . . . a german alliance a drop of this blood that runs in my veins runs also in yours. This is too far off for me to call you my dear cousin but it means that I have no interest in trifling with your feelings, on the contrary.

The longest and most peremptory epistle was reserved for the President of the French Republic; it ran to several thousand words, and ended: '*En vous rappelant que je vous remets, ce jour, de la part de Dieu, un ordre au sens militaire du mot, je vous prie de' agréer. . . .*'

Inside the folder cover of this mighty manuscript was affixed a printed label *Please accuse reception.* I am afraid we never did accuse it, any more than did United Nations or the heads of states.

Darkness on the waterfront in Algiers; a scuffle and a high bubbling cry. A burst of submachine-gun fire close at hand and a window splinters somewhere overhead. I turn the corner; no one has moved him. He lies there, an elderly Arab with beard jutting to the sky. There is more blood than I would have believed possible; I had not seen a slit throat before. A group of French parachutists swagger by; one kicks the corpse. Curfew, and an ill-hidden microphone in my bedroom.

Morning, and the city under lashing rain; all along the water-front the high waves rolled in, not Mediterranean blue nor nordic grey, but mud brown with dark Algerian sand, and when the crests curled over and the spume streamed back on the wind it too was brown. A French bar-tender looked out on it and said: 'It is an omen – the brown tide, the Arab tide that will sweep us all away, and unlike this tide it will not recede.' I ordered cognac; he poured two and raised his glass, 'Algérie Française'. He looked to me to respond; I raised my glass vaguely and said, 'Algérie!' What other answer could there be?

One night I wandered on a salt-marsh; I left the streets of the city in which I was living because without solitude I could not resolve the tangle of my thoughts. When I set out the moon was bright; I walked upon turf causeways imposed rectilinearly upon pans of flooded land stretching endlessly to the edge of a river delta. Before me rose ghostly flocks of flamingoes; they wheeled pale but colourless in the moonlight, and alighted always ahead of me, so that their numbers became illimitable and all-enveloping. After a long time the moon was hidden by cloud and I could no longer follow their flight. The only possible paths were the now unlit causeways, running always at right angles to each other, and I had lost my bearings. In utter darkness I came upon a *bidonville* shack. A figure little darker than the sky was somehow beside me and drew me into the warm darkness of the shelter. A bellows fanned a charcoal brazier, a bearded face thus lit by firelight glanced at me without apparent curiosity. '*Min fdl'k*,' he said. '*Min fdl'k*' (make yourself at home), and leaving the brazier he spread a blanket on the floor. I drank mint tea and then slept; in the cold hour of the dawn I was aware that small children came and laid more coverings upon me. No one asked me any questions.

Two hundred miles away from the beggars and my *garçon-nière* is the other room round which my life centred during the haywire winter. The number of times that I have traversed that route seems now uncountable, though a precise analysis would no doubt be disappointing. It is enough, anyway, to know every curve, every undulation. As with any long road that a traveller follows often, it has stretches that seem inimical and others that are reassuring. Physically, it is virtually without incident, the vast plain is given life only by small human activity and by changing sheets of flowers. Early in the year I would watch the harnessed camels ploughing the red earth, followed by a snowy froth of cattle egrets, as gulls follow the plough in Europe. There were league-long carpets of big white daisies where no green showed between them, and low hills between whose scrub were unbroken acres of mingled orange and purple flowers, painted, one would say, by a pointilliste such as Seurat. Other images of the road: high wind and tossing avenues of eucalyptus trees showing the white undersides to their leaves, eddies of red dust racing in high spirals along their ranks; biblical shepherds in tattered robes watching over piebald sheep who at the edge of green and unprotected corn graze conscientiously upon nothing; slow processions of camels laden with dates or halfa grass; bobbing, tittupping rows of donkeys whose white-turbaned riders sit side-saddle far back upon the crupper; a small mêlée in mid-road which, as the car surges down upon it, resolves itself into two tiny children trying to wrest the tail from a squashed jackal; the wreckage of a giant Cadillac wrapped round the stem of a eucalyptus tree, a bloodless corpse in a white *djellabah* hanging through the glassless window.

This road, after several hours of fierce driving, leads to the home of Prudence Hazell. Her wide window, fringed by a collection of cactuses that seem to have nothing at all to do with her personality, looks out over an orderly modern square in a town of progress. Here the men wear European clothes; the women, however, remain veiled, anonymous, and Prudence's maid, Aysha, becomes a totally unrecognizable figure of mystery as soon as she steps outside the door.

Everything else but the cactuses reflects some aspect of Prudence's personality. The sparse furniture, of which the *pièce de résistance* is formed by two twelve-foot-long mattresses, one against each wall; the bright North African blankets and cushions that cover them; the elaborate wall-hangings from Far Eastern civilizations; the great debris of papers and books, that occasionally starts within itself a landslide and spreads contemporary events over the floor like rock-fall on a mountain road; the telephone with its apparently inexhaustible length of flex; the overworked typewriter whose style has become staccato owing to the death of its minor punctuation marks – all these things belong as unmistakably to Prudence as does a thorn bush larder to a desert shrike. Contrary to impression, every book and document in the paper-storm of her table is securely impaled upon some mental thorn; she holds them under the calm surveillance of her glass-grey eyes as she holds friends, enemies, and acquaintances of many nationalities. Impaled too, upon the million spines whose zareba forms the periphery of her consciousness, is every fact that she has ever read or learned, every face and name that she has ever known; for though Prudence in middle age has travelled and read more widely than do most men in a lifetime, she has a memory whose precision retains the minute detail of every experience, whether firsthand or vicarious.

While by no means lacking in the domestic virtues she is pleased on occasion to allow her guests a display of their dexterity. At this moment that I picture her she sits at a table in the corner of the room, alternatively sucking a red pencil and deleting with it portions of a typewritten document; on one of the long mattress sofas the Utopian Ambassador, as black as night, is repairing one of her gloves whose finger-seam has split; at the opposite end squats the Chief of the Balongan Trade Delegation, sewing a button on to her jacket sleeve. I am between them, trying to repair the zip-fastener of her mountaineering anorak. She looks up. 'I'm sorry to be so unsociable, my dears, but I must get this done tonight – Nkrumah is coming to lunch tomorrow, and all those Ambassadors. . . .'

The doorbell rings. Prudence steps quickly into the hall and closes behind her the frosted-glass sliding doors that separate the sitting-room from the hall. There is a long muted conversation beyond them; it may be in any one of the ten languages that Prudence speaks fluently. At the end of ten minutes she returns and resumes her interrupted work without comment. Her guests leave very late, but if it is before two o'clock in the morning they are inevitably re-placed by newcomers before I can dispose myself to sleep upon one of the long mattresses. When I do so there is usually a representative of some unliberated or imperfectly liberated country snoring upon the sofa opposite. Such men live in an atmosphere into which I am drawn as inexorably as a fly into the maw of an insect-eating plant, an atmosphere of intrigue and sudden death. They are good enough to explain to me that our fortuitous association may be interpreted to my disadvantage; in Africa, they warn me, everyone is assumed to be partisan, and a British author at large is a suspect figure. They advise me to inspect my car for bombs every morning; at this, while my more habitual proficiencies flag, I have become quick and unforgetful. My existence became shaped like a dumb-bell; at one end the or-bit of my own dimly lit and squalid room, at the other the international clearing-house of Prudence Hazell's flat. Far to the south were the bright deserts where I longed to be, the deserts of shimmering castellated mirage and bounding gazelles, the flowering deserts where from waterless stone *jol* grew the miracle of mauve blossom upon pale thorn; but far to the south, too, were the columns of burning gas from the oil wells at Hassi Messaoud, pillars of smoke by day and of fire by night.

I would try sometimes to think of Camusfeàrna in March sunshine, of the waterfall and the budding birches, of primroses among dead bracken, of the soft mountain distances and blue sea, but always the image would dissolve before it was complete. Before it was strong enough to draw me from where I was. Again and again I postponed my return, unable to break through the confines of a barrier I could not understand. I was aware that I needed some jolt into reality to awaken me and to bring me home, and that that jolt could only come from some part of Camusfeàrna. As a result of this slender awareness I took the first positive step towards mental self-preservation. I wrote to England saying that I had been unwell for some weeks and suggesting that Jimmy Watt be sent out to help me with my return journey. I knew that he himself would be overjoyed, for he had always wanted to travel, but I was still afraid that the sight of him, and all its associations with homely, peaceful things, would not be enough to lift the cataract from my eyes, and that I would return in the same twilight state as I was.

Aberrant mental conditions are difficult to convey other than by implication or soliloquy; prose becomes overcharged in an effort to communicate emotion that is not fully understood by the writer. That, anyway, is nearly all that I can write of the haywire winter. I awoke, in some sense, when I saw Jimmy's face in the queue at the passport barrier, and all that Camusfeàrna was came back to me like the breaking of a dam. As we drove in a taxi from the airport he told me of a hundred trivialities at my home, and suddenly it became the only important thing in the world.

Jimmy stayed in North Africa for a fortnight, learned to drive the Land Rover on flat desert, acquired a curious dragon-like living lizard that, among a whole witch's compendium of dried vultures' wings, hyenas' teeth, ostriches' eggs, and a hundred other unsavoury magic properties, was obscenely demonstrated by a medicine man as a cure for impotence.

Moulay Ahmed's documents still had their last and climactic function to fulfil. Our homeward passages and that of the Land Rover were booked on a Dutch cargo boat sailing from Casablanca to London, and on the previous evening we were in the Tour Hassan Hotel at Rabat. I had not seen Moulay Ahmed since the Duke of Blitz's moufflon hunt several weeks before; now, in the bar of the Tour Hassan, he requested me to attend a duck shoot in a Northern province the following week. I explained that we were leaving for England the next day. He asked how we were travelling, and I told him by cargo boat from Casablanca. 'That,' said Moulay Ahmed triumphantly, 'will not be possible. Tomorrow is the state visit to Casa of Marshal Tito, and all routes into Casa will be closed. Your route into the town would actually be the processional route. It is absolutely impossible.'

'Even with the aid of the documents you gave me?'

'Even with those. You can forget the whole idea.'

Jimmy and I conferred privately. We had, we decided, nothing to lose and everything to gain by the attempt. There was at least a chance, and the documents, together with the highly official appearance of the car, formed a *combine formidable*. We did not announce our intentions to Moulay Ahmed.

We left Rabat early the next morning. The route had certainly been well prepared; every two or three miles there was an army or police road-block; and although the *coupe file* remained effective we decided upon a diversion by the minor coastal road. Upon entering Casablanca itself, however, I realized at once that Moulay Ahmed had not exaggerated, and that things were going to be very difficult indeed. Moroccan protocol for reception of heads of states is elaborate and traditional and, on such an occasion as this, included the mass importation of tribespeople from distant districts. These line the processional route, often for miles; they carry drums and tambourins, and at the approach of the state procession they begin to drum and to sing and sway to the rhythm of archaic tribal dances.

From the extreme outskirts of Casablanca all traffic was diverted away from the broad processional route that led to the port. I did not follow this diversion; instead I drove straight up to the police point and presented my documents through the window of the car. I had not really believed their efficacy in this situation, and I was amazed when the car was waved on without question. But when I saw what lay ahead of me I came near to panic. The broad empty road stretched away for a mile or more, festive with flags and bunting, innocent of a single wheeled vehicle, but densely lined at its sides with many thousands of spectators. As we moved on, a long ripple swept forward among them; turbaned heads craned to get a view, white *djellabahs* fluttered, hands waved. There was a diversion of opinion as to how this lone vehicle should be treated, the first, evidently, that had passed that way all day; some, clearly, took us for outriders or heralds, and accorded us no more than a burst of clapping or a ragged cheer; the tribespeople of the hills, on the other hand, unable to interpret the Arabic lettering upon the car, and doubtlessly unaccustomed to the format of a state procession, took us, if not for Tito himself, at least for some part of his entourage. We were clearly not Moroccans, we were driving along down the processional route, and it must have seemed reasonable to assume that we were foreign guests of honour. The adherents of this viewpoint behaved to us as they had been instructed to behave to Tito; they drummed and danced and sang and cheered, and it was a little difficult to know how to respond to this undeserved ovation. We compromised with more or less fixed smiles and an intermittent gesture between a wave and an official salute; but all the time I had a deep irrational fear that somehow Moulay Ahmed would suddenly appear like an avenging djinn from a bottle and tear our thin disguise to ignominious shreds.

But there was no disaster, no further checkpoint, the police who were in great strength nearer to the centre of the town plainly had full confidence in their colleagues at the outer defences, and eyed us almost without curiosity. The parking of the car seemed for a moment to present insuperable problems; then I reflected that no one was likely to question us further. Outside Casablanca's most luxurious hotel, which lay right on the processional route, was a car park over which was written 'Police only', and into this I drove with confidence, flashing my *coupe file* as I did so. Jimmy and I then ascended to the lofty roof of the Land Rover to watch the procession in comfort. A police officer called a question to me, and I was preparing myself for lengthy explanations when I realized that he was asking whether he might join us on the roof.

The next day we shipped the car aboard a small boat carrying a hold cargo of oranges and a deck cargo of tortoises, and lurched homeward across the Bay of Biscay below great white cumulus clouds, the blue sea and white water hissing and foaming at the ship's sides.

A year of mishaps and disasters at Camusfeàrna lay ahead, but at least I was awake and had shaken off the haywire winter. I have buried the rest of it in the compost heap of my subconscious, and now it only returns to me in the poignancy of dreams, urgent and febrile, in which are implicit the sense of some task unfinished, some goal unattained – sometimes I have thought it was death, either my own or that of the scapegoat. But only Holman Hunt could contrive the death of his goat; the others are immortal, rancid and septic, ready always to return and be driven forth again.

THE ROCKS REMAIN

In completion of our ritual of sorrow
I drove you from my fold with whip and goad;
Through wildernesses where I could not follow
You bore my shed intolerable load.

Groping after you now my purpose wanders
Through dry defiles upon the world's roof;
On dimly lit Saharas of unknowledge
I trace the double imprint of your hoof.

Goat calls to goat across the distant mountain;
Your outcast taint is rank upon the air;
Your herd forms, and the lowered horns turned outward
Deny my right, long shed, to all you share.

The she-goat standing for the scapegoat's mount
Takes on her back his double load of weight –
To bear a scapekid. When we drive him out
He will come here to find a willing mate.

So in the smell of sin you will discover
That my shed load held more than guilt and pain,
And in these Ishmael herds may mate another
With love that I cannot recall again.

5

All the Wild Summer Through

WITH THAT SPRING following the publication of *Ring of Bright Water* the privacy of Camusfeàrna came abruptly to an end. A great number of people who read the book accepted the disguise of place names as a challenge, and were determined to locate and visit the place; they came by their hundreds, and because at first we did not wish to appear churlish the once orderly routine of the house became chaotic. As spring turned to summer and the tourist season reached its height we became desperate, for the inroads upon our time meant that I was able to work only sporadically and without concentration. We erected *Private* notices on the two tracks by which the house may be approached, but these had little effect, and gradually our days became almost wholly occupied with warding off uninvited visitors. The number of notices that these had to pass before reaching Camusfeàrna was formidable; at the distance of more than a mile all gates already carried estate notices at the entry to the forestry ground, reading *Strictly Private – Young Trees*; after a further half mile the hardy encountered the first of my own signboards – *This Is A Private Footpath To Camusfeàrna – No Unannounced Visitors Please*; then, for those who had penetrated all the outer defences, came an elaborate signboard with a drawing of a beseeching otter and the words: *Visitors: There Are Pet Otters Here – Please Keep Dogs On Leash*; and finally, at a range of two hundred yards or so from the citadel, the single word PRIVATE, in foot-high red letters. Despite all these precautions, a steady stream of rubbernecks arrived daily, often with loose and undisciplined dogs, to bang on the single door of the house and demand, as if it were their right, to see the otters and all that had figured in the story.

One of the most extraordinary and revealing aspects of this unconcerted invasion was the conviction of each that he or she, and he or she alone, was the pioneer; that it could not have been possible for any other to have discovered the true location of Camusfeàrna, or for any other to have wished to do so. Each claimed to have established the position by hours of labour with charts and deductive power worthy of Hercule Poirot; by a long past familiarity with the coastline that had yielded a sudden and vital clue; by private information given by a friend of a friend of an acquaintance; by some recognized piece of landscape in a published photograph – always, in sum, by some feat of mental or imaginative agility of which no other could be capable. After one long day, when we had wrestled many hours with such well disguised angels, and when we were at last sitting down to eat for the first time since the previous evening, there came an authoritative rap on the door and a murmur of perceptibly transatlantic voices. I refused to move, and sent one of the boys to deal with the situation. The message he brought back was that the gentleman (the name eludes me) had travelled three thousand miles to see Camusfeàrna, and could not believe that I would be so in-hospitable as to refuse him entry. For the first time since the beginning of the siege my temper broke; I replied that if indeed he had wished to travel three thousand miles to visit a total stranger he might have shown more courtesy than to arrive unannounced at half past nine in the evening. This churlish outburst set a precedent, and when a few days later I looked out from my window to see a party of five people

Terry and the Greylag geese on Camusfeàrna beach

Reunion between Edal and her original parents— Jimmy, Edal, Malcolm and Paula Macdonald

Above: Camusfeàrn winter 1961-62

Left: The frozen waterfall

Above right: Monday and Lavin

Right: Nicholas

Far right: Simon

Monday on the day she arrived

Mossy and Monday

Monday's experiments in wate

leaning over the wooden palisade and baiting (I can find no other word) Teko, I found the instinct for battle strong in me. I went out and asked them with hostile civility from where they came. Manchester, I was told. 'And in Manchester,' I asked, with what coolness my rage could master, 'is it the custom to treat your neighbour's house and garden as a public exhibit?' There was a shocked silence; then the paterfamilias said plaintively: 'But this is not Manchester; in Scotland we've been told there's no law of trespass!'

This extraordinary situation does, in fact, obtain; in Scotland there is nothing but the unwritten rule of common civility to prevent any stranger entering the garden of a suburban or other house and making himself thoroughly at home. If he picks the flowers or otherwise damages the garden it is possible to secure an injunction against his future entry, but if he has a hundred friends lined up to repeat the performance it will be necessary to take out an injunction against each of them severally and in succession. An Englishman's home is his castle, but not a Scotsman's. Scottish law contains many such whimsical quirks; for example, a homicidal maniac may not be reincarcerated on the original findings if after escape he succeeds in remaining at liberty for three weeks. Research into the origins of such legal curiosities might be rewarding but not, one cannot help feeling, edifying.

As month succeeded month we became, in self-defence, more and more ruthless, because the very life of the place was at stake. If one of the boys was at Druimfiaclach collecting the mail and happened there to encounter a party of prospective visitors, he would give elaborately misleading directions as to how to arrive at Camusfeàrna; by these ruses I suspect, our household has forfeited the sympathy of a section of the public, but in order to survive we had no alternative. To not one of these victims of our seeming misanthropy had it occurred, apparently, that they were on holiday and we were not, that each of us had a full day's work to get through as much as, or more than, if we had been holding down an urban office job. We became, in the broadest sense, xenophobe, and resented any intrusion, because each day ended with work undone and a gradually increasing sense of handicap in earning our livings.

There were more precise, definable irritations. Those who were deterred by our final, flaming PRIVATE notices diverted their routes to the surrounding hilltops overlooking Camusfeàrna from a distance of perhaps three hundred yards; from these vantage-points they would scrutinize the house and its environs with field-glasses, telescopes and long-focus ciné-camera lenses, and on one Sunday morning when it was possible to count the heads of five such parties a female guest came to me almost in tears. 'Look,' she said, 'you told me you'd got no sanitation and I said I didn't mind using the countryside – but it's a different thing when four pairs of field-glasses and a ciné-camera are trained on you from all angles.'

What angered me perhaps more than anything else was an incident during the summer of 1961. A very smart small yacht came to anchor in the bay below the house, flying some pennant that was to me unrecognizable. There were three or four very fat men and women aboard. One of the men settled himself in some sort of deck chair in the stern, with a ·22 rifle across his knees. His companion began to throw bread to the gulls, and as they alighted on the water in response to this invitation he shot them. We sat at the edge of the sand-dunes and watched. At the end of five minutes I began to grow exceedingly angry; as a blood sport this particular exercise seemed to me despicable. It is academically true that for the protection of other species the greater gulls should be kept within numerical limits, but the method of procedure outraged in me some quite illogical approach to the subject; it seemed wanton and destructive. I sent Jimmy to the house to fetch the ·350 big game rifle. When he returned I waited until the fat man had shot a herring gull, and as it drifted away from his yacht, I shot at the dead bird. The noise of that rifle is considerable; the scene dissolved, figures hurried about the deck, the anchor was aweigh and the yacht's auxiliary engines started almost before I had made up my mind to fire another shot astern of her.

The acquisition of my own present motor vessel *Polar Star* was one of the many minor follies with which my life has been sprinkled. When I began to find myself comparatively prosperous it was agreed by my new company, who took over the running of Camusfeàrna, that we had a strong case for a substantial and fast boat. High speed was an absolute necessity, for because of the otters we could never be absent for very long from the house, and distances in the West Highlands are great. Such a boat would, we felt, solve many of our transport and supply problems, and could also be used as emergency accommodation for guests, whose numbers seemed always to increase. The expenditure agreed for this project clearly precluded the purchase of a high-speed luxury yacht; in fact there seemed few craft that would satisfy our requirements for sale at any price. At length an advertisement from a Yorkshire shipyard caught my eye: it read, 'Ex-RAF, TSDY 1945, 40 × 9·5 × 3 ft. draught, diagonal mah. hull, Transom stern, modern bow, twin Perkins 100 h p 1952, 20 knots, accommodation four, large cockpit, stated in very good condition, £2,000.' The fact that this miracle was within our agreed price limit should have warned me; I had once before, in the shark fishing years, bought a boat unseen on the strength of the Surveyor's Report, and I should have remembered the deplorable results. It is aggravating to repeat a stupid mistake, and thus to demonstrate that one is slower to learn than many an animal. However, as I could not at the time leave Camusfeàrna, I decided to rely upon an independent surveyor's report, together with advice from expert friends as to the suitability of the type of craft. By them I was advised that no hard chine boat could be expected to stand heavy seas, but that round-bilge construction of equivalent size and speed would be very far beyond the agreed expenditure. I therefore decided to buy the *Polar Star*, subject to a satisfactory survey; apart from a misleading attention to unimportant details, the report was excellent, and on 14 July Jimmy Watt left Sandaig for Bridlington to accompany the boat north with her two Yorkshire crew.

The *Polar Star* sailed from Bridlington on 16 July, to pass through the Edinburgh–Glasgow Canal, then the Crinan Canal, through the Mull of Kintyre, and so up the West Coast to Camusfeàrna. The voyage had an inauspicious beginning. The boat was no more than half an hour out from Bridlington when Jimmy saw fierce flames leaping from the stern between the diesel tanks and the calor-gas cylinders. The crew were in the wheelhouse. When Jimmy raised the alarm 'they started charging about all over the ship looking for fire extinguishers, cursing and swearing and expecting an explosion any minute. I had a look myself and there was an extinguisher in the wheelhouse all the time, so I took it and got the fire out myself.' After this mishap she made remarkable progress during the earlier stages of her voyage.

On the third day I was sitting writing at my desk at Camusfeàrna when I found my mind wandering to the probable position of the *Polar Star* at that moment. She must, I decided, be in the Crinan Canal itself – and then a thought came into my head that sent a sharp shock of fear through me. A boat emerging from the Crinan Canal finds itself in the Sound of Jura, almost landlocked, and with only two northward passages to the open sea, those to the north and south of the Island of Scarba. To any uninformed person looking at a chart, the southern passage, between Scarba and Jura, would appear very much the more direct route to clear the southern end of Mull and reach the open sea. That passage, however, is a death-trap, the famous Gulf of Corryvreckan where many, many a boat bigger than the *Polar Star* has met her end in savage whirlpools or the roaring wall of water that is the main overfall. On board the *Sea Leopard* I had watched it from a respectful distance years before, a mad leaping confusion as if the tides of all the world had met in that one place. The CCC Sailing Directions call it 'the worst in the West Highlands . . . at any time there is such risk that it is inadvisable to attempt it'. Now it struck me as just conceivable, but conceivable enough to bring out a fine cold sweat, that the East Coast crew aboard the *Polar Star* had not heard of Corryvreckan and were sailing without proper written directions.

I grabbed the telephone and spoke to the canal authorities at Crinan. The *Polar Star*, they told me, had left the canal some minutes before; I explained my fears, and they offered to try to call her on her radio and telephone back to me. The next quarter of an hour passed slowly at Camusfeàrna, the slower for two incoming calls unconnected with my predicament, in the course of which I was barely able to remain civil. The third time the bell rang it was Crinan and they were reassuring. They had been unable to contact the *Polar Star* because, like much else about her, the radio was out of order, but they had talked with a fishing-boat who had seen the *Polar Star*. She had passed, this boat reported, at about twenty-five knots, and appeared to be on course for the northern channel, not for Corryvreckan. I returned, a little uneasily, to my work. Jimmy had agreed to telephone from Mallaig, and that could not be for some hours.

It was late in the evening before he telephoned, and his voice sounded odd and strained. 'Are you in Mallaig?' I asked.

'No, we're in Tobermory.'

'Tobermory! But you left Crinan hours ago – is everything all right?'

'Well, not exactly. We ran into some trouble. There's no glass left in the wheelhouse, for example, and its hatch flaps have gone too. We ran into a sort of wall of water – like a head-on collision. Nobody was hurt – much.'

The *Polar Star*'s English crew had indeed steered straight into the Gulf of Corryvreckan, at its most dangerous of all tides, half ebb springs, and had charged the main overfall at maximum speed.

It was not until after Jimmy's arrival that I heard the full story of this adventure that might so easily have proved tragic. He had not seen the actual impact, for he had been making tea in the galley just aft of the wheelhouse. The *Polar Star* was travelling at full speed, slamming from wave top to wave top as hard chine boats do, when she seemed to Jimmy to ram something solid. The teapot was thrown from his hand and he himself was flung violently against the bulkhead; as this happened a wave of water some four feet deep swept through the double doors leading into the wheelhouse. Entrance for'ard thus effectively blocked, Jimmy made his escape aft. The roll hatch separating the cabin from the after hold was pulled down against the wind; raising it, he looked out upon a chaotic sea. It had, he said, no real form or shape beyond an impression of confused violence, for so many things appeared to be happening at once; there were fierce down-sucked whirlpools, waterspouts and waterfalls, and towering waves truncated at their ends. He climbed out on to the narrow unrailed side-deck and began precariously to make his way for'ard to the wheelhouse. While he was doing so the helmsman put the *Polar Star* about, still at full speed, and she came round in a wide arc, with seas coming up at her from all sides, from ahead and astern, from port and starboard all at the same time. Once clear of the worst of it Jimmy and one of the two Yorkshiremen worked furiously at the pumps, for the boat was half full of water. Jimmy asked what had happened. 'Dunno – something to do with the wind against the tide, I suppose.'

The *Polar Star* made Tobermory harbour three hours later, and there, past caring for rigid etiquette, her crew picked up the first vacant moorings that held a dinghy, and rowed it ashore.

I was reassured by one thought only; there could be very few vessels of the *Polar Star*'s size that could have attempted that folly and survived it.

The following afternoon the *Polar Star* came up on the southern horizon. Watching her through the field-glasses I could see little but the enormous bow wave she was throwing up; whatever her defects, twenty knots seemed a very conservative estimate of her speed, for from the moment at which she was first visible some ten miles away until she hove to and dropped anchor in the bay was no more than twenty-five minutes.

Terry and I rowed the dinghy out. This was my first sight of my new acquisition, and once aboard her I found it difficult to conceal my disappointment. Potentially, she was all that I had expected, but everything about her reeked of neglect and indifference, from the rusted and functionless instruments on her fascia board, to her uncaulked decks and damp-stained cabin.

As with so many other 'bargains' she required an enormous amount of expenditure before at last she became both trustworthy and socially presentable. At the outset she had, like some aboriginal woman, little but speed and a sound hull; for the rest she was dirty, neglected, squalid in appearance both inside and out, and with a highly unreliable transmission system from the wheelhouse to the two big motors in her stern. These were controlled, if the word may be applied to any operation so imprecise, by two throttles on the fascia-board, and two gigantic and rusty gear levers not less than four feet high. The neutral position in the forward and backward travel of these monstrosities was exceedingly difficult to achieve, and when found remained, so to speak, an armed neutrality, for the vessel would still creep ahead until the engines were finally stopped. The system was obsolete, and had in recent models been replaced by two small levers on the fascia board, operating a hydraulic gearbox and acting simultaneously as throttle and gear levers. This innovation, we discovered, could only be fitted to the more modern type of engine. In every sphere of life I have always found that one of the most difficult decisions for me has been to determine the moment at which to cut my losses; now, rightly or wrongly, we decided to replace both engines and transmission. We should then have a sound hull and sound engines, and during the winter months we could work at bringing the interior woodwork and fittings up to the same high standard.

This decision, however, we did not take until the autumn; and immediately after her first arrival at Camusfeàrna she had perforce to be sent to the nearest shipyard to remove the evidence of her encounter with Corryvreckan. There she spent some weeks, and we had little use from her that summer; none, in fact, beyond shopping runs to the village, a journey that we found she could accomplish in twelve minutes as opposed to our usual forty by foot-track and road.

August 1961 stands out with a terrible vividness in my mind. Before I began to write this book, I wondered whether in the narrative that month should be omitted, whether people who through *Ring of Bright Water* had become vicariously fond of us and of our animals could take even at secondhand the shocks and blows that we sustained, for they came near to bringing about the disintegration of Camusfeàrna as we had known it. The shattering chain of events began with a single episode which, though alarming, did not prepare me for the nightmare that was to follow.

We had staying with us Caroline Jarvis from the London Zoo, who, the previous year, had arranged Terry's employment as an otter-keeper. At that time Edal had the run of the house for most of the day; she would go for her walk in the morning and sleep and play in the living-room; only if there were very many people, or if she was particularly obstreperous, would we shut her up in her own quarters, a part of Jimmy's bedroom that he had divided by a four-foot high plasterboard partition. Caroline, who has enormous experience and love of animals of all kinds, got on extremely well with Edal; they had gone for walks together, and only the evening before Edal had gone to sleep on her lap. There was no tension in the atmosphere, nothing to warn us of what was coming.

The next morning Caroline, Jimmy and I set off for a walk with Edal. We had crossed the burn and were walking up the green slope beyond it when I saw Edal, who was close to Caroline, stop suddenly, almost like a pointer, and direct a malevolent glare at Caroline's foot. There was something so unfamiliar in Edal's expression that I called to Caroline to stand still, and hurried towards them. But it was already too late – Edal gave one piercing scream of rage and buried her teeth in Caroline's ankle. Jimmy and I pulled her off and attached a lead to her while Caroline limped home, making light of her injury. Jimmy and I went on with Edal to the islands, discussing all the way the possible reasons for her outrage. At first we were inclined to think that there might be some brain damage remaining from her long illness, but on the veterinary evidence we were forced to discard this theory as untenable. If the nerve itself had been damaged she could never have recovered the full use of her limbs and tail; it must have been the nerve sheath only, and that could not affect her present behaviour. It was, we concluded, some sort of explosion of jealousy; Edal considered herself polyandrously married to Jimmy and myself, and had put Caroline in the position of a rival. We made up our minds not only that she should not meet Caroline again, but that we should be very careful about letting her meet any woman at all. Caroline left two days later; I did not know then that she had given to Terry the thick woollen sweater she had been wearing. I went to London on business for a week, drove north in the Mercedes, and did not get back until after dark on a Monday night.

It was so late that I was surprised, as I approached the village pier, to see in the headlights of my car the figures of Jimmy and of Raef Payne, an old friend who had taken over the holiday occupancy of the empty croft adjoining Camusfeàrna. They both looked grave and worried; I knew at once that some sort of disaster had taken place at Camusfeàrna.

It did not take long to say; Terry had been very badly bitten by Edal, and had been taken the previous day to Broadford Hospital on the Isle of Skye. The local doctor had stitched him up as well as she could, but there was the possibility that one finger would have to be amputated. No one seemed to have any very clear idea of how it had happened; Edal had been in her own room, and Terry had gone up to play with her as he often would. He had been entirely alone in the house – Jimmy was out, and Raef had been in his own house a hundred yards away. Both hands were badly damaged. Terry had run over to Raef's house more or less holding on a finger that would otherwise have dropped off.

There was no way for me to get to Skye that night, for it was hours past the time of the last ferry-boat; I would have to wait for the morning. I do not think any of us slept very much.

I went first to see the hospital doctor, so that when I went on from his house to the hospital I was not quite unprepared, for I had been told that Terry might lose one finger on each hand – it depended on how much deterioration there had been overnight. We agreed that in any case I should bring Terry from the hospital to the doctor's house for a confirmatory examination, that I should bring him home to Camusfeàrna, and that the following day I should drive him to Glasgow for plastic surgery.

When I reached the little hospital I could at first find nobody; the place seemed deserted. I peered this way and that, and at length found myself looking down a corridor to the open door of a ward where a patient was visible sitting up in bed. He was not only sitting up, he was sema-phoring wildly with his discarded pyjama-top – suddenly I realized that it was Terry, and that the signals were directed at me. I hurried down the corridor.

There were only two other patients in the ward, an old man and a child, and both were somnolent. Terry could hardly keep his voice down as he demanded over and over again: 'Do I get out of here? Are you going to take me away? You won't leave me here?' At close quarters the smell of gangrene was overpowering; its implications made my voice unsteady as I reassured him.

Back in the doctor's house, I tried to persuade him to close his eyes while his hands were being examined, for I knew by that stench what their appearance would be; but he would have none of it, and took a keen, almost clinical interest in the proceedings. The removal of the bandages revealed a sight so unpleasant that it is better not to attempt description. The top two joints of the second finger of the right hand had literally been chewed off, as had a slightly lesser portion of the same finger of the other hand. The local doctor had somehow contrived to stitch them on again, but now they were very dead indeed. Terry looked at them dispassionately: 'Chop 'em off, Doctor,' he said, 'that ruddy lot's no good to anyone.' Terry was only just fifteen; he never shed one tear either in pain or in self-pity.

The next day we drove to Glasgow, where his father had come to meet him, and he was installed in a nursing home. There he quickly became everybody's pet, and the ten days passed more quickly than he had expected.

When we drove back together to Camusfeàrna we had agreed upon deception for the time being – we were both frightened of the Press getting hold of the story (Edal was at the height of her fame), and also frightened of a local scandal, scandal that might end in her being killed. We owned a portable petrol-driven saw, and outside our circle it was to be given out that Terry had lost his fingers when the chain of this struck a nail in wood and flew off.

I had questioned Terry so closely that he had brought to light the knowledge of which he himself had been unaware – when Edal attacked him he had been wearing Caroline's sweater for the first time. Yet even with this partial solution to her behaviour, the savagery of the attack and the massiveness of the damage made it out of the question for her to meet anyone but Jimmy and myself in the future. It was plain that no amount of attachment to her could justify the risks inherent in her continuing to live in the house and being petted by visitors. If we were to keep her at all there was only one possible course to pursue, and having made the decision we put it into action as quickly as possible. At the seaward side of Camusfeàrna cottage we would erect a pre-fabricated wooden house at right-angles to it, so that the two formed an L; this new house Edal would share with Jimmy, and through a hatch in its wall she would have permanent access to a spacious enclosure with two pools and every kind of waterworks we could devise. Her living conditions would not be greatly changed, for she could still share Jimmy's bed as was her wont, and she could be taken out for walks on any occasion that the coast (literally) was clear. As an insurance policy against Teko some day surprising us by a similar attack, I decided that he, too, must have a large pool adjoining his lean-to shed.

Jimmy's new house arrived by sea in half a gale of wind, and its unloading presented a weird spectacle as we poled ourselves about on its sections, steering them clear of the rocks and painfully hauling them above the tide's edge. My mind went back to the Island of Soay, and the building of the factory seventeen years earlier; I realized that once again, as if it were an inescapable pattern, I was in the initial stages of constructing and maintaining a complex organization on an almost impossibly remote site.

When the building was finally erected, decorated and furnished, it made an imposing room, thirty feet long by twelve feet wide, with eight large windows. The furthest ten feet were divided by a waist-high partition to form a bedroom for both Jimmy and Edal, and, since she was now to have permanent access to water and we could not dry her every time she emerged from it, we adopted the technique of an infra-red lamp hanging above a bed of towels just inside the hatch. This extremely practical idea had not, in fact, been ours in invention; it had been devised by one of the few other people in the British Isles who keep otters,

Mr Jeremy Harris, and it ensured that the otter's bedding would always be dry whether or not there was a human in attendance.

At this point, while I am describing what may appear an excessive concern for Edal's comfort and well-being, I should perhaps explain my own attitude towards her in the light of all that had taken place. She had inflicted terrible damage on someone for whom I was responsible and of whom I was fond, but for several seemingly valid reasons I did not feel I could send her away. Any private home to which she went would be exposed to the same risk, and it seemed an act of wanton cruelty to send this house-living animal to a life sentence behind the prison bars of a zoo. She was extremely and affectionately attached to Jimmy and to myself; she had acted instinctively; moreover, it was in some sense to the exploitation of her person in print that I owed my present prosperity. There will, no doubt, be those who feel these loyalties to be misguided; I can only say that in our own minds we had no option.

The prefabricated house was the easiest part of our plan to put into operation, though it involved much time, labour and expense; the installation of pools of the size we felt to be necessary was a very much more formidable task. In broad principle there are two main types of swimming-pool marketed for use in, say, suburban gardens; those which are circular, made of sectional steel sheeting standing upright upon the ground and holding a giant bag of waterproof material, and those which are rectangular, made of some such substance as fibre-glass, designed to be sunk into a prepared pit of the same dimensions. Both are almost unbelievably costly, but of the two the sheet-metal-and-bag type is less so. This, in view of the general heavy outlay, decided us upon the wrong choice, and we ordered three, two of four yards diameter and one of six yards. One small and one large were to be installed at different levels, partially sunk, in Edal's new quarters, and the third was to be erected in a new enclosure surrounding Teko's house, in case he too should at some time in the future have to be treated with caution.

Teko's pool burst on the first day that it was filled with water, and, being immediately outside my ground-floor window, it flooded the house with all its four thousand gallons. It did more, for it laid flat the wooden paling of the enclosure, and had Terry, who was standing beside the pool, not seen the metal beginning to bulge, he might well have been killed. The containing wall of the pool burst on that side only, and I think my calculations are conservative when I say that the metal sheets must have been slammed down by not less than twenty tons of water. A week later we replaced the wreckage by a sunk fibre-glass tank sixteen feet by eight by four-and-a-half feet deep. This object, looking like a giant's washing-up basin, arrived by the usual combination of rail and boat travel, and was delivered in Camusfeàrna south bay by a hired launch. (The *Polar Star* was absent, as so often that summer, undergoing some minor surgery to her fuel system.)

Edal's pools were partially sunk, and boarded outside to resemble huge vats; in their case there was no such disaster as had occurred with Teko's, but she began early to take a mischievous delight in ripping the PVC lining with her teeth, so that the level of the water could never be relied upon, and the complicated system of syphon and waterfall that we had devised was rarely in working order. We had, nevertheless, solved the problem of her continued existence at Camusfeàrna.

6

The Wreck of the Polar Star

SATURDAY, 7 OCTOBER 1961, began in a calm and orderly manner and ended in chaos. The events of the evening formed one of the chain of disasters, greater or lesser, that have punctuated the attempt to make Camusfeàrna, in all its isolation, a place of semi-permanent residence. At some time in the morning Miss Jean Alexander, who manages the Invermoriston Hotel, telephoned to say that she had staying with her Mr Lionel Edwards, known to several generations as a painter of hunting scenes, together with his daughter and son-in-law. Mr Edwards was particularly anxious to visit Camusfeàrna and see the otters, but he was by now a man in old age, and the long, steep track between Druimfiaclach and Camusfeàrna was beyond his capacity. The visit was possible only if we could take the *Polar Star* to the village pier four miles away and collect him there, returning him in the evening to the same place where his car would be waiting. There appeared no possible reason against this; the weather was flat calm with intermittent light rain and we had nothing on hand but the normal routine of the household. We arranged to collect Mr Edwards's party from the pier at about two-thirty.

Everything went smoothly until the visitors, who had lingered long watching Edal and Teko disporting themselves in their respective pools, began their homeward journey in the evening, and even then I was unaware of anything amiss. We cast off the *Polar Star*'s moorings at about a quarter past six; it was a dull grey evening with heavy rain hammering down on to a completely smooth sea, and there was not a whisper of wind from any quarter. There were some parcels to be fetched from the village, and it was dusk before Jimmy, Terry, and I set out again for home, the beginning of one of the worst nights I can remember.

The very high speed of the *Polar Star* reduces the time necessary for the journey to a little over ten minutes and we used all her speed because I thought that the very poor visibility might make it difficult to find our moorings; I was the more concerned when as we approached the Camusfeàrna islands I saw patches of dense grey mist. There was still no breath of wind to disperse them, and still the vertical rain streamed down and hissed into an unmoving sea; it was with real relief that I saw the big white buoy loom up through the mist no more than ten yards ahead. Jimmy and Terry lifted it aboard. I saw from their gestures that something was wrong, but the continuous rasping screech of the clear-glass circle in the windscreen made it impossible to hear their voices. Then Jimmy came down through the wheelhouse hatch. 'There's no dinghy on the moorings – just a cut end of rope!'

It was clear to me at once what had happened; I had been careless for the first time, and must have cut the rope with one of the *Polar Star*'s propellers as we left for the village. The full gravity of the situation did not immediately strike me; in that dead calm sea it seemed easy enough to calculate the drift of the dinghy during the hour of our absence and to recover her by one means or another. The only real trouble at this stage was the mist and the increasing darkness in a spot so strewn with rock and reef. The tide had been ebbing for nearly an hour and a half, which meant that in the absence of any wind the dinghy should have drifted southward and come ashore somewhere on the lighthouse island, whose dark bulk was by now only faintly discernible against the clouded night sky. The only point on the whole island where it might even theoretically be practicable to land one of the boys was at the lighthouse itself, where two L-shaped lengths of heavy-gauge piping led down into the water to form a rough-and-ready pier usable at any tide higher than three-quarter ebb springs. On one engine and minimum possible revs I crept cautiously round the north end of the island; the searchlight lit only a solid wall of rain, and as the lighthouse came into view its flashes seemed like torchlight shining on fountain spray, lighting nothing below them. We were no more than five yards from the pipes before I could make them out in the thin light of Terry's torch, and it was a tribute as much to his agility as to my manoeuvring that he contrived to scramble ashore while with enormous relief I put the engine astern. It was about then that I realized that this was the darkest night I had ever seen.

Terry's task was tough even for one who had not had two fingers amputated only a few weeks before. He was to search the northern shore of the island with its thousand weed-covered outcrops and treacherous crevices, and if he found the dinghy he was to bring it where we would lie at anchor as near to our moorings as we could judge. If he found nothing, he was to wait until nearly midnight, wade waist-deep to the next island in the chain, and so to Camusfeàrna south bay, where the tiny pram dinghy was drawn up on the sand beach. From there it would be a two-mile row right round the south side of the islands to reach where we lay at anchor, but at least the sea was so far in our favour. We had chosen Terry for this role because his hands made it difficult for him to handle anchor or rope, while his rowing was little affected.

Jimmy and I returned to the north side of the island and

dropped anchor, though by now the darkness was so total that, with the lighthouse obscured by the headland, we had little real idea of our position. At first we thought we could make out the faint flicker of a torch from time to time on the island shore, but then everything was black outside the lit cockpit of the *Polar Star* and the only sound was that of the rain. So it was for an hour or more; then came the first whine of wind in the rigging of the wireless mast, and a little later the first slap of breaking water on the ship's side. The wind was southerly and we were lying in shelter; it was plain now that Terry's alternative course, to row the pram round the lee shore of the islands in pitch darkness, would be little less than suicidal. Jimmy and I conferred, and decided to take the *Polar Star* round to the south bay and anchor her there, so that Terry, if he could launch the pram at all, would have but a short row out to us. It was then a little after half past nine.

We weighed anchor and very gingerly we set off again. It was as if one were deprived of all one's useful senses – the utter enveloping blackness and the deafening scream of the clear-glass combined to produce a sensation of claustrophobia such as I have never before experienced. I wanted to shout 'Let me out of here! Let me out of here!' We passed well to the west of the lighthouse and kept on southward for what I thought an amply safe distance before turning up for the south bay; but, no doubt subconsciously accustomed to the *Polar Star*'s normal high speed, I overestimated the distance we had covered. The lighthouse was obscured by the headland, and the only visible thing outside the wheelhouse was the intermittent pinprick of another lighthouse miles to the south-west.

I did have a split second of warning, but it was too brief to be of any value. The searchlight had shone only upon the unvarying wall of rain; now, only feet from our bows, I had a sickening camera-shutter image of solid rock. Then we struck and struck hard, and the bows reared. Both engines full astern produced only a hideous grinding sound, and after a few seconds we stopped them.

The worst of it was that we had no clear idea of our position, nor whether we were aground on an island or a reef. The whole of the area of the Camusfeàrna islands is a death-trap, even in daylight, to any boat unfamiliar with it; now, with more than four hours ebb tide, we might be on any one of fifty rocks. The *West Coast Pilot* with an inspired typographical slip, describes the south side of the islands as 'foul fround', and never had the fround seemed fouler than now with the *Polar Star* hard aground in the middle of a black night and a rising wind.

When I went aft I thought the hull was holed, for the floor-boards were awash, but then I saw that the angle at which her bows had reared must have sent all the bilge water to the stern and that this might be no more than the accumulation of rainwater over many hours of downpour. We decided to try to explore our surroundings, and we clambered overboard, Jimmy holding the head rope and I the stern. The rock shelved steeply and it was slippery and weed-covered; feeling upward in the darkness there was only more weed. We did little speculation aloud as to our whereabouts, for the evidence so far pointed to a reef, and neither Jimmy nor I could swim. There was one life-jacket in the *Polar Star*, and Terry had the other.

The wind rose steadily and the waves came out of the dark and broke over us, and as they grew greater they broke, too, over the *Polar Star*'s starboard quarter, so that she began to ship green water into the after cockpit. Then she began to bump and slam upon the rock that was holding her, and it was clear that she would break up if she stayed where she was. We went back aboard her and tried the engines again;

she would not move, but there seemed a faint chance that if we were both ashore on the rock we might push her off on the crest of a wave to take her chance of finding sand or gravel. We pumped her bilges, and for another despairing half hour we struggled in the slimy seaweed and the breaking waves until at length a slight veer in the wind did our work for us and suddenly she was free. All we had salvaged from her was a boat-hook. Our watches had stopped owing to immersion, but I think it was then about eleven o'clock. As the *Polar Star* drifted away from us we both felt very desolate.

We were surprised by how quickly her mast-light was obscured – no piece of rock formation that we could visualize could have hidden her so quickly, but by now it was almost dead low tide, and this was no guarantee that we were not on a reef. We could explore only by touch, for the blackness was utter and complete; passing one's hand before one's eyes they registered no faintest change of shade. Jimmy said: 'This is what it must be like to be blind, stone blind.'

The first thing seemed to be to get above the waves; this was no very logical process of reasoning, for we had no inch of dry clothing between us, and the rain was now lashing in on a force six southerly wind. The first ten feet were almost vertical and all weed-covered, and we could only raise ourselves almost inch by inch. More weed and more; I began to have a chilling certainty that we must be on a reef and not an island, and high tide would be before dawn. A small glow of hope warmed us when my hand touched the roughness of rock for the first time, but it was barnacles that I felt beneath my finger-tips. Jimmy found bare dry rock first, but it was smooth and sheer and he could find no fingerhold. He felt out to the left with his foot and there was nothing there; I did the same to my right and found nothing either.

We were evidently climbing some sort of narrow buttress. I remember saying: 'There just isn't a piece of rock like this anywhere round Camusfeàrna.'

That first twenty or thirty feet until we came suddenly on rough, tussocky grass must have taken us more than half an hour. We went on climbing, grass, rock, then grass again. Jimmy said suddenly: 'There's only one piece of ground like this – we're at the gull colony on the south face of the Lighthouse Island. I bet that in another quarter of an hour we'll see the lighthouse.' We did, and we were safe, but our troubles had only begun.

Even in the best of daylight conditions, the traverse of the half-mile length of the Lighthouse Island is no easy matter, for it is one of the roughest, toughest pieces of ground that may be conceived. Its uneven, rocky shore is split by deep fissures many feet deep, and these are camouflaged, as are pitfall traps for wild animals, by a rank growth of heather and briar. Above the shoreline the surface is never even; it is as though a truddle of big boulders had been flung together by some giant and then roughly coated over with the coarsest vegetation available to the climate. There are patches of dense, waist-high scrub willow through which it is entirely impossible to force a passage; ankle-twisting areas of tussock grass where each football-sized clump is as hard at its base as a stone; rooty heather growing three feet and more from treacherous holes and gulleys; and, worst of all, bramble thickets like barbed-wire entanglements. When in summer we would come here to count the eider ducks' nests or harvest herring-gull eggs we would pick our way with difficulty through this defensive jungle and often have to retrace our footsteps and seek a new path through the undergrowth; now we were confronted with the whole length of the island without even the use of our eyes. Also we were in a hurry now, both because of the urgency of calling salvage to the *Polar Star* and because soon the depth of water would increase between us and the next island of the chain.

We joined hands like children, and with Jimmy in the lead with the boat-hook we began to feel our way forward foot by foot. We stumbled and fell and swore, the briars tore at our legs and we bruised our shins and twisted our ankles among the rocks, and our teeth were chattering and all the time the rain came deluging in on the south wind; it ran in at our collars and trickled out into our shoes, and there was no speck of illumination in all the black night. Before each step forward Jimmy felt ahead of him with the boat-hook; it was fifteen feet long, but often it touched nothing and we had to skirt our way along the edge of a long rock-fissure only to find ourselves brought up short again by the density of undergrowth. At some point in this nightmare journey, we came into sight of a small white light that could only be the mast-light of the *Polar Star*; it seemed stationary, but we found it impossible to estimate the distance or judge whether she was on rock or soft beach. It must have taken us the best part of an hour to reach the north-eastern tip of the island, from which by wading we might gain the next, and by that time both of us were very near to the stage at which it seems simpler to lie down and give up. Of Terry we had heard nothing, and it would be superfluous to add that we had seen nothing.

The water between the islands was chest-high; sometimes, when our feet slipped deep among the weedy rocks, it was head-high and we were floundering. Jimmy led me on by the hand, feeling his way before him with the boat-hook, and it struck me what a bizarre spectacle we would present if some miracle could suddenly lift the darkness and leave us flooded with light.

'Even the weariest river winds somewhere safe to sea', and it was where the Camusfeàrna burn does this that there occurred the artistically climactic incident of the night. We had been on flat grassy ground for some minutes when I heard in front of us the familiar sound of the burn running over shingle and boulders; I forsook Jimmy's guiding hand, and shouting: 'We've done it! We're saved!', I stepped briskly forward. Never had pride a swifter fall; I had been at the very brink of the low sand cliff where the sand martins breed, and I stepped straight into space to fall ten feet and land on my head. For the first time that night I was truly unconscious for a little while, to be brought round by the full weight of Jimmy's boot on my face.

Terry reached the house perhaps half an hour after we did, and he had passed as bad a time or worse; for he had been for even longer without light. All hopes of finding the dinghy had ended abruptly and painfully after the first ten minutes, when a long slithering fall among the slimy rocks of the tide-line had smashed the torch and hurt the newly healed stumps of his fingers. He went on searching in the dark, hoping to stumble on the dinghy by accident, but he only stumbled on everything else. He saw us begin to move the *Polar Star* from where we had her anchored, and feeling the freshening wind he guessed our purpose. He began to cross the island to put his alternative plan into action, but without the aid of the boat-hook that had saved us from broken limbs, he fared worse and his progress was even slower than ours. When at last he was on the south side of the island he saw the mast-head light of the *Polar Star*, stationary perhaps a quarter of a mile from him, but no port or starboard lights. At first he could not bring himself to believe that she had been abandoned; then he tried to visualize her position, and realized that she must be aground. He had a life-jacket and he tried to swim to her, but he was exhausted and beginning to feel the effects of exposure, so he dragged himself ashore on the first piece of land he could

reach. This was another island, if possible rougher and more
inhospitable than the Lighthouse Island, and it took him some
time to recognize where he was. By the time he reached
Camusfeàrna he was far gone, but still as indomitably cheerful as his chattering teeth would permit him.

As soon as I had reached the house I had telephoned to
Bruce Watt, who had long ago been skipper of my shark-
fishing vessel the *Sea Leopard*, and who now possessed three
sizeable boats for the diversion of tourists. He was also coxswain of Mallaig lifeboat. For purposes of report to the
necessary authorities the events of that interminable night
were condensed into two brief reports, one by myself and
one by him:

'Report on Abandoning of Polar Star'

'On Saturday 7 October, I took a party of visitors in the
Polar Star from my moorings NE of the Camusfeàrna
Islands, to the village pier, some four miles up the Sound of
Sleat, accompanied by two employees, J. M. Watt and
T. P. Nutkins. Weather conditions when I left moorings at
6.45 pm were flat calm with heavy rain and poor visibility,
tide approximately at half-hour's ebb. I left the pier for the
return journey at approximately 7.20 pm and arrived at my
moorings a little after 7.30 pm. It was then after dusk; there
was a thick local mist and continuous small rain. On picking
up my mooring buoy I found that my dinghy was not on
the moorings and that the dinghy's painter had been cut,
leaving some two feet attached to the mooring-rope.
Visibility at this time was some 15 yards. Tide (two knots)
being stronger than wind, it appeared possible that the
dinghy was on the north-facing shore of the Lighthouse
Island, which is steep-to but not clean. I succeeded in putting Nutkins ashore at the Lighthouse, where an arrangement of heavy-gauge piping forms a pier which is usable

until three-quarter ebb springs. Nutkins was instructed to look for the dinghy and, if he failed to find it, to wait until he could reach the mainland by wading waist-deep and fetch a second dinghy (pram) from Camusfeàrna South Bay. Owing to visibility conditions, no contact with Nutkins was possible after he was put ashore. *Polar Star* remained on anchor ENE of Camusfeàrna Lighthouse. At approximately 9.30 pm it began to blow force 5–6 southerly with heavy rain and practically nil visibility, and it was plain that the passage of the pram from Camusfeàrna South Bay round the lee lighthouse point would be dangerous to Nutkins. I therefore decided to take *Polar Star* round into the South Bay to shorten the row for Nutkins as much as possible. I proceeded on the starboard engines only at 600 rpm, approximately 3 knots. After Camusfeàrna Lighthouse was obscured, visibility was literally nil and heavy rain rendered the searchlight useless. No light was visible except Halstray Lighthouse, $3\frac{1}{4}$ miles WSW. At approximately 10.15 pm I struck a reef, and, despite putting both engines full astern immediately, remained fast. Investigation revealed a rock, dry about one fathom, on our port side, but owing to foul ground all the way SE of the Lighthouse Island, I was unable to determine our exact position. Wind was approximately force 6 southerly; *Polar Star*'s port side began to slam on the rock and she appeared certain to break up unless freed. She was also shipping green water over the starboard gunwale aft. She would not drive off on the propellers, but there seemed a small chance of pushing her off on a wave crest if Watt and myself were both ashore on the rock. I therefore decided to try this, on the chance of her subsequently being driven ashore on sand or gravel, rather than the certainty of her breaking up where she was. After pumping her, and after a long time of trying, we succeeded in pushing her off as the result of a slight veer in the wind, and she began to drift NE. From the moment she was free, there was no means of regaining the vessel. Our watches had stopped owing to immersion, but I should estimate the time at approximately 11.00 pm. Watt and I made shore after the greatest difficulty and arrived at the house at 12.45 am. I immediately telephoned to Mr Bruce Watt, coxswain of Mallaig lifeboat, who also regularly undertakes salvage with his own craft.

'Nutkins was not able to wade from the Lighthouse Island until 11.30 pm, and visibility was so poor that he did not reach the house until after our arrival.

'I do not know how Mr Bruce Watt effected the salvage, but at first light in the morning he had the *Polar Star* alongside his boat, *Western Isles*, on my moorings. He then removed *Polar Star* to Mallaig.

'The dinghy was recovered 4½ miles N on the afternoon of the same day.

'Gavin Maxwell.'

'Report on Salvaging of Polar Star'

'At 0045 hours on Sunday 8 October 1961 Major Gavin Maxwell phoned myself (Bruce Watt) to say that his vessel the *Polar Star* was ashore to the East of Camusfeàrna Lighthouse and that he and his crew had managed to get ashore on the lighthouse island. He had left a light burning in the *Polar Star* and hoped that we would arrive in time to salvage her.

'I dressed immediately and went down to my ship, the *Western Isles*, and sailed at 0115 hrs. The night was extremely dark with showers of rain and winds of force 5–6 SE to S.

'At 0230 hrs on approaching Camusfeàrna Lighthouse, we observed a small light to the approximate East of the said lighthouse. On account of the darkness of the night and foul waters we were unable to approach any further and decided to go round to the lee of the lighthouse and anchor the *Western Isles*; and then to get ashore with the dinghy and investigate the position of the *Polar Star* and the possibilities of salvaging her. On getting ashore, we carefully made our way to the windward side and by torch light observed that the *Polar Star* was aground on a rock just breaking surface about 10 yds from the main reef. The boat was unmoored and abandoned. The *Polar Star* was aground forward with her stern rising and falling with the incoming surf.

'We decided that something would have to be done quickly if the boat was to be salvaged as the weather was deteriorating with the flood tide. We made our way back to the *Western Isles* as quickly as possible and came round to the windward side of the lighthouse where we sounded our way into a suitable position and dropped anchor. We fell in towards the casualty and rode to 30 fathoms of cable. When we felt sure that our anchor was holding, a crew member left with the dinghy to pass a rope to the *Polar Star*. With great difficulty a noose was passed over the winch on the bow of the *Polar Star* and the crew member returned to the *Western Isles*.

'Conditions by this time had steadily worsened and the *Polar Star* was now beam on to the rocks on her port side and bumping heavily. We moved slowly ahead with the *Western Isles* and at the same time winching in our anchor cable. The *Polar Star* by now had come head to wind and after a few minutes pause finally came clear.

'With great difficulty, owing to the *Polar Star*'s sheering and extremely bad visibility, we managed to get her round to the lee side of the lighthouse island and moor her along-side the *Western Isles*. During this operation it was observed that in the after well of the *Polar Star* there was several fathoms of rope with one end of it attached to the boat and the other to an oil drum. This we assumed was to have acted as a marker should the vessel sink. The time now being approximately 0500 hrs, we rested and awaited daylight.

'After daylight, when we were trying to assess the seaworthiness of the casualty and what damage had been sustained, Major Maxwell and his crew hailed us by megaphone from the shore.

'We rowed across to Major Maxwell and it was decided that the *Polar Star* should be towed to Mallaig.

'The following Tuesday, owing to the slipway being full, she was beached on wooden battens and the extent of the damage investigated. As far as could be seen by ourselves, Lloyd's agents and the local carpenter the damage was as follows:

'Both propellers buckled.
'Port A bracket supporting propeller and shaft strained and pushed upwards into the skin.
'Keel badly chafed and strained.
'Planking chafed, very deeply in places.
'Port chine strake loosened.
'Approx. 2 ft of Keel knocked out of fore foot.
'Hull generally strained and leaking.

'*Bruce Watt.*'

7

Teko Revisited

IT WAS WELL that we had given thought to the possibility, however improbable it appeared then, that the friendly, bouncing, affectionate Teko might one day commit the same outrage as had Edal, for by the time it did happen we were entirely prepared. He had his own heated house, his own enclosure and pool, and it had been planned in such a way that a dividing gate could exclude him from either one or the other. In emergency, he could be tended by the most timorous.

The emergency was not, in fact, long in coming. In November I became engaged to be married, and in December my future wife, Lavinia, and step children Nicholas and Simon Renton came to Camusfeàrna for part of the Christmas holidays.

Terry was at that time still looking after Teko and taking him for his daily walk, in company with the deerhound Dirk. Dirk was a comparatively recent acquisition, a gigantic yearling standing nearly forty inches at the shoulder, and it had been a joy to discover that he and Teko regarded each other as natural playmates, Dirk making rings of dazzling speed around the otter, or leaping over him high in the air. Simon, then aged thirteen, had accompanied the party more than once, and Teko had given him no more than a casual and friendly greeting as they set off.

As in the case of Edal and Caroline, the attack came without warning or apparent reason, and not long after they had left the house. They were on their way to the island beaches, and Simon was walking a little in front; the two animals, who had not yet begun to romp seriously, were walking sedately between him and Terry. Suddenly something detonated in Teko's brain – akin, I am certain, to Edal's past explosions of jealousy. He flew at Simon from behind, knocked him down (it must be remembered that Teko weighed little less than fifty pounds) and bit him savagely in the thigh. It was not just a single bite, it was a sustained attack, that might have been extremely serious had not Terry done a flying rugger tackle and pulled him off by the tail. It was the first of two rescues carried out by Terry after he had lost his own fingers. Teko responded instantly to Terry's authority; there was at no moment any sign of the attack changing direction from Simon to himself.

From what emotional rag-bag these outbursts are pulled it is impossible to say with any certainty, but I am convinced that the emotion is basically that which we describe as jealousy. To the otters, Caroline and Simon were interlopers; the otters sensed, if it is permissible to anthropomorphize so far, that something they had regarded as being their exclusive right was being shared with a stranger.

The immediate consequences of this incident were less grave than might have been feared, and were greatly helped towards this end by Simon's cavalier attitude to his injuries. He was unable to play football for a week after going back to school, and he will never lose the scars, but, like Terry, he shed no tear and made no complaint.

I left Camusfeàrna for London on 19 January, to be married on 1 February, and on the 22nd Teko attacked Jimmy. He and Terry had taken Teko and Dirk for a walk, and as usual the dog and the otter had indulged in wild games in and out of the sea. They had begun to walk home,

Jimmy leading with Dirk and Terry following with Teko. Jimmy stopped for a moment to pat and caress the dog, and in that instant Teko flew at him from behind. The first deep bite was in the calf of the leg, but by the time Jimmy had realized that Teko's rage was too great to yield to any persuasion, he had received other severe bites in the shin and the foot. Jimmy did the only thing he could do; he ran for it, with Teko in close pursuit. Normally he would have outdistanced Teko quickly, but he was handicapped both by his injuries and by heavy boots, and he fell once, to realize as he recovered himself that Teko was almost upon him and that Terry was still some yards behind. By now this demoniac and breathless procession had reached a point immediately above the small sand cliff where the sand martins breed, the point from which I had fallen on the night we had abandoned the *Polar Star*; and Jimmy, remembering that Teko had always evinced a dislike of heights, jumped from this cliff and floundered across the burn. The moment's pause that this manoeuvre had given Teko had been time enough for Terry to overtake him and attach his lead. Jimmy was in a state of virtual collapse at the other side of the burn.

All this was kept secret from me until my return to Camusfeàrna sixteen days later.

Terry is convinced that this disaster too was due to jealousy, that there existed some close bond between dog and otter, and that Teko saw this relationship threatened by Jimmy's apparent affection for the dog. It was Jimmy, in any case, who was in that situation the outsider; both Teko and Dirk were specifically under Terry's charge, and the three formed in some sense an independent unit.

Whatever the reason, I was faced on my return with a situation not easy of solution. I was to leave for North Africa in the near future; during my absence only Terry could look after Teko, and only Jimmy could look after Edal. If either of them were ill one otter would have to be treated as a zoo animal, tended without contact. I had become, and remain, the only person who trusted both otters and had no reason to fear either of them.

There have been times when, despite their consistently affectionate attitude to me, it has been difficult to forget the terrible injuries they have inflicted upon others. These moments have arisen mainly with Teko. He has always possessed a genius for removing his harness and an intense dislike for having it refitted, which is in itself an exceedingly difficult task when the otter is uncooperative. Teko resists the operation with all his really enormous strength and eel-like sinuosity, accompanying his motor actions with vocalization calculated to intimidate the most courageous. His sound of displeasure is an essentially cockney vowel sound 'wow-wow-wow', each syllable prolonged and yelled out somewhere in the middle range of a tenor's voice; there have been times when I have almost expected this to change suddenly into the scream that accompanies an attack, but I have at no moment truly lost the sensation of mastery in which lies my salvation. The occasion when I have come nearest to doing so was in the autumn of 1962, when Terry, who had by that time given up looking after otters and was engaged entirely upon the construction of new buildings, came to tell me that Teko had a terrible wound. This proved not to be an exaggeration – it was an enormous incision that looked as if it could only have been made with a scalpel as a first stage to removing the limb, and it stretched from under the arm almost to the shoulder. Behind the elbow, where the forelimb joins the body, an otter has a great baggy fold of skin which becomes almost like a wing when the limb is extended forward; this had been cut right through to reveal not only flesh but sinew. The wound was at least three inches deep and, because a side-strap of the harness had sunk right into its depth, it was gaping four inches wide. Seen in profile as he stood on his hind legs, the whole animal looked as if he had virtually been cut in two.

The first task was clearly to remove the harness, and I was the only one of us who could attempt it. Knowing that Teko must be in great pain, and remembering how much he hated his harness being handled even without this added stimulus to anger, I thought it very probable that my moment had come; it was, however, impossible to leave him in his present condition. (It may be worth mentioning that no form of thigh-boot or glove provides any protection, as armour, against an otter that is attacking with serious intent.) It would clearly be impracticable to hold him in such a way as to undo the two buckles securing the harness, and the material itself was of extremely hard nylon so that I did not think it possible to cut through with a single stroke of any blade that I had; moreover, any sawing action would necessarily drag the strap deeper and deeper into the flesh. In the end I settled for the kitchen scissors, and I entered his enclosure trying consciously to repress the fear that I felt, for however the emotion of fear is communicated to an animal the fact of its communication is unquestionable and disastrous.

Teko stood up and put his forepaws against me – they reached almost to my hip – and whimpered. I put my face down to his and spoke consoling, caressing words to him while my hands were busy about his shoulder, trying to work the scissor blade under the nylon. It cut slowly, but it cut; after the first strap gave way there was a second, and then finally I had to pull the shoulderstrap out of the wound in which it was deeply embedded – throughout all this Teko made not one single angry sound.

For eight days thereafter I had to go into his house and

treat the wound by blowing powder deep into the sulcus, and though my manipulations must have been exceedingly painful he made no demonstration of protest whatsoever. (As a further safeguard against infection we put an enormous hunk of rock salt in his pool; this fascinated him beyond measure, and at the end of the first hour he had somehow contrived to hoist the whole forty-pound lump to the surface and to manhandle it out of the water on to the bank. Then he put it back and repeated the performance.)

Whereas Teko always gives me delighted welcome when I return after absence from Camusfeàrna, repeating again and again his greeting sound of 'whack-o, whack-o', Edal would as invariably shrill her rebukes to myself or Jimmy for a desertion of even a day or two. (At first I was at a loss to interpret this phenomenon, and it was not until recently that I learnt that it is commonly recognized among human infants, the form of protest ranging between behaviour superficially akin to Edal's and enuresis; the rebuke, when it is not overtly expressed, is implicit.) Edal would wail and snarl and lie on her back scrabbling at the air with her hands, her voice a shrewish and feminine variation upon Teko's, lacking the consonant but retaining the cockney intonation, so that it emerges as 'ow-ow-ow', with a richness of disyllabic vowel-sound that might have baffled Professor Higgins had he encountered it in Eliza Doolittle. It was not until whichever of us had been absent had adequately apologized for his inconstancy that she would abandon her outraged attitude and seek the reassurance of caressing hands. What, one asks oneself, would Lovelace have felt had Lucasta's only reaction to his poem (and, after all, Edal enjoyed not only four brief verses but several thousand words of prose) been 'ow-ow-ow' until he said it was all untrue and he was never going away again?

It is an appropriate moment to place on record an unpalatable opinion, in which I hope that I may be proved wrong. Whatever may be true of other species, I do not believe that any fully adult otter of that to which Edal and Teko belong is to be trusted completely with any human other than its acknowledged foster-parents. The emotions are too intense, the degree of affection accorded by the otter too profound. To achieve placidity, to enjoy to the full the company of one of these wholly fascinating creatures one would have perforce to live the life of a hermit, with only animal companionship.

Edal and Teko will not, I think, have forfeited the final sympathy of their fans by the momentary violence that I have described. They acted instinctively and within the framework of their heritage, a framework in which violence was essential to survival and reproduction. It is not the existence of these explosions that should excite attention and comment, but that a carnivorous wild animal, never domesticated in the early history of mankind as were the wild dogs, should in the first generation of captivity or other association with man display so much that he finds acceptable and approvable. Several million people responded sympathetically to these aspects of Mijbil and Edal, described without selection or rejection of fact, and those with any sincerity should respond with understanding to the whole character of the creature as it emerges into maturity. An animal, like a human, who displays nothing but charm becomes insipid. ('I was right years ago,' said Anthony Blanche, the archetype of articulacy in Mr Evelyn Waugh's *Brideshead Revisited*, 'when I *warned* you. I took you out to dinner to warn you of charm.' Sebastian Flyte, against whom the tirade is directed, never escapes from the narrow confines of his charm; the only positive action of which he is capable is that of self destruction, that of dying as a dypsomaniac in a

North African monastery.) Any wild animal displaying nothing but charm is doomed, metaphorically, to the same end, and by the same process of denying his instinctive needs. In either case we must pose a pattern of behaviour desired by the majority – in Sebastian's case that of the English Roman Catholic Church in which he had been indoctrinated; that, in particular, of a prominent *clique* whose actions were subject to the super-ego of Farm Street. I am aware that to many this equation of humans, with their various religious criteria of behaviour, with the animal situation when interfered with by a 'master' set of rules equally unrelated to instinct, will appear both offensive and ridiculous, but the parallel is valid. Had Edal and Teko not allowed liberty to instinct they would in time have shed the rest of their positive qualities as well and have been left with nothing but charm.

8

Accident, Fire and Flood

WE HAD LITTLE USE from the *Polar Star* during the autumn months; what time was not taken up by repairs after her wreck and the fitting of her new engines was filled, for the most part, by gales and heavy seas.

Meanwhile, before she could be brought ashore in February, we had to arrange the building of a cradle for her, for she could not be beached in the ordinary way without damage to her propeller-shafts. A wheeled cradle to carry a boat of nine tons deadweight is a substantial vehicle, costly to construct and exceedingly difficult to transport to a site as remote as Camusfeàrna. Ours was built on the Clyde, some 250 road miles to the south of us, and carried by heavy lorry to the village pier five miles away; from there we hired one of the semi-local car-ferry boats to bring the massive structure in sections to the south bay at low tide.

The cradle had then to be assembled in shallow water before the tide rose; the whole operation had to be timed with military precision, for the *Polar Star*, lying seventeen miles to the southward, was to be floated on to her cradle as the tide came up. The whole eleven tons we then intended to winch up the beach and on to the grass beside the house, using for this purpose our own Sahara Land Rover. The car was already at the house, for, after the narrative of *Ring of Bright Water* had been brought to a close, the proprietors of the estate on whose land Camusfeàrna lies had decided to bulldoze a track to a neighbouring bay, and we had paid for three extra days bulldozing to branch this track to Camus-feàrna. The result could hardly be called a road; in places, indeed, the bulldozer seemed to have succeeded merely in removing the floating crust from stretches of peat bog, but by Land Rover the track was usable after a spell of dry weather, when its gradient of one in three was not mud-covered nor its flatter stretches reduced by rain to seemingly bottomless morass. The downward journey was usually practicable in theory, though the fording of the Camusfeàrna burn, which cut the upper section of the track, was difficult in spate; but to ascend in anything but the dryest conditions we had become used to putting out anchors ahead of the Land Rover and hauling her up on her own winch. Certain sections of the track were by now littered with broken anchor flukes in evidence of past failure.

Our plans did not run with clockwork efficiency. The two-ton cradle came apart as it was dropped into the sea, and its massive metal parts proved very difficult to reassemble in the water. When Jimmy Watt in the Land Rover began to winch it to the position chosen for floating-on, the *Polar Star* was still on the horizon, but long before we were ready she was cruising impatiently round the bay. It was a further two hours before she settled solidly on to the heavy timbers of her cradle, and our work was only begun.

The Land Rover was able to move the whole eleven tons a hundred yards up the beach to the edge of the grass, but the step up from the shingle on to the field itself was beyond her capacity, and we succeeded only in burning out the clutch. For the completion of the work, and for the removal of the now useless Land-Rover, we had two days later to hire a breakdown lorry from a garage twenty miles away. The lorry was able to winch the *Polar Star* on to the grass, but the removal of the reluctant Land Rover presented greater difficulties. At the end of three hours the cortège had progressed less than a hundred yards up the one in three gradient of the track, and it was some seven hours after the beginning of the operation when, after midnight, the exhausted pall-bearers reached the metalled road at Druimfiaclach. It is such frequent incidents as these that render life at Camusfeàrna more costly than that of many a great mansion house nearer to the amenities of civilization.

All this was after the great freeze-up. First had come tempests and hurricanes that knocked the fences flat, whisked the slates from the roof like leaves in autumn, blew dinghies about as if they were pieces of paper, while the surf fell upon the windows of the house and crusted them thick with salt. The gentle slope of the high sand-dunes to the sea became overnight a vertical cliff some ten feet high as the invading waves roared in and battered the dunes into a resistant wall; the racing torrent of the burn in spate undermined the roots of the alders and the trees fell; the length and breadth of the field, where the bent-grass itself lay flattened by the wind, was scattered with seaweed and flotsam from the beach. It had been impossible to watch the sea, for one could not stand upright without support, much less keep one's eyes open as the hurricane hurled mingled spume and sand landward at a hundred miles an hour.

When the days of tempest were over it began to snow, and – something I had only seen once before at Camusfeàrna – it lay right down to the sea's edge. Slowly it turned intensely cold; the burn froze over and then finally the waterfall itself. It froze solid, still in the form of a waterfall, so that only the lack of movement betrayed its sculptural substance. Giant icicles formed a fringe from the banks of the pool beneath it, icicles more than seven feet long and as thick as a man's arm, and the deep pool itself was solid for more than two feet. The snow fell as though it would never end. Flat on the field and down to the tide it lay nearly two feet deep, and on the margin of the sea itself floated a tink-ling crust of ice. On the hill above us the road was blocked; there the snow lay evenly more than a yard deep, and there were drifts into which an elephant could have disappeared.

We had staying with us a Sicilian, Eugenio Vicari, who had never seen snow lie before; months earlier, when his visit had first been planned, I had tried to disabuse him of the image he had built of Camusfeàrna, that of a cottage in deep snow surrounded by Christmas trees. I had told him that it would be wet and windy and dark and that the only snow would be on the hilltops. Now he looked at me and grinned and said: '*Credo che non conosci bene la Scozzia!*'

His arrival at the station thirty-five miles away had pro-duced a moment of fine farce, a linguistic misunderstanding that it would be hard to better. Sitting in the hotel lounge and looking out over the small bleak village, he asked me whether there were any churches in the town. It was a natural enough question, for every Sicilian village is domi-nated by its church tower, and from where we sat there was no evidence of any ecclesiastical architecture whatsoever in the whole community. The word he used for church was, I thought, '*moschea*,' literally a mosque, but used in some parts of Sicily to denote any religious building; a result, no doubt, of the long Arab occupation of the island. I replied that there were, in fact, three, but they were on the outskirts of the town. What, he asked solemnly, were they like? He would find them very different from his own, I said; some of them did not even approve of music or bells, considering such things frivolities. In short, I summed up, he would find them very serious-minded, they might even seem to him to be preoccupied by death and the day of judgement. At this moment he could contain the joke no longer and he exploded. He was so helpless with laughter that it was minutes before I could understand – he had not used the word '*moschea*', but '*mosca*', the plural forms being nearly identical. He had, in fact, asked whether there were no flies in the town. When at the end of his visit he left from the same station he asked me to say good-bye to the three serious-minded flies and tell them not to worry so much about the day of judgement.

There was one further equally glorious misunderstanding during his stay, but it is difficult to convey the full nuance without offence. It was New Year's Eve; inside the house the wireless was blaring, the fire blazing, the room hung with Christmas decoration. Outside was the ever-intensifying cold of frozen snow and bare starlit skies. Jimmy had been out, and came back in a high state of excitement. 'The burn's frozen solid!' he announced. 'I've just walked right across it where it's deepest – I jumped up and down and it didn't even creak!' Eugenio, interested by Jimmy's obvious mood of high enthusiasm, asked me to translate. I said: '*Ha camminato sul torrente gelato*' – he walked on the frozen burn. Eugenio looked very puzzled. 'Why?' he asked, with great insistence. 'Why?' This seemed to me unwarrantable obtuseness; but perhaps, I thought, to a Sicilian who had never before seen natural ice there was nothing odd in being able to walk on it at sea-level. I said somewhat testily: 'What do you mean "Why?" It is a very remarkable thing to be able to do, and certainly the first time we've ever been able to do it here.' His astonishment deepened visibly; his forehead was furrowed with the effort to understand. 'Is it a ritual?' he asked, plainly anxious to enter as fully into the curiosities of Scottish life as I had once attempted to be absorbed into peasant Sicily. 'A ritual?' I replied. 'No, it's not a ritual, although in the old days, on big rivers like the Thames, these things became almost a ritual – things like roasting an ox whole on the ice of the Thames, or driving a coach and four horses across it. Here, it is just extraordinary to be able to walk across a small frozen river at sea-level – if it happened every year I suppose in time we'd make a ritual of it. Do you understand now?' I saw the same expression creeping into his big dark eyes as when he had begun to comprehend our confusion of issue about flies and churches. He was now obviously controlling a fit of giggles with the greatest difficulty. 'Would you mind,' he asked with painful politeness, 'would you mind repeating what you first said when I asked what Jimmy was so excited about?' I repeated it: '*Ha camminato sul torrente gelato.*' He began to choke with suppressed giggles, then the dam gave way altogether and he was helpless, rolling from side to side, literally crying with laughter. Although I had not yet understood the joke his mood was irresistible, and I began to find myself in the same state. 'What did you think I'd said?' I kept on demanding, but it was minutes before he found enough control to answer me. Then he gasped out: 'I didn't hear the letter "c". I suppose it was the wireless making all that noise – I thought you said "*ha minato sul torrente gelato!*" ' Now *minare* is the Italian slang verb for solitary sexual indulgence. Thus the picture of a strange esoteric ritual had been forming in Eugenio's mind, a ritual more weird, surely, than any of the archaic practices of his country. The year the Thames froze over and Charles II masturbated on the ice. . . .

Everywhere the snow went on falling, but the days were for the most part bright and sunny and the sea blue, and the plantation of young firs on the hillside above us became a regiment of Christmas trees. We improvised a toboggan, to the huge delight of Teko, who would straddle it to be towed round at ever-increasing speed. He seemed to understand the idea very soon, and when we pulled the toboggan to the top of a slope he would climb on to it and wait with obvious impatience for someone to shove it off down the slope. As it began to slow he would kick with his hind legs to maintain the impetus, and when his chariot finally came to rest he would work angrily at the ropes with his teeth, as if by so doing he could once more coax it into movement. We sent to London for a real toboggan, but by the time it arrived the snow had long gone and had given place to mud and quagmire.

The geese had left us, the wild grey geese that I had domesticated at Camusfeàrna two and a half years before. The day before the snow began they had taken wing, spiralled high above Druimfiaclach and made off southward at a great height. Of the eleven that left, only three came back in the spring; the rest, no doubt, suffered the common fate of wild creatures that have been taught to trust their worst enemy.

During all this time we had, as I have said, little use from the *Polar Star*, yet one glorious morning will always stand out in my memory. Since the roads were still blocked by snow when the time came for Eugenio to return to Sicily, we could only reach the distant station by sea. The winter sun was just up in a bare blue sky, the shadows still long and blue upon the snow, and the great white hills all about us were salmon-pink above a smooth enamel sea of beetle-wing blue. On every side so little showed through the snow that the only colours of which one was aware were those of its varying tones, from shadows to sunlit brilliance, and the two blues of sea and sky. The *Polar Star* roared north between the frozen mountains, and her great leaping seething wake held the reflected light of the sun and the snows; to us on board her the racing boat seemed the only moving thing in a world of ice-cold colour, her speed the direct expression of human exhilaration.

In February 1962 Malcolm and Paula Macdonald, who had given Edal to me in the spring of 1959, came to Camusfeàrna to visit her after an absence of nearly three years. I had told them of all that had happened during the past six months, of her attack upon Terry and of her apparent hatred of women, and they both agreed that it would be inadvisable for Paula to meet Edal face to face. Malcolm would go into her room with Jimmy, and Paula would watch over the waist-high partition that separated Jimmy's sitting-room from Edal's quarters. We were in the living-room when we reached this sensible decision, and a moment or two later I was called to the telephone to take a long-distance call. The telephone conversation was prolonged, and it was some quarter of an hour later that I returned, to find the living-room empty. I went across to Jimmy's house, and as I entered his sitting-room I at first saw nobody. Then I heard voices from beyond Edal's partition, and hurried forward. Sitting on the bed were Jimmy, Malcolm and Paula, and to the last two Edal was making every demonstration of the profoundest welcome and affection. It might have been thought surprising that Edal should remember them at all after that long lapse of time and the mental and physical crises through which she had passed; this, however, was not a question of mere recognition but of positive joy. She squirmed and beamed and pushed her fingers into their mouths; then, as Paula talked to Edal the baby language to which she had been accustomed as an infant, Edal reverted to behaviour that she had not displayed for a full two years. When Paula had first brought her to Camusfeàrna Edal had a well-established and slightly inconvenient method of displaying her affection for her foster-parent, that of sucking and nibbling at Paula's neck. This she had reserved for Paula only, and had never transferred the pattern to Jimmy or myself; now she climbed up on Paula's lap and went into her old ritual as though it were days rather than years that Paula had been away.

It was, in some respects, a heart-rending reunion, for some

six weeks before, the two West African otter cubs that Malcolm and Paula had brought back from Nigeria to replace Edal had been killed. These two were without exception the most domesticated and endearing otters I had ever seen, living totally free and behaving like very well brought-up but extremely playful dogs. A minister of the Church of Scotland, mooching along the foreshore with a shotgun, found them at play by the tide's edge and shot them. One was killed outright, the other died of her wounds in the water. The Lord gave man control over the beasts of the field, as this minister reminded a journalist.

In the course of that winter of 1961–2 we fortuitously acquired two more otters, and once again with the element of coincidence that would seem by now to have become a stereotype. First, a gamekeeper telephoned from the south of Scotland. That afternoon, he told me, he had been walking along a river bank when he had come unexpectedly upon a bitch otter with four very small cubs; one had been farther ashore than the others and found his route to the river blocked by a man and a dog. He just squatted and blinked, as though considering at leisure the correct course of action in these totally unfamiliar circumstances. Probably it was this certain gormlessness of personality which has to some extent characterized his existence ever since, that saved his life – for the gamekeeper, seeing this very small creature just sitting there and blinking hopelessly at him, threw a gamebag over it and picked it up. He took it home, put it in a box with some wire-netting over the top, and telephoned to me.

Despite the complications of the existing otter *ménage* at Camusfeàrna, I did not hesitate. I had always wanted a British otter, and had come near to realizing this ambition when in a previous summer a local keeper had brought me a small female cub that his terriers had caught, but alas she proved to have a double compound fracture of the lower jaw, and were it to remain unset she would for all her life have been unable to feed herself. Jimmy and I bottle-fed her and tended her wound for a few weeks, but when at last the necessary surgery was carried out in a distant town she died of post-operational shock. Now this completely un-damaged cub was more than I could resist.

Transport, however, presented problems. As nobody knew whether or not the cub was weaned it clearly could not be sent unaccompanied on a long train journey; Jimmy was on holiday in the south, Terry was not yet old enough to drive a car, and I could not leave him in sole charge at Camusfeàrna. I hired a driver and my neighbour, Mary Mackinnon, volunteered to make the three hundred mile journey in my Land Rover.

When two days later I went up the hill to Druimfiaclach to meet them I carried on my back a wicker fishing creel, thinking this to be an ideal container for a small and possibly very active creature intent upon escape. This picture, how-ever, proved entirely false. When I entered the kitchen at Druimfiaclach, Mary was sitting with the cub on her knee and it looked remarkably domesticated if not particularly intelligent. I carried it down to Camusfeàrna inside my shirt, and it fed contentedly from a bottle immediately after arrival.

A few weeks later, after I had gone to London to be married, another unweaned cub arrived. The first had been a male, the second, to dot the i's of the coincidence, was a female. Jimmy received a telephone call from the Isle of Skye, to say that a bitch otter in milk had been shot a few days before and now a road-mender had found a tiny un-weaned female cub in a ditch. Within three days the two were together in the upstairs room that Edal used to occupy.

The male we had named Mossy, after the earlier cub that

died; the female was christened in my absence by the day of
her arrival, Monday. How the characters of each of these
two would have developed in the absence of the other, it is
impossible to say. Mossy, certainly, would have demanded a
great deal of patience. As long as he was kept in a large box
and only lifted from it to take his bottle he appeared docile
and promising, but when he was liberated in the room he
did not display the confidence I had expected. I had to sleep
on a mattress on the floor before he would consent to curl
up in the crook of my knee as all my other otters had liked
to do, and he would avoid being handled if he could. It took
a fortnight of patience before he would allow us to begin to
handle him again and before he started to play with such
moving objects as a screwed-up ball of paper on the end of
a string. Perhaps he would have developed into a truly dog-
like creature had I not had to go south to London and had
Monday not arrived a few days later, but I fancy that his I Q
would always have remained noticeably low.

Monday, by contrast, was from the beginning utterly
confident and of a very high degree of intelligence. She was
visibly the younger of the two, being little larger than a big
rat when she arrived. At the start Jimmy kept her separate
from Mossy; she lived in a large basket by the kitchen fire,
and if she had remained alone there can be no doubt that
she would have become an apotheosis among domesticated
otters. When, however, after a few days, she climbed from
her basket, explored her new surroundings, and fell wol-
fishly upon a plate of roast mutton, Jimmy decided that the
time had come to introduce her to her future mate.

Carried upstairs to Mossy's room she at first stayed quite
still, while Mossy advanced and withdrew from her again
and again. At last she followed him, a little uncertainly, as
he moved away from her, and from that moment he took
possession of her. He nuzzled her, and climbed all over her,

Beaching the *Polar Star*

Lavinia and Dirk

The *Polar Star*, April 1963

Camusfeàrna, February 1963

What remained of the Mercedes

making a small, high wickering sound in the back of his throat, and when Jimmy went to pick her up Mossy made an angry dart at him with the explosive breathing noise in the cheeks that is his sound of aggression.

Every day Monday spent a little time in that room, before being returned to the kitchen, and each day Mossy became more possessive and more angry when she was removed. In less than a week she took up permanent quarters with him, and from then on Mossy took no interest in human beings except as purveyors of eel meat. Though Monday remained confiding, the two were self-sufficient. They indulged in endless mutual grooming, though in this as in all else Monday remained the subservient partner and Mossy retained his demanding male arrogance. A typical and oft-repeated tableau was that of Mossy lying at ease upon his back, preening, in a desultory way, his chest and forearms, while at the lower end of his body Monday performed for him services that afforded him the greatest evident delight. They slept much throughout the day, showing a preference for darkness; sometimes they would curl up together underneath a chest of drawers, but more often they appeared as a conspicuous and faintly stirring lump under the carpet. Towards evening they would awake and begin to play games that gathered tempo until from the living-room the noise above resembled nothing so much as a couple of toy trains running on the rimless spokes of their wheels. Round and round the bare boarding next to the walls they would race tirelessly, the thunder of their progress interrupted only by Mossy's inevitable catching of Monday, when the sounds of galloping feet would change to prolonged and concerted wickering. This wickering is extremely difficult to describe; it is a very rapidly repeated staccato but musical note of which the effect is almost of something mechanical. It is in the treble key; perhaps the nearest parallel would be the concept of a motor-mower whose voice had not yet broken, and the nearest approach to accurate reproduction is to rub a wetted finger-tip quickly to and fro over half an inch of glass surface.

Humans, in their role of providers, remained creatures of enormous importance to Mossy and Monday, and at the sound of a step on the stairway they would make a single competitive rush for the half-door that separated them from the landing. After the first few weeks we had removed the carpet until such time as outdoor quarters could be arranged for Mossy and Monday, so that by now there was nothing to deaden the patter, or thunder, of their tiny feet on bare linoleum. We tape-recorded the noise of this race from one corner of the room to that diagonally opposite, and the effect is that of a sound-track deliberately speeded up, so that it becomes simply a solid roar, without perceptible impact of individual feet. At the end one can distinguish one single tap on the drum, so to speak – the sound of their forepaws hitting the door as they stood up against it in frenzied anticipation.

Sometimes Dirk the deerhound would accompany whoever went up to feed them; he would put his paws up on the half-door and gaze down with benign interest at the sharp little faces looking up at his.

At this time we fed Mossy and Monday by hand upon pieces of chopped eel, partly so that they could thus be forced daily into human contact and so retain some domesticity, but partly, also, in order to ensure that each received a due share; for Mossy, despite his possessiveness towards his consort, had proved himself an apostle of enlightened self-interest, and ungallant to the ultimate degree. Anything he could possibly snatch from her he did, and when we had first offered them whole eels he had contrived to carry the whole lot in one journey to a distant corner, where while eating the first he snarlingly guarded the remainder. If during this display of anti-feminism one gave another eel to Monday, he would shoot across the room from his corner, whisk it away from her, and add it to his own defended store. There was no solution but to feed each with inch-long lengths of eel from a pair of tweezers; these were necessary because, while Monday took these bonbons with all the gentleness of a well-trained dog, Mossy was by instinct a grabber, and cared nothing whether or not his needle-sharp teeth enclosed more than a piece of eel. At the time I resented Mossy, and thought only what a rewarding animal to domesticate Monday would have been without him, for it was not until some three months later that we moved them outside and had all the unwearying joy of watching two wild otters at play in a glass tank.

Meanwhile both these otters had to receive the injections necessary to ensure their future health. The injections were in two doses at a fortnight's interval, and in this matter, too, Monday displayed most strikingly the quality of intelligence that Mossy lacked. Neither of them was handleable in the sense that they could be held still while being injected with a hypodermic needle; but to this problem the same resourceful vet, Donald MacLennan, who had saved Edal's life, had as always brought answers. He introduced us to an instrument I had never seen, a dog-catcher; a long metal tube from the distal end of which protrudes a noose that can be drawn tight from the butt. Neither animal being familiar with the function or potentialities of this device, the first injections produced no difficulty at all, and the work was completed in five minutes. We began with Monday, because she was the first to go into a corner where she could be walled off and confined by a piece of boarding some three feet high and four feet long. After that initial mistake on her part, she displayed, however, a cunning in avoiding the noose that no human brain in the same body could possibly have surpassed. She had, after all, only her jaws and her two

fore-paws at her disposal, for after the first quarter of an hour
we had closed her in so completely that she had no room to
manoeuvre. Again and again as the noose descended towards
her head she would anticipate trouble by going to meet it –
she would spring up and seize it between her teeth, worry it,
and throw it back over her shoulder with a flick of the neck.
More than once, when someone had momentarily succeeded
in distracting her attention and we had the noose almost in
position, she would get her paws inside it and pull it open
with that extraordinary strength which even very small
otters can display. It took three-quarters of an hour, and the
cooperation of three people, before we finally secured her;
it had been a hateful proceeding, and I dreaded its repetition
with Mossy.

I need not have worried. While Monday had clearly retained an acute recollection of the noose – almost, one is
tempted to write, an understanding of its mechanical
principle – that great booby Mossy, although angry and
blustering at being boarded off into a narrow corner of the
room, had no more idea of how to avoid capture than he had
shown on the river bank in his extreme infancy. With him
it was all over in three minutes.

For both of them, in however varying degree, I felt that
the experience must have been traumatic, and I expected that
it would be a long time before they recovered their trust in
us, even as providers of food. I thought it would be weeks
before we again heard that rush of scampering feet at the
sound of a boot on the stair. In fact it was less than an hour;
neither seemed to bear us any ill-will for the outrages we
had committed upon their persons.

They were, however, rapidly growing up, and both our
own pressure upon the limited accommodation of the house
and their increasing agility made it necessary to move them
to outdoor quarters. It was, perhaps, the second factor that

forced the decision upon us, for one incident made it evident that we could no longer ventilate the room by leaving the top of the window open without running the risk of their exit. We had removed a top drawer from the chest of drawers in order to sort through its contents, and immediately Mossy and Monday saw the resulting dark cavern as an ideal retreat from unwelcome human visitors. That this new den was some four feet from the ground troubled them not at all; the exact process by which they progressed from the floor to invisibility was too quick for the eye to follow, but the fact remained that the vertical distance was greater than that which they would have to ascend to reach the window. We made somewhat hasty preparations for their removal to an enclosure immediately outside the living-room window. From then on they became Lavinia's special care, and it is better that she rather than I should write the next chapter of their history.

'When I became engaged to Gavin in November 1961, it was inevitable that I was asked by a great many different people a great number of questions such as: "How will you like living a great deal of the time at a place as remote as Camusfeàrna?" "Do you like the otters and get on with them?", etc. All these questions I answered in the affirmative because in marrying, a woman consciously takes on not only the man, but also the pattern of his life and whatever it contains. For me, this pattern was in theory entirely acceptable but the reality only began after we returned from our stay in North Africa following our marriage, when the real work began of fitting into a long-established bachelor establishment, of putting down my own roots in my new home. I was a new girl, and above me in seniority of time were Gavin, Jimmy, Terry – and Edal and Teko. The difficulty here was that in a *ménage* in which otter and human lives were inextricably woven, I found that, whereas I had complete contact with the humans, I could, by virtue of being a stranger and a woman, only have the remotest contact with the otters; nothing more than talking to them over a dividing fence as I went to and fro during the course of the day; or at most sometimes throwing their food to them and thereby establishing that I was friend and not foe, even though a somewhat distant and negative one.

'It was not until the two babies, Mossy and Monday, were moved out into their enclosure, that I suddenly realized that I was not after all the only new girl. They had, in fact, come to Camusfeàrna at exactly the same moment as I had, and all three of us were busy settling in in our various ways. The realization of this made me view them in a completely new light, and I began to see them not as just two more of these strange, fascinating but remote creatures of whom I had no experience and with whom I had no personal contact, but as two highly individual animals with their own distinct personalities; animals with whom I could, given time and patience, establish a much more rewarding relationship than that of a mere interested and appreciative onlooker.

'When we returned to Camusfeàrna in the late spring, Mossy and Monday were still in their winter quarters in one of the upstairs rooms, the only home, in fact, that they had known since they were tiny cubs and had first come to us. They were shy, timid creatures, made more so by the facts of their mutual companionship, and that none of us had been able to give them enough of our time to accustom them completely to close human contact. Then came the day when their new outside enclosure was ready for them; their house was built and their blanket put on the sleeping-perch inside it; the glass water-tank, dismantled from Gavin's London house and brought up by me in the Land Rover, had been reassembled (but not yet filled); their empty giant tortoise shell in which they played hide-and-seek for hours on end had been carried down and put on the grass; and finally, Gavin and Terry had by some super-human effort of strength and incredible precision managed to roll an enormous old tree stump through the gate, making both a decorative feature in the enclosure, and a practical stepping-stone for them in and out of the tank. While Gavin and Terry were resting, panting from their exertions, I followed with handfuls of earth and clumps of sea pinks, hoping they would take root in the crevices of the wood; but when eventually the two little otters discovered the fun of scrambling all over the stump, the garden we had so quickly created for them disappeared with equal rapidity. The moment finally came to move Mossy and Monday themselves – a manoeuvre which was accomplished with far greater ease and speed than any of us had dared hope for. They were lured into a forty-gallon oil drum placed on its side; this apparently held no terrors for them, for after a very short time they nosed their way inside with true otter inquisitive-ness, and someone standing behind was able to fold down the cut lid and turn the oil drum upright. The bunghole in the side we left open and all the way down the staircase and out to their new home, they were jostling for a place at this window and looking out with their bright beady eyes at the unfamiliar world beyond their bedroom door. Once inside the enclosure, we laid the drum on its side once more and stood back to watch them slowly and cautiously emerging. It was a bright, sunny day, and this added to their confusion, for their eyes were totally unaccustomed to anything but the subdued light of the pine-panelled room in which they had spent their earliest months. However, the warmth of that day and those following was on the whole fortunate, for the temperature change from indoor to outdoor life was not too abrupt for them.

'We watched them nosing their way blindly round their

strange new surroundings, passing by their familiar tortoise shell with not so much as a flicker of pleased recognition, and finally finding the open door to their house, they bolted inside, into the darkest corner beneath the sleeping-perch. That was the last we saw of them for many days, but for their brief and timid sorties in the late evening in search of food which they grabbed and carried back at once to the safety of their house. We knew they emerged sometimes in the darkness of the night because from inside the house we occasionally heard little squeals and wickering noises, but at the slightest sound of human footsteps they would bolt back to their hideout.

'It was at this point in their lives that I found myself becoming more and more absorbed by the thought of these two tiny bewildered creatures who remained so obstinately out of sight; how they could be lured out and given the confidence to remain out in daylight without this precipitate flight at the first sound of clumping boots. We did attempt one day to break them of their nocturnal habit by closing their door behind them when they had emerged to find food, but they looked so pathetically miserable, huddled together in the shaded right-angle of their house and the fence, that we very quickly relented and reopened the door for them to return to the reassuring darkness of their home. But as the days went by and there was little noticeable improvement in this situation, we began to fear that they would remain as creatures of nocturnal habit.

'At this point, in early June, I had to go down to London for about ten days, and whilst I was away, Gavin tried new tactics by changing their feeding times. They had been having breakfast-eels at the same time as Edal and Teko had theirs, but that meant that no sooner had Mossy and Monday grabbed their ration, than they disappeared straight back into their house, and were not seen again until in the late evening the need of more food forced them to emerge once more. By postponing their morning feeding time we achieved exactly what we hoped for; they now ventured out and nosed their way round the enclosure with steadily increasing confidence and curiosity, simply through the dictates of their stomachs. Moreover, this enforced waiting period even began to awaken their enthusiasm for any passing human who they thought might be the bearer of their eagerly awaited eels.

'When I travelled up again, Gavin was already on his way down as he had to be in London on business for a few days. We broke our journeys for a couple of days at a mutual rendezvous, and then continued our separate ways north and south. When I got back to Camusfeàrna, I took over where he had left off in trying to win the confidence of the baby otters. It was entirely fascinating, especially as for me the attempt to establish contact with otters was a completely new experience. Although to the trained eye Mossy and Monday were easily indentifiable, to begin with I found myself getting very muddled and mistaking him for her, and vice versa – unless of course they were both in view, when the difference in size was obvious. We had all of us also adopted a sort of sing-song call to them, joining their names together, so there was no question of each coming to their own name at that stage. (Later, when feeding them by hand, I always made a point of talking to them each indi-vidually, and by name.) Now I began to see very clearly not only the physical difference, but also how unalike they were in character. Mossy, always the larger of the two, was by far the less intelligent and had a definitely boorish streak both in his treatment of Monday and of humans. His manners are, on the whole, appalling; he is a grabber by nature, and his ungentlemanly conduct towards Monday together with the expression on his face, altogether broader and flatter than hers, earned him the nickname of Reggie, after one of Evelyn Waugh's more oafish characters.

'Whereas Mossy's personality remains consistently dull – and thereby very often comic – Monday's by contrast is brilliant, gay and quick-witted. Her small, pointed face is always alive with curiosity and silent laughter, and she very quickly became the leader in all enterprise, though her devotion to her slow and unenterprising companion never wavered. Invariably, when food was thrown to them over the fence, it was Mossy who grabbed the first eel with a furious warning squeal at her, and one could almost see her shrug her shoulder as she waited, unmoved, for the next one. Sometimes he went too far with her and tried to take an eel from her, but at this a quick nip, a well-timed warning to watch his manners, would send him flying.

'We had a lot of trouble with the glass water-tank which we had hoped to have filled by the time the otters were in their new enclosure. One of the sheets of glass, of which there were three on each side and one at either end, had cracked when we first filled the tank, and we had to wait some days for a replacement. In the meantime we put the old hip-bath on the grass, but it was so shallow that after a few minutes of Mossy's and Monday's vigorous splashing nothing remained but an inch or two of almost pure mud, and the ground around it became more and more like a soggy ploughed field. But from their obvious enjoyment of it, it was plain that they would spend far more time out of doors when they had a permanent pool; we waited with growing impatience for the arrival of the new piece of glass, and then for the cement to dry and harden before we could again fill the tank with water. This was finally accomplished, but it was now late June, the time unfortunately which Gavin had to spend in London. Terry was also away on holiday so only Jimmy and I witnessed the great event of their introduction to deep water.

'Before describing this, I should explain that the tank had

been set up directly in front of the living-room window; across this window with its back to the light is a sofa, and by kneeling on it we had a perfect view of the tank. It was in that position that Jimmy and I spent many hours during the next few days. The tank itself measured approximately eight feet long by three feet wide by three feet deep, the glass panels held together by an iron frame, giving it an all-round rim of about three inches wide, and two surface cross-bars. We knew that entering the tank presented no problem to the otters; they could either go via the tree-stump, or simply by jumping straight from the ground on to the rim. This they had in fact been doing with the greatest of ease when the tank was empty, balancing their way along it and the cross-bars. Now, with the tank filled to the brim with clear water, we waited by the window in the long evening light and watched for the reward of our work.

'As was their wont at that time, they emerged from their house about sundown, when the bustle of the day was over and the light had begun to fade. They had a small doorway at the furthest corner of their house, just where it formed a right-angle against the fence; from this they would creep out slowly and cautiously, with wary glances all round as they advanced, and at the slightest noise would dive back to security. Later, as their confidence increased and with it their acceptance of the household, they watched everything with interest – footsteps still brought them clamouring to the wire-netting in the hope that every passing friend was a bringer of food, but if the footsteps were those of a stranger they would vanish immediately.

'On this particular evening, they explored the way step by step, and finally reached the tank. When they leapt up on to the rim and found not empty space but cold clear water, their astonishment was enormous, and their balance nearly upset. From this point their two separate personalities emerged even more clearly than before – Mossy the backward boy, Monday the forward girl. She dipped her nose in the water, and then again, deeper, shaking the drops from her face each time she withdrew her head, but each time plunging it a little further down until finally the inevitable happened; she lost her balance and fell in. With a twist of remarkable agility she was already holding on to the edge with her hands, as I clutched Jimmy's coat sleeve with anxiety and muttered "Are you sure she will be all right, Jimmy? Are you *sure* she will know how to swim?" However, she hauled herself out on to the rim with ease and then repeated the whole manoeuvre, but now deliberately and with obvious relish and greater daring each time. For quite a while she splashed in and out, but always she clung to the edge with her hands. Every now and then she would leap down to terra firma, where Mossy was moving about in a puzzled, aimless manner. She seemed to be both teasing him for his timidity, and yet encouraging him to be brave and join her in this delicious new game, but the most he could achieve was an occasional cautious prowl along the edge.

'Quite suddenly she was in and somehow out of sight; I found myself holding my breath, as one does when watching a swimmer who has dived. Unlike a human swimmer, however, she did not reappear, and with an awful sensation of choking I burst out: "Jimmy, *quick*! She's stuck." Jimmy shot out of the door, and at the unexpected interruption Monday shot out of the tank and bolted into her house.

'We watched her until it was too dark to see out of the window any more, and it was the most wonderful spectacle of under-water *joie-de-vivre* I have ever seen. After that initial plunge she appeared to have every movement, every trick of swimming, at her finger-tips; she had grace, and speed and beauty – a water ballerina. She was totally absorbed and had completely forgotten the luckless Mossy, who was still no further than the stage of dipping his big toe in at the water's edge. Jimmy and I finally turned away from the window and nibbled at our long-forgotten supper, but we could hear the splashing in the tank for the rest of the evening, and perhaps Monday swam all night long, for she was still at it when I fell asleep.

'The advent of water brought about completely the change we had hoped for in the habits of Mossy and Monday, and eventually they were as content by day as by night in their routine of swimming, eating and sleeping. But before this happened Jimmy and I had two more days of watching before Mossy mastered the art of swimming – two days in which he clung to the side, somersaulted over the cross-bars, kicked with his hind legs, thrashed with his tail; he would lose his balance and go in head-first and still manage to keep a grip on the side with his back toes. It was very funny and very clownish; but he would not, could not bring himself to let go. Monday mocked and teased him mercilessly, darting and diving below and around him, nipping at his tail and his toes. Finally she simply gave him a great shove and it was all over – to his patent surprise he suddenly discovered that he could swim. They began to evolve endless and intricate games together – water-ballets, which started in slow motion and worked up gradually to a long crescendo of movement, until the tank seemed a rapidly boiling cauldron and the two gyrating animals appeared to be twenty. Hide-and-seek, wrestling, boxing, "pat-a-cake" with hands or noses – in and out the tank, on to the tree stump, down the other side, hide under the tortoise shell. We have dawdled away many minutes watching their play.

'Gavin returned home a few days later and was delighted by the change he found. Now that the babies were so much less shy, he and Jimmy could hope to obtain some photographs or films of their underwater aquabatics whenever weather and light conditions allowed. We still referred to them as "the babies" but in fact they were growing fast, looking supremely healthy, and appeared to have insatiable appetites. At this stage they were supposed to receive four eels each for breakfast, the same in the afternoon, and a further two or three in the evening. But on going out at about ten or eleven at night, one would invariably hear a rush of tiny feet and see two small figures standing upright, side by side, holding on to the wire-netting and demanding more to eat. So we introduced a fourth feeding time; but Mossy and Monday were great believers in the theory that there is no harm in asking, and having many times received this extra meal from the hands of one of us they would pretend to the next passer-by that it had been forgotten.

'I was delighted with the change in their daily routine, for I wanted them to be much tamer than they were at present, and there was clearly very little hope of achieving this while they persisted in hiding by day. Now, however, Monday (in the lead as usual) began to come out when I called, with Mossy trailing behind suspiciously. I began to go into the enclosure with ready chopped-up eels, to draw out hand-feeding them for as long as possible. It was tremendously rewarding, and I found myself looking forward to feeding-times just as much as the otters clearly did – for our different reasons. Again, at this exercise, their two natures showed up markedly according to the now familiar pattern; I adopted a sitting position from the start, squatting back on my heels, and very quickly Monday came right up on to my lap to take her piece of eel. She was always absolutely gentle and deli-cate in her movements, and we have often thought that but for her strong bond with Mossy she could have become a complete household pet. He, as was to be expected, made a terrible fuss when being hand-fed; he took it all right, but with a lunge and a snatch, accompanied by furious squeals.

I have often expected to see a small chunk of my finger or thumb go with the piece of eel; but quite suddenly and to my surprise and delight he also grew gentle. But this may not have been so much a triumph of taming on my part as a result of the example of good behaviour from Monday.

'Their attitude to other animals was curiously matter-of-fact – far more so than to humans, with whom, as I have already said, they were extremely shy but for the recognized members of the household. Dirk the deerhound has always been a source of interest to them, and I have often watched long, snuffly conversations going on through the wire, the otters on their hind legs raising their small button noses to meet the dog's large wet one. But the funniest encounter occurred one day in the autumn between Monday and one of the greylag geese. I was in the otter's enclosure doing something or other by the tank, and caught sight of the geese stalking by the open gate in single file like slow, self-important sentries. The last one decided to turn in down the path to the front door, and at the same moment Monday came out of the side door of her house. They caught sight of each other simultaneously; the goose became quite hysterical, either with rage or fear, or possibly both, and danced up and down with wings extended, hissing loudly. Monday was by this time on her hind legs holding on to the wire with one hand, and a comical expression of mild surprise and interest on her face. I called as loudly as I dared to Gavin, who was working in his room, to bring a camera quickly before the scene dissolved; it was one of the occasions so frequent at Camusfeàrna, when I have wished that I carried a ciné-camera permanently slung round my neck.'

This was the autumn; both Lavinia and I were abroad during the early winter months, and we did not see Mossy and Monday again until the New Year of 1963.

Conventional insurance policies cover accident, fire and flood, and in a year of miscellaneous mishaps which included the first and last of these items it would perhaps have been unreasonable to expect fire not to have been attracted to Camusfeàrna by its general aura of crisis and vulnerability. I was, of course, alone in the house when it happened. I had been rendering down a great quantity of beef fat; when I had finished I placed the very large basin of liquid fat on the kitchen floor, put a frying pan of water on the electric hotplate with the intention of cooking myself some kippers, and then went to answer the telephone. The conversation lasted some ten minutes; I had a mental eye on the frying pan of water, but I did not think that, starting from cold, it could have evaporated in that time.

Exactly as I put the receiver down there was a muffled but heavy explosion from the kitchen, heavy enough to send a shiver through the pine-panelling of the whole ground-floor. Tearing through into the living-room I looked aghast at the entrance to the small kitchen – the whole doorway was blotted out in a roaring mass of flames whose tongues were even now shooting along the living-room rafters and devouring small pendant objects in their progress. Just inside the main door of the house was a large new fire-extinguisher; with this knowledge I felt quietly confident. I seized this impressive weapon rapidly, carried out the simple instructions printed upon it, advanced as near to the flames as the heat allowed me, and directed the nozzle towards the kitchen ceiling, for this, I thought, was the point from which the flames might take over the rest of the house.

The jet of extinguishing fluid lasted for something less than three seconds; then this pretentiously aggressive and brightly coloured instrument just began to dribble on to the floor. The only tap in the house lay beyond the wall of flames and the nearest water out of doors was Teko's pool.

I grabbed two buckets and raced for it; the bolt on his gate was stuck, and when I finally forced it open Teko was waiting to slip past me. By the time I had the two buckets full and the gate closed behind me I thought there was little chance of saving the house; for it is entirely lined with the ideal tinder of Oregon pine-panelling, and I was already considering what should be salvaged and how two irreconcilable otters might be rescued simultaneously with Mossy and Monday, whose room would be the first to go. The first buckets had little effect beyond a blinding cloud of steam; eight times I ran to and fro between the pool and the kitchen, throwing the water to the ceiling in cupped hands, and eight times Teko did all that he knew to make ingress or egress from his enclosure impossible. After the last of these nightmare journeys, I was amazed to see that no flame remained; the walls and ceiling of the kitchen, which had been repainted a week-before, were blackened and charred, but no living spark was left.

The first thing to catch my eye among the dismal debris was the remains of something that looked like the casing of a small home-made bomb, the ragged strips of thin, twisted metal that result from an explosion within a container. There were a considerable number of these scattered round the room, and then quite suddenly I saw their origin. Embedded in the basin of fat, now congealed by many gallons of water, was the warhead – the upper half of a deodorant spray of popular make. This tin, evidently, had stood too close to the hotplate on which I had prepared to cook my kippers; it had exploded, and with awful accuracy of aim the upper portion had travelled eight feet to slam into the basin of liquid fat. The force of the impact had sprayed fat all over the walls and ceiling; enough had fallen on the hotplate to start the fire, and this had in turn detonated two more deodorant cans, several pieces of which had also found their way into the fat and given fresh impetus to the flames.

Accident, fire and flood. Not long after the fire came the plague of rats. We had known for some months that for the first time in the history of Camusfeàrna there were a few in the house, but they did not appear to multiply, and caused us little trouble. Now there was a sudden population explosion and, far from our being able to ignore the rats, they became our major preoccupation. Whether they really numbered thousands I do not know, but certainly they gave that impression. Sleep became impossible at night as behind the panelling, they fought and mated, played and ran races, rolling, it seemed, some kind of resonant ball at high speed for hours on end; food disappeared from the most inaccessible places, and floors and furniture became foul with rat dung; they gnawed through the panelling to allow themselves multiple entry to every room and chewed the upholstery of soft furniture in order to build themselves nests; and worst outrage of them all, one of their number bit my head twice during one night. Possibly he too was in search of nesting material. To add to their other nauseous characteristics, they were cannibals by apparent preference, for if one of their number were caught in a trap he was invariably eaten before morning.

At first I was unwilling to use rat poison, for the memory of an experience long ago remained fresh in my mind. When I was an undergraduate at Oxford there was a small enclosure in the park containing ornamental waterfowl such as Mandarin and Carolina ducks and a few comparative rarities; every year these birds laid eggs and every year they were eaten by rats, insolently and in daylight before spectators. Waterfowl were in those days one of my major interests and I felt this to be a waste. The park keeper gave me permission to exterminate the rats and, full of youthful enthusiasm, I bought a packet of widely advertised and well known rat poison. On this packet were printed the words 'harmless to poultry and all domestic livestock'. I put poisoned bread and bran in the waterfowl enclosure, and the next morning every single bird in it was dead.

So at the beginning we tried every method of destruction other than poison. Outside, where we had refuse pits among the sand-dunes, they had formed a honeycomb of interconnecting burrows having their entrances many yards apart; into these we poured large quantities of petrol and ignited it to form a heavy subterranean detonation. This certainly did kill a great number of rats, but the birth rate evidently remained consistently higher than the death rate. We shot them with shotguns, rifles and pistols; we swiped at them with pokers, sticks and axes; we set for them snares and snap-traps and live-traps, but nothing made any impression upon their numbers.

The very first rat that we caught was in a live-trap on the living-room floor. None of us wanted the task of drowning it, and eventually it was left to me to carry the cage down to the stream. I submerged it immediately; the rat went on running round the cage as if it were in air and not water. No bubbles rose. After perhaps half a minute it put its paws up between the wire mesh of the trap and hung there, looking at me. It went on looking at me; it must have been a further minute or more before I realized that it was dead.

The live-traps were useless. The following day one trap held seven half-grown rats, and the day after there were another six; then no rat ever entered them again. By October the situation was unbearable and we consulted what the ungenteel used to call a rat-catcher, but is in fact a Rodent Operative.

There appeared to me to be only one possible poison, on grounds of safety, efficiency, and humanity, and even this,

Warfarin, could not completely be guaranteed harmless to the otters. The risk, however, was comparatively small, and in the event our judgement was wholly vindicated, for at the end of a week the otters were in excellent health and there was not a single remaining rat at Camusfeàrna.

In the course of the Rodent Operative's visit I learned much about rats that was strange to me. The common man, he said, tended to think of them as creatures of barnyard and building, in constant association with man; this was wholly fallacious and he would guarantee to find me rats on the pinnacles of the Cuillin Hills. As an example he cited the meteorological station on the summit of Ben Nevis; rats had arrived within a day or two of completion of the huts ments, and it would be unreasonable to assume them to have climbed 4,000 feet from the rich refuses of Fort William. It was due to the perpetually wandering habits of the rat, he explained, that they had settled at Camusfeàrna; not a square yard of countryside was unvisited by some rats in the course of six months, and they would stop wherever they found food plentiful. An open refuse-pit, which at Camusfeàrna was our only means of disposing of kitchen rubbish, was irresistible.

He also told me that I had been using the snap-traps, which were simply a larger version of the ordinary mousetrap, in a completely mistaken way. In my innocence I had asked him the best bait to use on these. 'None,' he replied. 'You don't bait them at all. I've never been able to understand why the makers put that little bait-peg on them – it gives people the wrong idea from the start.' He expounded his own method, which he said was foolproof. A rat in a room will at some time during the night run round the whole perimeter of the walls, and an unbaited snap-trap placed with the spring-platform against the wall was therefore infallible. But, he added, all traps became obsolete with the introduction of

Warfarin, and rodents need no longer present a problem to anybody.

Accident, fire and flood. Dirk the deerhound broke his leg. Any dog with a broken tibia produces many problems; when the dog weighs something like a hundredweight and the leg is the better part of a yard long, the problems are disproportionately increased. It had become a stereotype that after any absence from Camusfeàrna I would inevitably return to find that some disaster had taken place while I was away, and Dirk's accident conformed precisely to that pattern. Lavinia and I had been visiting friends some fifteen sea miles or 120 road miles to the southward; we had travelled by car, and had formed an intricate plan by which both sea and road transport were available for other family projects. My stepson Nicholas and Jimmy Watt had been invited to fish a salmon river the following day, in the area where we had been staying; we therefore decided to leave the car at the fishing port there, where the *Polar Star* had been undergoing some adjustments to her gear-box, and return to Camusfeàrna in her. We could then immediately transport Nicholas and Jimmy to the port by boat, leaving them the use of the car and ourselves returning to Camusfeàrna in the *Polar Star*.

This plan, surprisingly, we carried through without interference by weather or any of the many other factors that might have caused its dislocation, but when we dropped anchor in Camusfeàrna bay to take Nicholas and Jimmy on board, they brought the news that Dirk had broken his leg a few minutes before.

The dog had been in the house when Terry had announced that the *Polar Star* was on the horizon, and the whole party went out to watch her; Dirk, not in those days the best disciplined of dogs, had slipped out unnoticed and set out for a canter on the hill. No one was aware of his absence until a few minutes later, when a newly appointed estate manager who had been inspecting the forestry ground knocked at Camusfeàrna door and announced to Terry: 'Your dog's up there by the hill track, and he seems to have hurt himself pretty badly.'

Terry found Dirk at a distance of something like half a mile from the house, howling pitifully and unable to rise, each successive struggle causing him even intenser agony. It was obvious to Terry that Dirk had a fractured foreleg, and equally obvious to him that there was no way to get the dog home but to carry him, for to construct a stretcher would mean leaving Dirk for a long time in his present plight. It was fortunate that Terry, though past his sixteenth birthday by only four days, was constructed to the same Goliath specification as Dirk; two years at Camusfeàrna had transformed him from a pallid London child into a Hercules of six foot two and thirteen stone. Dirk had never been accurately weighed, but Bell's *The Scottish Deerhound* gives the weight of a dog standing thirty inches at the shoulders as 95 to 105 lb, and Dirk is very considerably over thirty inches. Terry simply picked him up, one hand under his chest and the other under his haunches, and carried him home. He remarked that had the incident taken place five days earlier he would have performed this feat at the age of fifteen.

The vet arrived soon after Lavinia and I had returned from our southward journey with the *Polar Star*, and in half an hour the dog's leg was set and plastered, but we were barely at the beginning of our troubles. Even an able-bodied dog of Dirk's proportions occupies a surprising amount of space in a cottage the size of Camusfeàrna; but only now, immobilized by his injury, did his vast extended frame reveal the enormity of his stature. In broad terms he occupies three feet by five, and the slightest attempt at movement of any kind caused him an agony so acute that he could not contain his voice, so that night and day became hideous with his screams. To move him out of doors so that he might relieve himself was the work of two men, carrying and manoeuvring through doorways his vast forequarters and thereafter supporting him in this helpless position until necessity overcame his inhibitions and he allowed his sphincters to relax. He required constant nursing night and day, and after the first two nights it was clear that we could not keep him at Camusfeàrna throughout his convalescence. We made arrangements for his reception at a hospital kennel in Inverness the following day and addressed ourselves to the problems of his transport. We spent the morning building a stretcher; this we covered with foam rubber cushioning and over it we nailed an army blanket, the free portion of which would be passed over the prostrate dog and in turn nailed down to hold him in position.

It was just after we had succeeded in carrying Dirk from the house and laying him on the stretcher that a party of unannounced visitors arrived. They were, they told Terry, friends of some people whom I had received earlier in the year, and who had told this party that they were sure I would not mind if they called. To the best of my recollection there were five or six of them, a comparatively modest invasion, for families holidaying in the West Highlands seemed often to consist of double that number. I told Terry to explain that I could not see them at present, but that if they cared to go for a walk and return in an hour it was possible that the present crisis would be over. They did not choose to leave immediately, but stayed to annoy Teko by peering at him over the paling, thus adding his penetrating voice to Dirk's pathetic howls as we arranged his sprawling carcass upon the stretcher.

We manoeuvred the huge wooden structure through the rear door of the Land Rover with the greatest difficulty, for the door itself was narrow, and we had to tip the stretcher at an angle of forty-five degrees before it would pass through and lie flat across the seats. The nailed blanket, however, held Dirk from sliding, and the stretcher settled neatly into its position.

The Land Rover set off very slowly up the steep track. At the end of half an hour it had progressed less than two hundred yards, for the tyres found no grip upon the slippery mud of the steep gradient, and Jimmy and Terry were once more reduced to hauling the car up by her own winch.

At this point the visitors returned; my apologies for inability to receive them after all evoked no other response than unconcealed and boorish anger that they had been sent on a fruitless walk instead of being informed of the fact when they first arrived. The very gaucherie of their egregious presumption deprived me of words. They retired huffily to a neighbouring hilltop, from where they watched with sour satisfaction our struggles with the improvised ambulance.

When at length Jimmy and Terry reached the metalled road their real troubles began. The braking power of the Land Rover being greater than her acceleration, Dirk was perpetually shifted forward and downward on his stretcher; since he could use only his hind limbs in an effort to rise or readjust his position, their pushing movements only propelled him further towards the bulkhead between him and the driving cab. Each one of these movements pressed the strained blanket against his plastered foreleg. Jimmy remembers the eighty-mile journey as a nightmare, Dirk screaming and helplessly defecating where he lay, so that the stench in the car became almost as unbearable as the pitiful sounds of the dog's distress. A score of times they halted to rearrange him, and by the time they arrived at their distant destination both Dirk and his stretcher were anchored by a spider's web of string and rope to every stable object in the rear of the Land Rover. Accident, fire and flood.

9

Société Anonyme

A FRIEND, WITH WHOM I travelled in the autumn of 1962 to Southern Europe and North Africa, had long suspected the existence of an international body whose French branch he knew to bear the title of *Société Anonyme pour la Confusion des Voyageurs*. That there were affiliated or subsidiary organizations all over the world was evident, but the locality of the ultimate HQ remained unidentified. During our journey I came to suspect it of being mobile; it was the off season for tourists, and the highest officials of the organization, who by their very skill could only be attached to HQ, appeared to be in constant touch with our progress or lack of it.

The new Algerian Cabinet had, in November 1962, a *Caisse d'Equipement*. A *Caisse d'Equipement* for an agent of the *Société Anonyme pour la Confusion des Voyageurs* would at its most basic level contain the following items, to be used at discretion and to create the greatest confusion. A well-trained agent will go far with the following signboards; they are designed specifically to reduce to captivity or lunacy the driver of a motor vehicle, and each *caisse* must be assumed to contain the essentials for one town or village only. The following list for a French-speaking country is deductive, and applies to the off-season in summer; when the flow of foreign tourist traffic is greater, and funds derived from fines are ploughed back into the firm, the number of items can be greatly expanded without loss of profits.

(*a*) 1 sign *Toutes Directions;*
(*b*) 8 signs *No Entry* (International Code);
(*c*) 4 signs *Défense de Stationer* (1 verbal, 3 International Code);
(*d*) 10 signs *Fermé sans Date;*
(*e*) 10 signs *Tirez* and *Poussez* (to be reversed);
(*f*) 4 signs *Hommes* and *Femmes* (to be reversed).

As an example of how the first three items can be employed to the greatest effect by an intelligent agent I cite the following two alternatives; both, clearly, are taught in the primary course of instruction, and both are seen here from the traveller's eye viewpoint.

Upon entering the purlieus of a considerable village or medium-sized town one is surprised to see that the main, the obvious, route to the town's centre is blocked by a *No Entry* sign, while an arrow with the words *Toutes Directions* points to a side-street on the right. This street is straight and narrow and leads into a square. Sometimes the centre of the square is ornamented with an equestrian statue, but always it is made hideous by a huge notice *Défense de Stationer.* A few cars of foreign identity are touring round and round the square in a hesitant, jerky fashion; one, with Swedish number-plates, has run out of petrol, and several gendarmes are gathered round it with notebooks and snarls of triumph. The Swede does not speak French; his wife is in tears. Still unsuspecting, one follows the sparse traffic. Only slowly does it dawn upon one that all exits from this square – let us say five in all – bear No Entry signs, including the street from which one has emerged. *Défense de Stationer.* Round and round the square, hope dying, despair growing, the close press of circulating cars ever increasing, the cruel gloating gaze of the gendarmes following like vultures behind a wounded animal. Time must have a stop, defiance is useless; the car coasts to rest and the vultures close in with their notebooks, their bills, their beaks. Later, they will have the car removed and direct the traveller courteously to an hotel bearing the *Fermé sans Date* notice. (If it is open items (c) and (f) may be used to advantage, but only after the first quarter of an hour.)

Alternative: the same *Toutes Directions* sign, but this time the diversion is not short and straight into the trap. It begins as a reasonably broad street, and after a hundred yards it turns at right-angles to the left. It grows narrower and turns at right-angles to the right. Then very much narrower still, room for one small car only, and another corner to the left. By this time the walls of the old town are scraping the car's wings, and it is with a sense of enormous relief that one sees ahead the sunlit stone of a spacious square. It is true that one sees simultaneously the familiar *Défense de Stationer*, but one has not yet learned the lesson. Beyond is no exit from the square, and once again the street of emergence carries the No Entry sign. Many gendarmes are gathered gluttonously round a hundred helpless cars. The *tirez* and *poussez* upon the police HQ doors have been reversed; there are broken hinges, and broken glass, and *papillons* are being scattered to the limit of vision.

Surprisingly, it is often in the remotest places that the organization achieves its greatest virtuosity. Once, lost at midnight on desert tracks in southern Morocco – wind, sand and stars – the headlights of my Land Rover showed a distant but unmistakable signpost. Eagerly I approached it and eagerly directed the searchlight beam full upon its legend. It read, quite plainly and without any possibility of doubt, '*A Sodom et Gomorrah*'. For hell's sake, I thought, this is the turning-point of sanity. I'm several thousand miles off course, and several thousand years behind time. I got out of the car and investigated the outrage in detail. It was a wooden board, and the paint was quite fresh; near to its foot was a pile of camel dung, also quite fresh.

It was not until several days later that I learned of an American Film company who had tentatively chosen the fantastic desert city of Ait Ben Haddou as the setting for the expenditure of a sum that was phenomenal even by Hollywood standards. Other, as then unrecognized, activities of the organization came to mind. Approaching the outskirts of Hamburg at 11 pm the main oil-feed pipe of my car breaks; I am due at Le Touquet the following day; I speak no German other than that learnt parrotwise in early childhood from German Poetry for Recitation. *Der Alkoenich* and *Der Alte Barbarossa* are inadequate to the present situation. . . . Entering the Spanish frontier at Irun; despite the fact that one could throw a stone into France, no official speaks one word of French. My Land Rover, heading for North Africa via Gibraltar, contains various firearms including a pistol. From the frontier I am driven in a police car to a police HQ in a town some ten miles distant. There is no competent official. When he arrives an hour later there is no interpreter. He appears entirely fortuitously after the competent official has left again. After three hours I am allowed to retain rifle and shot-gun, the case of each now fitted with some sort of chastity belt, but the pistol is confiscated. I may recover it at Algeciras police station in two days' time; it will be there long before I can get there myself by car. I wait a week in Gibralter and visit Algeciras daily, but no one has heard of the pistol. Through the good graces of an officer of the Gibraltar Garrison I receive it in England, four months later.

My object has been to explain the principle of the organization before narrating the story of a journey made hideous by its activities.

I left England by car in late November 1961. One of the more childish hobbies that I have carried with me into middle age is the driving of very fast cars, and the year before I had bought a Mercedes-Benz 300 S L Roadster. While not appreciably faster than the old converted Grand Prix Maserati that had preceded it, the Mercedes was by contrast, utterly reliable, comfortable and weatherproof. I accorded to this car the feelings conventionally appropriate to the most costly single possession that one has ever owned, and a scratch upon its glossy coachwork disturbed me as much as would a boil upon my own face.

I had business in France, Majorca and Algeria, and our itinerary required a strict time schedule to avoid total disruption. We were to drive from Le Touquet to Barcelona, ship the car to Palma, and fly on there ourselves the following morning. After four days in Majorca we were to fly to Palma – Nice – Algiers, leaving the Mercedes in Palma, spend eight days in Algeria, fly to Algiers – Nice – Palma, and after a further fortnight in Majorca ship the car back to Spain and drive north to various rendezvous in France. The second of the two periods in Majorca I intended to regard as a holiday without responsibility, the first that I had taken for years.

It was pouring with rain when we landed at Le Touquet, and it went on pouring with rain all that afternoon and all the following day. As we drove further south we came into snow and ice; finally, as we left Perpignan, a wind sprang up and increased until it cannot have been less than Force 11 on the Beaufort scale. Zig-zagging down the sea-cliff roads towards the Spanish frontier at Port-Bou the storm plucked and tore at the car until more than once I thought that we should literally be blown off the road and over the edge of the precipice. At the frontier post itself the force of that tearing wind was so great that it took all one's strength to open and close the doors of the car and fight one's way across the road to the frontier buildings.

In Spain it began, inevitably, to rain again, and the

windscreen was once more coated with the slush barrage of heavy transport. We arrived in Barcelona after dark, more than an hour after the scheduled time at which the car should have been at the docks.

During my few visits to the country Spanish traffic regulations have remained wholly enigmatic to me; whatever I do or do not do, whistles are blown, accusing fingers pointed, and I am brought to a halt. After some penetrating inquiries the relevance of which is not apparent (for example, the full Christian names of my father, who died in the same year that I was born); after documentary formalities lasting long enough to allow the last hundred laboriously overtaken lorries to repass, I am fined a preposterous sum in hard cash and allowed to set off in dispirited pursuit of the heavy convoys. It must be coincidence that the policeman simultaneously heads for a tavern.

Madrid and Barcelona appear to have given enormous study to the technique of confusion. To a running commentary of chirruping police whistles (sometimes it has seemed to me that these sounds are the true language, the primitive vocalization of the species, and that human articulation must have been laboriously learned) the packed traffic surges always straight forward, unable to turn left or right or stop without incurring a veritable orchestra of furious chirping.

Thus to say that our entry into Barcelona was filled with frustration would be an understatement; the inexorable flow of traffic, moving to the tune of angry or purely conversational chirps, bore us ruthlessly past every desirable goal. Our immediate destination, I had decided, must be an hotel, from where some employee would accompany us to the shipping company's offices in the town and then direct us to the docks. A simple and eminently sensible programme, but in practice very difficult of achievement. For, although hotels of all types flanked both sides of the long tree-lined avenue down which we swept, any attempt to turn right or left was greeted by the same outraged grasshopper chorus. There were no *No Entry* signs such as are customarily used by the *Société Anonyme*, no *Toutes Directions*; only the relentless, jostling surge of traffic. Caught up in the stream, we were swept onwards, whirled round a great fountain and back down the avenue by which we had arrived.

By some whim of the Society's agent responsible for this street, the whole block of traffic of which we were a unit was suddenly herded off the avenue and right to the doors of the Ritz. This, though clearly disconcerting to some of the cars surrounding us, was the apotheosis of our dreams, and our simple and sensible programme was carried through to the letter.

Meanwhile, however, agents of the Society had been in touch with Palma, finalizing the details of our total rout.

The Mercedes had been left at Barcelona dock, complete with her keys, in charge of the shipping company concerned. In exchange for these keys we received the document necessary to reclaim the car at Palma dock on the following day. Euphoria set in.

In the morning we flew from Barcelona to Palma, arriving at the airport a little before midday. As the expensive part of the itinerary still lay ahead of us, we took the airport coach to the town terminus. Entering the outskirts of Palma, and thinking of nothing in particular except that Majorca ought to be warmer in winter, I was amazed to see my own car approaching from the opposite direction. The bus was so high, and the Mercedes so low, that I could see nothing of the driver as he passed; looking back after him I could make out through the rear window of the Mercedes that there was no passenger, and that the head and shoulders of the driver had the contours of a very young man with ruffled hair. Somehow I retained an impression of overalls or dungarees. Then the Mercedes had disappeared round a bend, and our bus continued on its sedate way into Palma.

We did, immediately, jump to conclusions, but we were anxious to give them the benefit of the doubt. Upon arrival in the town we left our luggage in a café and went immediately to the port. The sentry of the port police, clearly a minor employee of the Society, informed us that the port was closed until four pm. It was then half past one. Neither of us spoke enough Spanish to argue the point with any persuasion.

Resigned by now to passing the day making sport for the organization, but still unaware of the magnitude of the disaster it had prepared for us, we took a taxi back to the airport. It was just possible, we argued, that some employee of the shipping company had tried to deliver the car to us there. The taxi-driver spoke a little French, and when we had explained our predicament he joined enthusiastically in the treasure hunt.

The airport knew nothing of the Mercedes, nor had it at any time visited the premises.

The taxi driver suggested that whether or not the port was officially closed it should be possible, with his local knowledge, to visit the dock office of the shipping company and there to pursue further enquiries. We returned to Palma.

During the drive we speculated as to the probable fate of the car. All the facts pointed to theft, yet they refused to fall into place. A vehicle of the Mercedes's striking, not to say garish, appearance (the body was scarlet, the head white) could not possibly be concealed in an island the size of Majorca, much less removed from it and converted into cash elsewhere. From the start I leaned to the theory that the car had been illicitly borrowed, possibly for a joy ride, by someone whose place of work was inside the docks, and that she would eventually be found abandoned somewhere in the countryside not too far from Palma, for the thief would presumably have to return to the docks by some specific hour. In all these suppositions I proved to be right, but nothing had prepared me for the circumstances in which she was to be found abandoned.

At the dock office of the shipping company the taxi-driver was forceful and voluble. An alert-looking young clerk of the company hustled us through the throng and bustle of busy warehouses and finally ran to ground a small, seedy and exceedingly shifty looking Majorcan of some fifty years. Nature had never endowed him with beauty, and now his obvious apprehension did not help to produce a reassuring mien. After two or three minutes of unintelligible Majorcine conversation he produced the ignition key of the Mercedes from his trouser pocket; it required no advanced knowledge of the language to understand that here was the man responsible for guarding the car, and that he had no knowledge at all of its whereabouts. It had disappeared; so much was evident.

At this point we explained to the clerk that we wished to put the matter into the hands of the police. In broad principle he agreed, but urged that we should approach the port police, since it was from the port that the car had disappeared. We concurred, with the reservation that we should also approach the Guardia Civil, since the Mercedes had been last seen, not in the docks, but upon the open road. He brushed this rider aside and led us to the office of the port police. Here a tired looking civil servant informed us that there would be no competent officer on duty for some hours. We returned to our taxi and directed the driver to the Headquarters of the Guardia Civil.

Inside the swing doors at the top of the broad flight of steps the equivalent of a constable sat upon a bench reading the daily paper. We asked to see the officer in charge. Later, perhaps, he said; the officer was having lunch . . . an hour, two hours . . . no, there was no available officer at the moment. My companion, who, though as helpless as I was in Spanish, was completely bilingual in French, exploded. What would happen, he asked with little unction, if there had been a murder or a bank robbery? The constable asked whether there had been in fact a murder or a bank robbery. Finally my companion delivered himself of a summary: 'We wish,' he said, 'to talk to no one else than the Chief of Police for all Majorca. A car of great value, unique in this island, and possibly in all Spain, has been stolen from the docks and is now upon the open roads of Majorca.' The constable began to reply that if it had been stolen from the docks we should address ourselves to the port police, but during the course of my companion's impassioned speech a door had opened, and an officer of unidentified rank had emerged and listened. Something in this speech had evidently touched off a train of ideas, a link, apparently, with something he already knew. He looked thoughtful. Asking us to wait for a few moments, he disappeared into an inner courtyard. We waited for more than a few moments, but eventually he returned and ushered us through the courtyard to a small upstairs office. The taxi driver was allowed to accompany us as interpreter; none of the officers spoke any other language than Spanish.

Upon entering this office the first thing that caught my eye was a portable Olivetti typewriter in a soft case. Olivettis are not rare, but this particular one was either my own or its twin in every respect, even to the staining of the case. Then, as I took in the rest of the room, I became aware that the whole multiple contents of the Mercedes was stacked against one wall – suitcases, cameras, books, tins of engine oil, all that had been crammed into the boot and locked there before the car was shipped from Barcelona.

My first reaction was one of profound relief that the Mercedes had been traced; then almost in the same instant I realized that the exhibits included the tool kit and the tonneau cover. The removal from the car of literally everything that was portable could only mean one thing. Almost simultaneously with the thought I heard the voice of the taxi driver: 'Your car has had an accident, a very bad accident. It is *kaput* – it is not possible to repair it in any way, ever.'

We rallied; we asked who had been driving it. 'It is not known. The remains of the car are now being towed to Palma. The police request you to return here at six o'clock this evening to complete all formalities.'

It was clear that we needed linguistic allies of more official status than the taxi driver. We needed an authorized interpreter and a lawyer. We went to the British Consulate, where we learned that the Consul was confined to bed with *la grippe*. From there we went to the agent of some English friends, and arranged for him and a lawyer of his choice to accompany us to police headquarters at six o'clock.

The four of us were punctual. The police officers present were now of high rank and appeared keenly, if slightly suspiciously, interested in the unfolding of the drama. To set the ball rolling they gave us the bare facts. At a fashionable seaside village some five miles from Palma, the Mercedes, evidently driven at a very great speed, had come into contact with a concrete column, and had been virtually cut in two. What connected the two halves, they added with relish, was bent in the form of a semicircle. Shortly after the accident, which was unwitnessed, a young man had presented himself at a first aid post in the neighbourhood. After treatment for contusions he had asked to go to the lavatory, from which, it was discovered quite a long time later, he had made his exit by the window, never to reappear.

The preparation, translation, and typing of my statement took an interminable time. The introductory paragraph held a note of caution, not to say disbelief. 'The holder of British Passport No. 24022, who claims that his name is Gavin Maxwell, and says that his father was called Aymer and his mother Mary, tells the following story. . . .'

At the close of these lengthy and ponderous proceedings, my companion was mysteriously whisked away by an officer of the flying-squad, dressed entirely in black leather. At the same time it was politely proposed that I should go to inspect the remains of the Mercedes in the garage to which it had been towed. 'Where are they taking him?' I asked the interpreter. 'To the first aid post to see whether it was really he and no other that was the driver of the car. These boys don't leave a lot to chance once they get going.'

We walked to the garage, the Mercedes agent for Palma, where a multilingual foreman greeted us. 'I have seen many fantastic accidents – accidents of all kinds – look,' he pulled an envelope of small photographs from his inside pocket and began to display his fantastic and lifetime-long collection of improbabilities (one was of two saloon Mercedes, of which the larger was parked foursquare on the roof of the smaller; '*he* was killed,' said the foreman, 'very dead'), 'but never I have seen an accident like your car and the driver still alive.'

The description of the Mercedes's condition had been no great exaggeration. The shape of the chassis was such that the car could only have been parked with accuracy upon the circumference of a rather small circle. Only the fact that the car had left-hand drive had saved the driver; just forward of the passenger's seat a great square extending right to the midline of the car had been, as it were, removed *in toto*. Into this space two men could walk in and stand. This was the shape and form of the concrete column that had sunk into her, as violent a bodily rape as could be imagined. There was clearly little worthy of salvage beyond the tyres, and possibly the upholstery. The mystery of the ignition key was explained; the wires had been pulled out from behind the dashboard and connected to each other by hand.

Our destination had been a village on the east side of the island; now we were requested not to leave Palma until further notice.

We stayed at a hotel whose pretentious restaurant printed a multilingual menu, a column in Spanish, another in French, and a third in English. This cheered us slightly, for the English column was headed with an unashamed declaration of cannibalism:

'Our chef suggests *you* today.'

He suggested, among culinary curiosities too numerous to mention:

> *Lamb soup Hodge-Podge*
> *The Short Broth with Egg Joke*
> *Spoked and granished Esturgeon*
> *Froce meat*
> *Balls, Catalonian style*

The following day was entirely occupied by legal formalities. In the evening an urgent telephone message arrived from police headquarters. The thief had been apprehended; would I present myself immediately before he was transferred to prison.

The same office, with my luggage stacked against the wall. Several police officials of steadily augmenting rank. Three-quarter rear view, leaning forward in his chair and holding his hands in his lap because they were handcuffed, sat a very blond and very young man. The interpreter asked me if this was the man whom I had seen driving my car. I moved round until I could see the back of the boy's head silhouetted against the white wall; it was a replica of the momentary image I had retained of the Mercedes driver. I said I could not be certain, but that there was a strong resemblance. The presiding police officer spoke rapid Majorcine; when he had finished the interpreter said: 'The officer says he did not bring you here to identify the boy. They already know that it was he. He asked you to come here so that you might see he had wasted no time in finding and arresting the criminal. And, because he knows that you are a writer and you may sometime write about Spain, he wanted you to see that it was not a Spaniard who had stolen and wrecked your car. This is a north German boy from a cargo ship in the port. He is an orphan and has no near relations. He speaks fluent English, and you may ask him anything you like.'

Disconcerted by the mass presence of police, I said less to the terrified boy than humanity demanded. He said: 'I don't remember what happened. . . . I had been drinking in the morning. . . . I'm very sorry I took your car, and very sorry I can't pay for it. I never meant to steal it, only to have a drive in it. Please believe me I'm very sorry.'

The following morning I had to make a second lengthy deposition, this time to the judiciary authorities. In the course of the preliminaries I learned that Ehrenfried Muller would probably serve four years in prison for the combined charges to be laid against him. 'Does he know this?' I asked. 'I expect so. By now the lawyer employed by the German consul will have told him.' I asked whether the Spanish authorities could charge him with the theft if I did not, and was told no; his time might thus be reduced to two years. It seemed to me brutal to have any part in such savage sentences upon the follies of youth, and I refused to lay charges that appeared to serve no purpose other than spite.

A few days later I left Majorca for Algiers.

It was not until some time later, after a week spent in Algeria, that I visited the scene of the accident, and failed utterly to reconstruct the circumstances. I had known the name of the village, Campastilla, and that the offside of the car had struck a concrete pillar at a very high speed. I also knew from Muller that he had been driving away from Palma, that the accident had in fact taken place a very few minutes after I had sighted the car.

In my hired SEAT 600 I left Palma with a very clear idea of what I was looking for and a certainty of recognizing it when I saw it. It had to be a left-hand bend – whether sharp or merely a long curve made little difference given the speed of which the Mercedes was capable – and somewhere on the right of the roadside there must be a concrete post or column. Campastilla was shown upon the map as a small coastal village, and it did not seem likely that the spot would be difficult to identify.

The approach to Campastilla was dead straight, and there was no concrete pillar anywhere. The village was short, with a detectable left-hand curve, it is true, and when one emerged from it there was the sea on the right-hand side, with no intervening wall or obstacle, and a ribbon development of *plage* hotels on the left. This situation obtained for a further two miles, by which time signboards showed us that by no stretch of the imagination could we be said to be still in Campastilla.

Utterly mystified, we turned the car, drove back to Campastilla and made inquiries. Ten minutes later we were at the site of the disaster. It was a concrete column, one of three or four forming a very short and modest arcade, and various small red relics of the Mercedes were discernible in the dust at its foot. The concrete had been extensively repaired very recently.

All this, however, was on the left-hand side of the road.

The shop behind the column was a small grocery. Through an obliging interpreter from a near-by hotel we learned all that he knew of the story. He and his wife had been in the back room of the shop, sitting quietly over a glass of wine, when there had been a gigantic crashing noise and the whole building had rocked and shuddered. Running outside he had found a red racing car impaled upon the pillar and facing towards Palma. At the wheel was a half-conscious young foreigner. The grocer gave him brandy and revived him, and then asked whether the driver would like to deposit the luggage from the car in the safety of the shop. The boy had replied hurriedly that the car was not his, and boarded a passing bus.

The grocer pointed out to me that one half of the pillar's width was of sandstone while the other was of reinforced concrete; had the car hit the sandstone portion the column would in all probability have collapsed and carried with it the roof above. Had the car missed the column it must inevitably have entered either his shop or the empty shop next door; in either case the driver must certainly have been cut to pieces by glass.

I had been looking for a concrete pillar on the right hand side of the road; now it transpired that for some unapparent reason the car had performed a complete *tête à queue* in a twenty-five foot width of dry road and had finished by facing in the opposite direction.

Twenty yards, two houses, beyond the site of the accident stood an elegant house upon whose ground-floor balcony a black monkey with a long tail and a jewel-studded collar diligently searched its fur. My interpreter indicated the creature with a pointing finger: 'The mother of that gibbon was looking at the sea – no car passed her vision. Then she heard the impact and she and her monkey run out, and there is a car, making part of the column, but pointing towards Palma. I know well the mother of that monkey; she invents nothing.'

At this juncture the monkey, the mother of the monkey and a small dog of indeterminate breed crossed the road ensemble; the monkey, stepping daintily, held its tail vertically and delicately curled forward over its back. I perceived that the mother of the monkey had no reason to invent anything; an aura of incredibility already surrounded the *ménage*; but they knew all, even though they might remain inscrutable.

'I think,' said the interpreter, 'that the German boy sees the monkey, walking in the road like that, and thinks he sees like pink elephants – so he slams the brakes – from 120 mph, and all the rest happens. But,' he added reflectively, 'it is all like a dream – one does not understand.'

I did not understand. My curiosity was aroused to the pitch at which nothing but Muller's own account of the disaster could satisfy me. Through my lawyer I arranged to see him in prison on the following Saturday, in three days' time.

On arrival at the prison it was plain that the Society was at work again. As I had laid no civil charges against him, Muller had been bought out on bail by the German Consul, forty-eight hours before. The prison authorities did not know his address. My lawyer, who had arranged the visit, was disconcerted but did not accept defeat. 'Now, we go to the court-in-law where haves the address inscribed, and the judge give.' But he did not give.

We went to the law courts. 'The judge's mother is staying mort yesterday; judge gone. Now we go to number two court-in-law.' At the second court, quite a long way away: 'The judge of number two court-in-law is sick at home. Now we go to the *audencia*; there I have much hope. But it is long way – you wait in this café, and I come back in ten minutes.'

After three-quarters of an hour he returned triumphantly waving a slip of paper. 'Here is Muller's address – it is in the suburbs, it is better we take a taxi. If he is not in they certainly know at what hour he return.'

We drove a couple of miles out of Palma into a district of surprisingly gracious villas. We found No. 23 without difficulty. An exceedingly suspicious-looking woman opened the door – partially – to the lawyer, and denied all knowledge of any German. When the lawyer returned to the taxi he was visibly ruffled.

'*Not* is possible to understand this,' he said. 'I see with my eyes the address inscribed in the book at the *audencia*. Perhaps the woman she is told say nothing. But *not* I understand. Now we telephone the German Consul.'

It being Saturday there was no answer, and a visit to the Consulate produced only echoes of our knocking at the door. The lawyer was baffled at last. 'Not I can do anything at all before Monday. By one o'clock on Monday I shall telephone you with all arrangements made.'

At one o'clock on Monday he telephoned to tell me that all offices were closed and that nothing was possible until the Christmas season was over on Thursday the 27th. He himself would unfortunately be absent from Palma until the afternoon of Friday 28th, and no official would thereafter be available until the following Monday.

Meanwhile the monkey motif remained curiously strong.

Jimmy Watt came to Majorca for a few days of his holiday; we went to the east side of the island, and there, jumping down into the dressing-room of a Roman theatre, he dislocated his ankle. By the time we reached a hotel the swelling was alarming, not so much by virtue of its size as by its extreme distension over a very small area, with very considerable extravasation. I thought that Jimmy should be X-rayed immediately.

We were ashamed to jump the gigantic queue at the clinic – if more than 150 amiably disposed and dispersed persons in the waiting-room and the corridors could be called a queue – but we excused our privilege on linguistic grounds.

The clinic was remarkable, both by its extreme formality and extreme efficiency. The doctors were voluble, human, expert. Everybody watched everybody else being treated; everybody smoked like chimneys, and appeared to expect everybody else to do the same. There was less formality than I have ever seen among official classes in any country. Jimmy's X-ray and diagnosis were performed in record time and a number of well-wishers came forward to talk to him while his bandage was drying. There happened to be a momentary visiting lull when he cocked his ears and said: 'That's a monkey – nothing else makes a noise like that.' I listened and said I thought it was some kind of mechanical toy, like an india-rubber dog that squeaked if you pressed it, Jimmy insisted, and as he was unable to walk himself I volunteered to investigate. The open doorway of the next surgery framed a strange scene. On the operating table sat a young woman who had recently undergone some nasal surgery; her nose was encased in plaster and strapping, from which protruded the ends of two small wooden splints. She was surrounded by a large number of people of all ages and sizes, some three or four of whom were engaged in taking flashlight photographs. On the outskirts of this throng stood a couple of nuns, and from somewhere on the floor, at a point hidden by their voluminous skirts, emanated the strange sounds that had attracted Jimmy's attention. I still leaned to the theory that it was produced by a child with a vocal toy. At that moment one of the nuns stooped and picked up something which she held cradled in her arms as one would hold a very small baby. The noise stopped. I was completely puzzled – no child of a size that could be hidden by the nun's arms could have been left on that foot-crowded floor. Taking advantage of the general policy of *laissez-faire*, I walked into the surgery and stood beside the nun as she bent her head and crooned over whatever it was that she held. A small arm, black and hairy and shiny, reached up from the folds of her drapery and put its hand confidingly round her neck. A moment later she turned, and I was looking into the face of the smallest chimpanzee I had ever seen. Now, a nun cuddling a baby chimpanzee in an operating theatre is an unusual composition, by any criteria, both in *dramatis personae* and in setting. Language difficulties prevented satisfaction of my curiosity from the nun herself, but the doctor attending Jimmy spoke French. When he returned to powder the zinc bandage I asked him, a little timidly perhaps, because I half expected him to say that the whole scene was a figment of my imagination, about the monkey.

'The chimpanzee?' he said. 'It's our mascot. Do you like it? I'll get it for you – wait a minute.' He went out and returned with the chimp; he put it into my arms and it put an arm round my neck and snuggled up to me.

'She came to us in a curious way. A rich man had a son born to him with club hands; the fingers were not only webbed but there was bone fusion, and to give him working fingers needed a very complicated operation. However, I knew I could do it, and I told the father so, but perhaps I didn't explain clearly enough that it was an operation that could only be done in stages – that I could not give the child ten workable fingers after one operation. Anyway, the child was admitted to the clinic, and I performed the first stage, which was a central division giving him two mobile units on each hand. When the father came back and saw this he supposed it to be all that I could do, and he was bitterly disappointed; he lost all confidence in me, and wanted to take the child to another surgeon. I protested that I would make those hands as mobile as a monkey's. He said: "If you really do, I'll give you the most expensive monkey in the world."

'Well, my operation was wholly successful, and he kept his promise; perhaps a baby gorilla would have been more expensive still, but we couldn't really cope with a gorilla here. This little chimpanzee is just two months old; she's affectionate and gentle to everyone and everyone loves her dearly. And she's so healthy because she's looked after by a team of expert doctors. Come my little one, and I'll take you back to your aunt.'

My long-delayed meeting with Muller took place the following week, by the simple expedient of leaving at the German Consulate a message and a proposed rendezvous. Thus our second meeting, at a luxury hotel, was in marked contrast to our first when he had sat handcuffed between his captors.

I realized very soon that from the point of view of illuminating the mystery of the Mercedes crash our meeting would be sterile, for he remembered nothing at all from a few seconds before the accident until he found himself once more aboard his ship with an agonizing right shoulder.

He told me everything he remembered, and in the greatest detail, for he was grateful to me for making possible his release from indefinite detention in a cell of some thirty hardened criminals. He also told me something of his history. His family had been landed proprietors in what is now East Germany; his father had been killed during the war against Russia, and his mother had escaped to West Germany. When he was fourteen years old she had died of cancer and he was entrusted to the care of an uncle; between him and this man there had long existed a marked mutual antipathy. He was sent to sea before his sixteenth birthday, the first time as galley boy and greaser's assistant in a small coaster. Since then he had changed ships many times, and at the date of his arrest he had been an apprentice third officer learning astronomical navigation. By this time he had visited nearly every port in the world, and had acquired something of the orphan sailor's predatory attitude towards life.

He had been drinking a little in the morning of the day in question but he did not think he had been more than very slightly drunk.

He had come ashore shortly before midday, meaning to walk into the town in search of diversion. As soon as he had passed through the dockyard buildings he saw the Mercedes standing glistening at the roadside. He was a car enthusiast, with considerable mechanical knowledge, and had even owned an elderly Mercedes himself. (He had crashed it.) A 300 SL was the apotheosis of his dreams; he had not seen more than a score or so in his life, and had fastened longing eyes upon all of them. At first he had no thought other than to admire this splendid toy. He walked round it and studied it from all angles. At length he decided that the owner could not really object to his sitting in the driving seat and indulging in five minutes' fantasy. (Those were his actual words.) He tried the door and found it unlocked.

As he sat at the wheel and felt the controls the open road seemed to stretch away in front of him; he seemed to see the speedometer needle soaring towards 150 mph, to hear the roar of the exhaust in his ears as the car rocketed forward in response to his throttle foot. For some minutes he was lost in a day dream.

It was the hour of siesta, and the port seemed utterly deserted. He could also see for a long way to each side of him. He did not try to pretend to himself that the owner would not mind his taking the car for an hour's drive; the temptation was so great that he did not even ponder to consider the near-certainty of being caught in an island the size of Majorca where such cars are extremely *rarae aves*.

Having made up his mind he worked quickly and skilfully. He pulled out the wires from the back of the ignition switch and began to make a junction. He received several electric shocks, but in his excitement hardly noticed them. His first junction produced an alarmingly loud whine from the fuel injectors, so he was quick to make the second, and the engine started at once.

He had no idea how he was going to get past the port sentries if he was challenged; he had that mentality. They stepped forward, indeed, but seeing an obvious young German in a German car they did not ask him to stop. He was past the first obstacle. For the first mile he was in traffic, and he drove slowly as he had been driving when I saw him from the airport bus. Then he was in the suburbs and began to drive fast, then on an open country road straight but narrow; he remembered that here he was doing between 120–30 mph. Then he entered a deserted village street, and thought that he did not slacken speed appreciably. 'Then I received some kind of terrible mental shock. I don't remember anything more till I was back on the ship. Perhaps a child ran across the road – something like that.'

'No,' I said, 'there was no child. No human being of any description saw the accident.'

After that he only knew what he had been told. Someone

took him to a first aid post and examined his torso for broken bones. He had gone to the lavatory and escaped through the window, but he did not remember that either. A man on a motor-cycle, a civilian, had followed him and brought him back. He had returned to his ship in an ambulance; he had no recollection of this, but remembered finding himself aboard with an agonizing pain in his right shoulder, greeting his shipmates with exaggerated *bonhomie*.

Later there had been an identification parade. Not knowing that he had been stripped at the first aid post he had not realized the absolute certainty of identification – he had a large brown birthmark on his left breast. When he saw his shipmates asked to open their shirts he gave himself up.

With the hope of shaking his amnesia by trauma, I asked if he would come with me to the site of the accident. As we drove out through the suburbs I noted that he remembered every detail. 'Here I passed a Cadillac', or 'Here in this bit I began to go fast, to use the car's acceleration, which was even more than I had expected it to be', and 'Here the road was quite clear and I began to race'. As we entered the village of Campastilla he said: 'This I remember, but I don't remember the road beyond it. Is it straight?'

'It is,' I replied, 'but you never got there.'

The long curve that formed the end of the village was a little more abrupt than I had remembered it. In the middle of this curve he gave a sudden exclamation. '*Here* something happened, I know it, things seem to be going round like they must have been that day.' I looked at him and saw that he had gone suddenly white. I waited, but whatever had caused that moment of blind panic would not break through to consciousness. 'It's no use,' he said finally, 'it was something terrible like the end of the world, but I don't know what it was.'

So we had to reconstruct the picture by circumstantial

evidence. We got out and walked forward. Where the houses came to an end on the right-hand side the sea began. The road had been built up from the sand, so that its seaward side, unprotected, dropped three feet sheer to the beach; twenty yards beyond the houses a part of the retaining buttress had sunk and left a depression some five inches deep and a yard across. Now I understood for the first time exactly what had happened.

As he had said, Muller had reduced speed very little upon entering the village and must have taken the gentle left-hand curve of the street at a full hundred miles per hour. The maximum pull to the right had thus coincided precisely with this hole at the extreme edge of the road, and the shock had thrown the offside front wheel to within inches of the drop. He must have panicked and braked hard while wrenching the steering-wheel to the left; this had started a slide which, when it became broadside, actually swung the rear wheels of the car out over nothing. Only the front wheels, on left lock, remained upon the road, travelling sideways at some ninety miles an hour. When the rear wheels regained terra firma a complete *tête à queue* was thus inevitable. The only remaining mystery was the fantastic chain of coincidences by which in this potentially holocaustic smash, no human being had suffered so much as a broken limb. It was as though the streets had been specially cleared and the reinforced-concrete column placed with a watchmaker's precision, at the one and only point where it could avert disaster.

'I think I have a charmed life,' said Muller. 'It has always been like this, that something has happened to save me. So much so that sometimes when I have thought of killing myself because the world is so bloody I have been stopped by the idea that it was impossible, and so not worth while trying. The first time was when I was four years old, and playing with another little boy on a farm. I fell down a sort of well, only it wasn't water but a tank of cow's urine. I couldn't swim at all, and this tank was enormous, with sheer sides. They told me afterwards that in the whole tank there was one, just one, little stanchion, or it may have been the end of a pipe, an inch or two below the surface. And I'd fallen in just at that point, so my hands found it at once, and I was able to hang on to it for a long time until I was rescued.

'Then when I was about seven or eight, there happened something even stranger. It was a very, very cold winter. On the way home from school there was a frozen lake, not a very big one, but perhaps a hundred yards across. Over most of it the ice was several inches thick, and we used to cross it with a run and as long a slide as we could make – everyone was always trying to see if they could get right across in one slide. There was only one dangerous place, a patch where a spring came up and the water was barely frozen. Well, one day I did a really wonderful slide, but I'd got the direction just wrong, and I went slap into this patch at high speed. The ice was as thin as paper, and I went straight into it and straight on under the thick ice beyond it. Now there was only one other place where there was little or no ice, a little patch where, for one hour a day only, the waste from the village houses ran in and thawed it. Well, get this – I went in at one hole in the ice and shot along under its surface for a dozen yards or so and popped up through this other hole, all in a matter of seconds. At any other time of day there wouldn't have been another hole. There have been a hundred things like that in my life; it would take too long to tell you them all. But the last two have been perhaps the strangest. Last year in Cuba a man in a port tavern wanted me to sell my watch; he became a nuisance, and I told him to f— off. He got very angry and said no one could speak to him like that, and he pulled out a big automatic – a Colt

·45 I think it was – and pointed it at my head. I thought I could see that the safety-catch was on, so I made a grab for it. But the safety-catch was not on, and he fired, and – look – the bullet went through the top of my left ear.' (He had very small ears, lying flush with the skull.) 'Just the difference of half an inch and it would have killed me, and your Mercedes wouldn't have been crashed by a crazy boy.'

If Muller had been unable to throw any clear light upon his crash he was able to contribute to the records of the *Société Anonyme* the story of its finest hour, the tale of a display of pure virtuosity achieved without any *caisse d'équipement*, without diversion of route or collaboration of recognized officialdom. Some prosperous German acquaintances of his had spent their summer holiday touring Italy in a large new Mercedes-Benz saloon. The party consisted of husband, wife and young children; the luggage, designed to meet every social occasion, had been comprehensive, including much jewellery and costly evening dresses. The family had arrived at the Leaning Tower of Pisa early one Sunday morning, planning thus to avoid a rush of international tourism, and had left their locked car at the foot of the tower from whose cock-eyed summit they surveyed an as yet unawakened world beneath them. The arrival of a breakdown lorry in the car park, a lorry equipped with a heavy crane for lifting cars on to its float, was therefore of some considerable surprise to them, but as yet no subject for anything but idle speculation. Then before, or rather below, their at first unbelieving and then outraged eyes, this lorry positioned itself beside their car, slipped chain slings around its tyres, hoisted it bodily aboard the float, and scuttled rapidly away. By the time the near-hysterical German family had reached ground-level and emerged from the tower there was no sign of lorry or car, nor did they ever recover one single item of all their lost possessions.

'So you see,' said Muller. 'I'm only an amateur really.'

Balls – Catalonian style.

In the end he was charged only with driving without documents, and received sentence of two months and two days, totally remitted for good conduct and character while on bail. He had, however, already served thirty ineradicable days in a provincial Spanish prison.

10

The Tides Return

WHEN AT LAST I had completed the interminable formalities connected with the loss of the car and was
able to return to Camusfeàrna I found much change. The
house now had many of the amenities of civilization, including sanitation, a bath and showers, and the tiny kitchen was
now all-electric. Every one of these innovations dependent
upon water was, however, functionless, for at the date of
my return the supply had been frozen for more than a
month, and remains frozen at the time of writing five weeks
later.

My arrival at the house had a curious, almost surrealistic
flavour. During my absence a jeep had been added to the
Camusfeàrna transport fleet, and in this we bucked and jolted
in the dark down the frozen track whose mud mountains and
ruts had become as hard as rock. At the house the headlights
showed a single greylag goose standing outside the door, and
Jimmy explained to me that of the five that we had imported
in the late summer to replace those that had left us in July
this was the sole survivor. Two had disappeared only a
week ago, fallen prey, probably, to foxes or wild cats whose
more usual sources of food supply were cut off by the snow
and the cold. Now this single goose tried to push past us
into the house, and having succeeded in entering the living-
room, tried immediately to jump up on to the sofa whose
entire surface was occupied by the sprawling form of Dirk
the deerhound. Deterred from this enterprise by Dirk's

uncooperative spirit, the goose then hopped into an arm-chair. At no time in the past had the bird even tried to enter the house. We removed it to the bathroom, and Jimmy had just remarked that despite all the many inconveniences of the month-long freeze we could at least be thankful that there had never been even the briefest power cut, when all the lights went off. We had very little coal, very little paraffin, and no cut wood.

Thus it was sitting in overcoats by candlelight in the freezing living-room that I learned in detail of recent happenings at Camusfeàrna, happenings of which I had heard only in the barest outline.

Terry Nutkins had left Camusfeàrna to become a Zoo keeper in London, and Jimmy was now in sole charge of an increasingly complicated *ménage*.

A few weeks before, a mate for Teko had arrived from Griqualand in South-East Africa. This otter proved to be an enormous animal, bigger than Teko himself, extremely domesticated and affectionate towards human beings, and her introduction to Teko had presented none of the problems we had anticipated. Placed in accommodation adjoining his, so that they might become accustomed to each other's voices and smells before closer acquaintance, she had brushed aside these formalities by climbing into his enclosure during the night, and in the morning they were curled up together in his bed. This happy and promising situation was cut short by her sudden and then unexplained death only two days before my homecoming. She had been healthy and in high spirits in the evening, and when Jimmy had gone in to her in the morning he had found her dead but still perceptibly warm, curled up in Teko's bed under the infra-red lamp, the tip of her tail in her mouth as though she had been sucking it – a habit, like that of Edal sucking her bib, that she had in life.

During the short weeks of her life with Teko, Mossy and Monday had discovered their unrivalled powers of escape from any enclosure in which they might be confined, and on more than one occasion all four animals had been found together in Teko's pool. It would perhaps be truer to say that Monday had discovered her powers of escape and had somehow coerced her moronic consort into cooperation in such matters as combining their strength to move heavy stones and taking alternate shifts in digging the long tunnels that she planned. Even then, owing to his greater size and absolute absence of initiative, Mossy often found himself left behind while she made her escape through some aperture too small to permit his passage. On this first evening of my return he was alone in the enclosure, but during the night she returned for him and from outside enlarged her latest tunnel until he could squeeze through. From then on, for the first three weeks of my stay, their capture and recapture became our major preoccupation, until at length I was forced to realize that nothing but a zoo cage could confine her, and I accepted defeat.

Monday could climb like a monkey, balance like a tightrope walker, dig like a badger, move stones that were heavy to a human, jump like a squirrel, make herself thin as an eel or flat as a flounder; no device nor ingenuity of ours could make her once relent her first avowed intent to be a pilgrim. But most of all it was her brain, the systematic application of her many skills and her single-minded pertinacity, that convinced me of the uselessness of the struggle.

She had tasted freedom and she would have no more of prison. It was not, in the prevailing circumstances, an inviting prison or one calculated to lead to resignation; the glass tank frozen, all running water stopped, the small patch of ground now hard as rock and without vegetation. Outside were the sea and the islands with their many habitable lairs among the rocks and the bracken and the rooty heather; outside was the freedom of the waves and the white sands and the weedy rock pools. There was nothing I wanted more than to let her go free, but with the knowledge of all the other tame otters that because of their confidence in man had been shot or bludgeoned to death by the first strange human being they approached, I felt that I must confine her. It took three weeks to convince me that this was not only an impossibility but would be more cruel than any death she could meet in freedom.

One wall of their enclosure was formed by the Camusfeàrna house itself; the other three were of continuous, smooth, wooden paling five feet high. The only points at which the woodwork did present a completely smooth face were the right-angles formed by their own house, of the same height as the paling, and a further right-angle where a heavy straining-post had been boarded round. At the base of the fence we had sunk fine-mesh wire-netting into the ground, extending six inches vertically into the ground and then two and a half feet horizontally inwards. As a further safeguard against tunnelling, we had placed heavy stones along the greater part of the perimeter. This was the prison from which, during a time of bitter frost when the ground was frozen as hard as iron four feet underground, Monday escaped time and again with contemptuous ease.

At the beginning I thought naïvely that our only problem was to catch them, for I could not seriously believe in the impossibility of making the enclosure proof against escape. We constructed in the paling a foot-square drop-hatch that could be closed by the release of a string from an upper-storey window. I disposed a number of eels temptingly a yard or two inside the trap, and at dusk I sat down with the release-string in my hand to await developments. The otters arrived very soon after dark; they came and went between the eels and the hatch so that there was never a clear moment when both of them were inside simultaneously. Eventually I decided that to catch one was better than to catch neither, and I released the string when only Mossy was in the enclosure. I felt certain that Monday would come in to him during the night; in this I was right, but at the time I did not know that she would as certainly perform a rescue, and contrive somehow to extract her clottish companion from captivity before dawn.

During the night I could hear her whistling impatiently to him from outside and his peevish and fretful responses as he explained the patent impossibility of reaching her; at some time in the small hours these sounds ceased, and in my innocence I imagined her to have joined him in their house and settled down for the night.

In the morning they had both gone. She had indeed climbed into the enclosure, but only in order to move a few massive stones, tunnel under the wire-netting and liberate the captive.

The following night, having as I thought made all tunnelling projects impossible, I reset the trap and again sat at the window with the string in my hand. This time I had to wait much longer and it was Monday that I caught. The front door of the house, in temporary disuse, led directly into the enclosure, and I went out to her carrying peace offerings. She ran straight up to me, emitted a breathy, explosive sound of challenge, and gave my boot a sharp, symbolic nip. She then ran to the corner where the paling formed a convex right-angle, and began to shin rapidly up it with the powerful hunching movements of a bear climbing a tree. I had literally to push her down, while Jimmy ran for materials wherewith to form an unscaleable overhang at the top of this corner. In the end it looked as if it would challenge even a monkey's capacities.

The next morning she had gone again. I attached pieces of

slippery Formica to the paling at the points where she was wont to climb. Miraculously they gave her no pause. Every night she came brazenly into the trap, insolently confident of her ability to overcome or undermine any obstacle that I might set in the way of her escape before morning. Every day my preparations became more elaborate, and every day she mocked me. The trap was by this time automatic; an ingenious system of strings ensured that when she pulled at eels the hatch would close itself and at the same time ring the ship's bell upon the gatepost. The whole of the area on which she had exercised her feats of climbing was covered by a great sheet of smooth metal, a relic of Teko's first ill-fated pool, and the night after the appearance of this fresh puzzle we caught both Mossy and Monday. They were still there in the morning, and all the day through they slept in their house. I had no doubt in my mind that they were now captive for as long as we wished them to remain so. Twenty-four hours later they had once more vanished, this time by an ambitious tunnelling scheme that involved the moving of a stone weighing some sixty or seventy pounds.

We made only one more attempt. The following evening, just before dusk, Jimmy called to me that Monday had come in through the door of her new extension building and that he had closed it behind her. She came through into the living-room and began to explore, briskly and impatiently, ignoring us altogether, rather in the manner of a testy colonel inspecting company lines. Having exhausted the possibilities of floor-level she moved upwards, displaying a degree of acrobatic power that appeared hardly credible. In the same way that water finds its way downward between and around all obstacles by force of gravity, so she appeared to be borne upward by some like but contrary force concealed within her. High on the shelves she stepped daintily and gracefully amongst the bottles and tins and groceries;

finding little to her liking, she returned to the floor with the same sinuously effortless movements, climbed on to the sofa and said something exceedingly rude to Dirk, and finally moved off to continue her researches in the new wing. When she entered the bathroom we closed the door behind her, intending to confine her there until we had secured Mossy. It was a sliding door; in less than three minutes she had discovered the principle of its operation and was back in the living-room.

We coaxed her back into the bathroom and this time secured the door so that there was no means of opening it.

Mossy did not return that night, and in the morning we found that Monday had chewed her way through the bathroom plaster-boarding and had already got to work on the woodwork that lay beyond it. She was, however, still captive against her will, and for the first time.

In the evening we caught Mossy, and brought Monday through to join him in their enclosure, which I believed to be now proof against any attempt at escape. During the night there was much whistling and the sounds of heavy stones being moved; at dawn I looked out from my window and saw Monday doing a high rope-walk along the top of the paling. She had not climbed up from inside, but had contrived her escape at ground-level and was now returning for her consort. In a further five minutes they were both on their way to the sea.

It was at this point that I abandoned the struggle, as much on humanitarian grounds as in the knowledge that by one means or another she would always outwit me. I hoped, but with little conviction, that Mossy and Monday would remain in the vicinity of Camusfeàrna and its islands, where they would be at least relatively safe from death at human hands. It was not until several days later, and after Lavinia had joined me from London, that I discovered how little grudge they appeared to bear us for our determination to make them captive, for they had taken up permanent residence under the floor of the new wing.

Their entry to this improbable refuge was under the door that now formed the principal entrance to the house; here, immediately below the threshold, was a small unboarded portion giving access to the space between floor and foundations. From this slit, some two feet long and four inches high, Lavinia found that she could call them at will to take food from her hand. The slit was divided in the middle by an upright plank; invariably at her call the two small faces, one blunt and one sharp, would peer out as though from letter boxes, and invariably it would be Mossy who was to the left of the upright and Monday to the right. This position they would assume at the first sound of her calling voice, and they remained completely indifferent to the tramp of human feet stepping over them to enter or leave the house.

Now that their freedom was established, it seemed to me that to encourage this unexpected domesticity we should take every possible step to make their self-selected quarters as luxurious as possible. Choosing a time at which they were both engaged with Lavinia outside, we cut a rectangle in the wooden floor of the room beneath which they had chosen to set up house, and sunk between it and the foundations a well-bedded and draughtproof kennel whose roof was formed by a raisable hatch in the floor of the room. This, to my surprise, they took possession of immediately, but they did not accord a like approval to other arrangements we had made for their comfort. With the idea of protecting them from the prevailing sea-winds we had built up earthworks that covered all the seaward-facing space between the new wooden wing and its foundations, thus leaving the otters only one common entrance and exit. We had forgotten an otter's insistence upon alternative means of egress;

the next morning the earthworks had been efficiently tunnelled in two different places. The amount of labour that they had put into this work was, however, an encouragement to believe that they considered themselves to be perfecting otherwise ideal and permanent quarters.

At morning and before dusk they would, as I have said, come out to Lavinia's call and take food from her hand, but as to where they went at night we had no knowledge until she followed them. It was a season of bitter cold; the days were for the most part still and bright with winter sunshine, but the nights were arctic, and the burn was frozen right down into its tidal reaches, with a layer of ice that capsized as the tide went out and floated up to form a new and thicker layer as it returned. A little before dusk one evening Lavinia, who had been down to the burn to break the ice and draw water, heard them calling to each other at some little distance from the house. Following Monday's small, urgent voice, she came upon them playing in a partly frozen pool, shooting under stretches of ice, and bobbing up where it ended, climbing on to it and rolling upon it, diving back and splashing as they sported together. Fearing that they would resent her intrusion, and read into it some further attempt at capture, Lavinia had approached them by stealth, crawling upon all fours; only when they began to move on down the stream did she stand up and call to them, but they found in her presence no cause for any alarm. As they neared the tide she walked beside them, their heads now no more than silhouettes on a sea blanched by sunset colours, until suddenly a curlew rose before them with its rasping cry of warning, and in a panic they turned and raced back upstream and into the darkness. The next night again she followed them down the burn in the dusk, and lost them in the thickening darkness as they swam out towards the islands.

With the liberation of Mossy and Monday, something seemed to me restored to Camusfeàrna, something that had been lost for many months, for once again these were wild creatures free without fear of man and choosing to make their homes with him. As if to reinforce this mood, two of the wild geese suddenly returned after an absence of seven months; one of them was the great gander who had sired all the young of the previous year, and now on the very day of his arrival came straight up to us to take food from our hands. Somehow, with all this unwary confidence in mankind, he had survived the autumn and the winter months and fallen prey to no wildfowler's gun; perhaps he had joined some vast flock of wild grey geese and during his long absence from Camusfeàrna had taken his reactions from them. It is sad that for the otters there is no such safety in numbers; sad to think that Monday's whole dynamic personality may be blotted out to appease momentarily the inner emptiness and frustration that causes the desire to kill.

Before me is a letter from Norway, telling of yet another pet otter done to death.

She was tame and she would follow me like a dog. The last days we used to go fishing in a near-by loch. She jumped about in the rowboat while I was pulling the oars. Now and again I left her alone in the loch, sure to pick her up again when I wanted her to stay at home. But this very morning a mason passing the loch on his way to work saw the kind and confident animal and gave her a kick with his heavy boot. I found her dead, resting on a pile of branches out in the water.

Destruction, empty and purposeless, unmitigated even by the strange intimacy that binds the archetypal hunter to his quarry. I hope that if ever again I write of Camusfeàrna the murder of Mossy and Monday may not mar the pages of my book.

THE TIDES RETURN

Cascades from our far distant mountain spring
Are scattered into spume by hurricane,
And the sweet vivid stains of childhood clinging
Are blanched from the brightness of their beginning
Into a conform of khaki. All that remain
Become elusive as a woodcock's wing
In autumn dusk. But still the bird of passage
Carries some undelivered, unsigned message,
Some testament, some favourable will;
And with this knowledge I pursued him as a hunter,
Though fleeing like him from some ancestral winter
– Believing that to inherit I must kill.

In bright oases of the desert south
Brown men eat the living hoopoe's heart,
Feeling the muscles pulse inside the mouth.
Only this death can give them back their youth,
Only this blood restore their childhood sight
And bring them knowledge of forgotten truth.
Hunter and hunted too near now, pursuer
Sensing his true role, rejected wooer,
Must kill what he cannot possess;
Knowledge of my true intent, destruction,
Hold me now in counter-poised inaction
And let my lover, bird of passage, pass.

GAVIN MAXWELL

RAVEN SEEK THY BROTHER illus. (30p) 6/-

Again set in the lovely West Highland surroundings of
Camusfeàrna, this is a remarkable self-portrait full of
marvellous photographs, anecdotes, descriptions of people
and landscapes, birds and animals, and times of comedy
and tragedy.
'Splendid for lovers of animals and fine writing'—
THE EVENING NEWS.

LORDS OF THE ATLAS illus. (40p) 8/-

The breathtaking story of the meteoric rise and spectacular
fall of a warrior Berber tribe, and their almost legendary
leader—T'hami El Glaoui, Pasha of Marrakesh.
'Romantic and horrifying'—THE TIMES.

RING OF BRIGHT WATER illus. (30p) 6/-

Now an enchanting film starring Bill Travers and Virginia
McKenna.
Camusfeàrna, a remote home in the Scottish Highlands, a
pet otter as intelligent and affectionate as a dog, this is
both a moving and a fascinating account of the author's
homelife.

THE ROCKS REMAIN illus. (30p) 6/-

This is the beautifully-written sequel to RING OF BRIGHT
WATER which describes, among other things, the arrival of
the new otters Teko, Mossy and Monday.
'As beautifully written, as vivid, and as moving as its
predecessor'—THE GUARDIAN.

PEACOCK BOOKS

Editor: Kaye Webb

THE GLEAM IN THE NORTH

Six years after the events told in *The Flight of the Heron*, Ewen Cameron still felt as if his friend and enemy Major Windham had died only yesterday. He still wore Keith's ring, and had named his second son after him. He even had a strange presentiment that before long he would meet someone connected with Keith Windham, and that the meeting would be fateful.

He was right, but he had not imagined how terrible the circumstances might be. As things turned out, his desperate anxiety to save his cousin Archibald Cameron from imprisonment and execution, and his longing to help the Jacobite cause, combined to brand him irretrievably as a traitor and a false Highland thief in the eyes of Keith's brother. It was torment to appear so unworthy of the friendship of a man who had never done a dishonourable act in his life, especially when it could be of no help to his cousin. Indeed, would anything save Archie now?

This is another of D. K. Broster's famous and romantic stories of loyalty and courage, set in the bustle of scheming eighteenth-century London and the remote, mysterious Highlands.

Cover design by Shirley Hughes

This edition has been abridged for Peacock readers

D. K. BROSTER

The Gleam in the North

A SEQUEL TO

The Flight of the Heron

PENGUIN BOOKS

Penguin Books Ltd, Harmondsworth, Middlesex, England
Penguin Books Australia Ltd, Ringwood, Victoria, Australia

—

First published by Heinemann 1927
This abridged edition published in Peacock Books 1968
Reprinted 1971, 1973

—

Made and printed in Great Britain by
Cox & Wyman Ltd, London, Reading and Fakenham
Set in Intertype Times

CONTENTS

In all that concerns Doctor Archibald
Cameron this story follows historical
fact very closely, and its final scenes
embody many of his actual words.

Chapter 1

THE BROKEN CLAYMORE

1

'AND then,' said the childish voice, 'the clans charged and they were so fierce and so brave that they broke through the line of English soldiers which were in front, and if there had not been so many more English, and they well-fed – but we were very hungry and had marched all night . . .'

The little boy paused. From the pronoun into which he had dropped, from his absorbed, exalted air, he might almost have been himself in the lost battle of which he was telling the story this afternoon, among the Highland heather, to a boy still younger. And in fact he was not relating any tale of old, unhappy, far-off things, nor of a battle long ago. Little more than six years had passed since these children's own father had lain badly wounded on the tragic moorland of Culloden – and would have died there but for the devotion of his foster-brothers.

'And this,' concluded the story-teller, leaving the gap still un-bridged, 'this is the hilt of a broadsword that was used in the battle.' He uncovered an object of a roundish shape wrapped in a handkerchief and lying on his knees. 'Cousin Ian Stewart gave it to me last week, and now I will let you see it. . . . You're not listening – you're not even *looking,* Keithie!'

The dark eyes of his little hearer were lifted to his.

'Yes, My was,' he replied in his clear treble. 'But somesing runned so fast down My's leg,' he added apologetically. 'It comed out of the *fraoch.*'

Not much of his small three-year-old person could be seen, so deep planted was it in the aforesaid heather. His brother Donald, on the contrary, was commandingly situated in a fallen pinestem. The sun of late September gilded his childish hair, which gleamed as no cornfield ever did; he was so well-

7

grown and sturdy that he might have passed for seven or eight, and one could almost have imagined the winged helm of a Viking on those bright locks. But the little delicate face which looked up at him was that of a gently brooding angel. Between the two, tall, stately and melancholy, sat Luath, the great shaggy Highland deerhound, and behind was the glimmer of water.

The historian on the log suddenly got up, gripping his claymore hilt tight. It was big and heavy; his childish hand was lost inside the strong twining basketwork. Of the blade there remained but an inch or so. 'Come along, Keithie!'

Obediently the angel took his brother's outstretched hand and began to move away with him, lifting his little legs high to clear the tough heather stems.

'Not going home now, Donald?' he inquired after a moment, tiring, no doubt, of this prancing motion.

'We will go this way,' replied the elder boy somewhat disingenuously, well aware that he had turned his back on the house of Ardroy, his home, and was making straight for Loch na h-Iolaire, where the two were never allowed to go unaccompanied. 'I think that Father is fishing here somewhere.'

2

Conjecture or knowledge, Donald's statement was correct, though, as an excuse for theirs, his father's presence was scarcely sufficient, since nearly a quarter of a mile of water intervened between Ewen Cameron of Ardroy and his offspring. He could not even see his small sons, for he sat on the farther side of the tree-covered islet in the middle of the loch, a young auburn-haired giant with a determined mouth, patiently splicing the broken joint of a fishing-rod.

More than four years had passed since Ardroy had returned with his wife and his little son from exile after Culloden. As long as Lochiel, his proscribed chief, was alive, he had never contemplated such a return, but in those October days of 1748 when the noblest and most disinterested of all the gentlemen who had worn the White Rose lay dying in Picardy of brain fever (or, more truly, of a broken heart) he had in an interval of consciousness laid that injunction on the kinsman who almost felt that with Lochiel's his own existence was closing too. So Ewen resigned the commission which he bore in Lochiel's own regiment in the French service, and saw again the old grey house and the mountain-clasped loch which was even dearer. But he knew that he would have to pay a price for his return.

And indeed he had come back to a life very different from that which had been his before the year 1745 – to one full of petty annoyances and restrictions, if not of actual persecution. He was not himself attainted and thereby exempted, like some, from the Act of Indemnity, or he could not have returned at all; but he came back to find his religion proscribed, his arms taken from him, and the wearing of his native dress made a penal offence which at its second commission might be punished with transportation. The feudal jurisdiction of the chiefs was shattered for ever, and now the English had studded the Highlands with a series of military outposts, and thence patrolled all but the wildest glens. It was a maimed existence, a kind of exile at home; and though indeed to a Highlander, with all of a Celt's inborn passion for his native land, it had its compensations, and though he was most happily married, Ewen Cameron knew many bitter hours. He was only thirty-three – and looked less – and he was a Jacobite and fighter born. Yet both he and his wife believed that he was doing right in thus living quietly and on his estate, for he could thereby stand, in some measure, between his tenants and the pressure of authority, and his two boys could grow up in the home of their forefathers.

Besides, Lochiel had counselled return.

Moreover, the disaster of Culloden had by no means entirely quenched Jacobite hopes. The Prince would come again, said the defeated among themselves, and matters go better ... next year, or the year after. Ewen, in France, had shared those hopes. But they were not so green now. The treaty of Aix-la-Chapelle had rendered French aid a thing no more possible; and indeed Jacobite claims had latterly meant to France merely a useful weapon with which to threaten her ancient foe across the Channel. Once he who was the hope of Scotland had been hunted day and night among these Western hills and islands, and the poorest had sheltered him without thought of consequences; now on the wide continent of Europe not a crowned head would receive him for fear of political complications. More than three years ago, therefore, poor, outcast and disillusioned, he who had been 'Bonnie Prince Charlie' had vanished into a plotter's limbo. Very few knew his hiding-places; and not one Highlander.

3

'My want to go home,' said little Keith, sighing, but Donald took no notice of this plaint; his eyes were intently fixed on something up on the red-brown slopes of Meall Achadh on the far side – was it a stag?

'Father not here,' began the smaller boy once more, rather wistfully. 'Go home now, Donald?'

'Be quiet!' exclaimed his brother impatiently, intent on the distant stag – if stag it were. This object was certainly moving; now a birch tree by the loch-side blocked his view of it. Donald himself moved a little farther to the left to avoid the birch branches, almost as breathless as if he had really been stalking the beast. But in a minute or two he could see no further sign of it on the distant hillside, and came back to his actual surroundings to find that his small brother was no longer beside him, but had trotted out to the very brink of the loch, in a place where Donald had always been told that the water was as deep as a kirk.

'Keith, come back at once!' he shouted in dismay. 'You know that you are not to go there!'

And then he missed the claymore hilt which he had laid down a yard or so away; and crying, 'How *dare* you take my sword!' flung himself after the truant.

But before he could reach it the small figure had turned an exultant face. 'My got yours toy!' And then he had it no longer, for with all his childish might he had thrown it from him into the water. There was a delightful splash. 'It's away!' announced Keithie, laughing gleefully.

Donald stood there arrested, his rosy face gone white as paper. For despite the small strength which had thrown the thing, the irreplaceable relic was indeed 'away' ... and since the loch was so deep there, and he could not swim ... Then the hot Highland blood came surging back to his heart, and, blind with a child's unthinking rage, he pounced on the malefactor. One furious push, and he had sent his three-year-old brother to join the claymore hilt in the place where Loch na h-Iolaire was as deep as a kirk.

A child's scream – two screams – made Ewen Cameron throw down his rod and spring to his feet. He had for a little time been well aware of childish voices at a distance, and had known them, too, for those of his own boys. But since it never occurred to him that the children were there unattended, he was not perturbed; he would row over to them presently.

But now ... He ran across the islet in a panic. The screams prolonged themselves; he heard himself called. Then he saw.

On the shore of the loch, looking very small against the great old pines behind him, stood a boy rigid with terror, screaming in Gaelic and English for his father, for Angus, for anyone ... and in the water not far from shore was something struggling, rising, disappearing. ... Ardroy jumped into the small boat in which he had rowed to the island, and began to pull like a madman towards the shore, his head over his shoulder the while. And thus he saw that there was something else in the loch also – a long, narrow head forging quickly through the water towards the scene of the accident, that place near land, indeed, but deep enough to drown twenty children. Luath, bless him, thought the young man. Before he had rowed many more strokes he dropped his oars and plunged in himself. Even then, strong swimmer though he was, he doubted if he should be in time. ... The dog had got there first, and had seized the child, but was more occupied in trying to get him bodily out of the loch than in keeping his head above water. But with a stroke or two more Ardroy was up to them, only praying that he should not have to struggle with Luath for possession. Mercifully the deerhound obeyed his command to let go, and in another moment Ewen Cameron was scrambling out of Loch na h-Iolaire, clutching to him a sodden, choking little bundle, incoherent between fright and loch-water.

4

The old house of Ardroy stood some quarter of a mile from the loch, rather strangely turning its back upon it, but, since it thus looked south, capturing the sun for a good part of the day, even in midwinter. Comfortable and unpretentious, it had already seen some hundred and thirty autumns, had sometimes rung with youthful voices, and sometimes lacked them. Now once again it had a nursery, where at this moment, by a fire of peats and logs, a rosy-cheeked Highland girl was making preparations for washing two small persons who, after scrambling about all afternoon in the heather and bracken, would probably stand in need of soap and water.

And presently their mother came through the open door, dark-haired like her younger son, slight, oval-faced, almost a girl still, for she was but in her late twenties, and combining a kind of effortless dignity with a girlish sweetness of expression.

'Are the children not home yet, Morag?' she asked, using the Gaelic; and Morag answered her lady that surely they would not be long now, and it might be that the laird himself was bringing them, for he had gone up past the place where they were playing.

'Ah, there they are,' said Lady Ardroy, for she had heard her husband's step in the hall, and as she left the room his soft Highland voice floated up to her, even softer than its wont, for it seemed to be comforting someone. She looked over the stairs and gave an exclamation.

Ewen looked up at the same moment and saw her. 'All is well, dear heart,' he said quickly. 'Keithie has had a wee mishap, but here he is safe and sound.'

He ran up the stairs and put the small wet thing, wrapped in Donald's coat, into its mother's arms. 'Yes – the loch . . . he fell in. No harm, I think; only frightened. Luath got to him first; I was on the island.'

Alison had seized her youngest almost as if she were rescuing him from the rescuer, and was covering the damp, forlorn little face with kisses. 'Darling, darling, you are safe with mother now! ... He must be put into a hot bath at once!' She ran with him into the nursery.

Ardroy, wet and gigantic, followed her in, and behind came the mute and coatless Donald, who stood a moment looking at the bustle, and then went and seated himself, very silent, on the window-seat. Close to the fire his mother was getting the little sodden garments off Keith, Morag was pouring out the hot water, his father was contributing a damp patch to the nursery floor. But Keithie had ceased to cry now, and as he was put into the bath he even patted the water and raised a tiny splash.

And then, after he was immersed, he said to his mother, raising those irresistible velvety eyes, 'Naughty Donald, to putch Keithie into the water!'

'Oh, my darling, my peeriewinkle, you must not say things like that!' exclaimed Alison, rather shocked. 'There, we'll forget all about falling in; you are safe home now. Towel, Morag!'

'Donald putched Keithie into the water,' repeated the little naked boy from the folds of the towel. And again, with deeper reprobation in his tone, '*Naughty* Donald!'

Ardroy, anxiously and helplessly watching these operations, knelt down on one knee beside his wife and son and said gently, 'Donald should not have gone near the loch; that was naughty of him, but you must not tell a lie about it, Keithie!'

'*Did* putch My in!' reiterated the child, now wrapped in a warm blanket, and looking not unlike a chrysalis. 'Did – *did*!'

'Yes, I did,' said a sudden voice from behind. 'It's not a lie – I did push him in.' And with that Donald advanced from the window.

His kneeling father turned so suddenly that he almost overbalanced. 'You – you *pushed* your little brother into Loch na h-Iolaire!' he repeated, in a tone of utter incredulity, while

13

Alison clutched the chrysalis to her, looking like a mother in a picture of the massacre of the innocents. 'You pushed him in – deliberately!' repeated Ardroy once more, getting to his feet.

The child faced him, fearless but not defiant, his golden head erect, his hands clenched at his sides.

'He threw my broadsword hilt in. It was wicked of him – wicked!' The voice shook a moment. 'But he is not telling a lie.'

For a second Ewen gazed, horrified, at his wife, then at his heir. 'I think you had better go downstairs to my room, Donald. When I have changed my clothes I will come and talk to you there.'

'Donald . . . Donald!' murmured his mother, looking at the culprit with all the sorrow and surprise of the world in her eyes.

'Naughty Donald,' chanted his brother with a flushed face. 'Naughty . . . naughty . . . naughty!'

'A great deal more than naughty,' thought the young father to himself, as he went to his bedroom and stripped off his wet clothes. 'Good God, how came he to do such a thing?'

He put that question squarely to the delinquent, who was waiting for him in the little room where Ardroy kept his books and rods and saw his tenantry. Donald's eyes met his frankly.

'I suppose because I was angry with Keithie for being so wicked,' he replied.

Ewen sat down, and, afraid lest his horror and surprise should make him too stern, drew the child towards him. 'But, surely, Donald, you are sorry and ashamed now? Think what might have happened!'

The fair head drooped a little – but not, evidently, in penitence. 'I am not sorry, Father, that I threw him in. He was wicked; he took my claymore hilt that was used at Culloden and threw it in. So it was right that he should be punished.'

'Great heavens!' exclaimed his parent, loosing his hold of him at this pronouncement, 'don't you think that your little brother is of more importance than a bit of an old broadsword?'

To which Donald made the devastating reply: 'No, Father, for I don't suppose that I can ever have the hilt again, because the loch is so deep there. But some day I may have another brother; Morag said so.'

Words were smitten from the laird of Ardroy, and for a moment he gazed speechless at this example of infantile logic. 'Donald,' he said at last, 'I begin to think you're a wee thing fey. Go to bed now; I'll speak to you again in the morning.'

'If you are going to punish me, Father,' said the boy, standing up very straight, and looking at him with his clear, undaunted eyes, 'I would liefer you did it now.'

'I am afraid that you cannot have everything you wish, my son,' replied Ardroy rather grimly. 'Go to your bed now, and pray to God to show you how wicked you have been. I had rather you felt that than thought about getting your punishment over quickly.'

But the executor of vengeance stuck to his guns. 'It was Keithie who deserved punishment,' he murmured, but not very steadily.

'The child's bewitched!' said Ewen to himself, staring at him. Then he put a hand on his shoulder. 'Come now,' he said in a softer tone, 'get you to bed, and think of what you would be feeling like now if Keithie had been drowned ... And you see what disobedience leads to, for if you had not taken Keithie to the loch he could not have thrown your hilt into it.'

This argument appeared to impress the logical mind of his son. 'Yes, Father,' he said in a more subdued tone. 'Yes, I am sorry that I was disobedient.'

Later, bending with Alison over the little bed where Donald's victim was already nearly asleep, Ewen repeated his opinion that their elder son was fey. 'And what are we to do with him? He seems to think that he was completely justified in what he did! 'Tis ... 'tis unnatural!'

And he looked so perturbed that his wife smothered her own no less acute feelings on the subject and said consolingly, 'He must at least have done it in a blind rage, dear love.'

'I hope so, indeed. But he is so uncannily calm and judicial over it now. I don't know what to do. Ought I to thrash him?'

'You could not,' murmured Lady Ardroy. Like many large, strong men, Ewen Cameron was extraordinarily gentle with creatures that were neither. 'No, I will try whether I cannot make Donald see what a dreadful thing he did. Oh, Ewen, if you had not been there ...' Her lips trembled, and going down on her knees she laid her head against the little mound under the bedclothes.

Chapter 2

LIEUTENANT HECTOR GRANT OF
THE RÉGIMENT D'ALBANIE

ALISON retired early that evening, but Ardroy did not go to bed at his usual hour; indeed, he remained far beyond it, and half past eleven found him pacing up and down the big living room. Now and again, as he turned in his perambulation, there was to be seen the merest trace of his memento of Culloden, the limp which, when he was really tired, was clearly to be recognized for one.

Deeply shocked at this fratricidal tendency in his eldest son, and puzzled how best to deal with it, the young man could not get his mind off the incident.

At last, in desperation, he seized an account book and bore it to the fireside. Anything to take his mind off the afternoon's affair, were it only the ever-recurring difficulty of making income and expenditure tally. For Ewen had never received – had never wished to receive – a single louis of the French gold buried at Loch Arkaig, though it had been conveyed into Cameron territory by a Cameron, and though another Cameron, together with the proscribed chief of the Macphersons (still in hiding in Badenoch), was agent for its clandestine distribution among the Jacobite clans. Ardroy had told Doctor Archibald Cameron, Lochiel's brother, and his own cousin and intimate, who had been the hero of its transportation, that he did not need any subsidy; and John Cameron of Fassefern, the other brother, representative in the Highlands of the dead Chief's family now in France, was only too relieved not to have another applicant clamouring for that fast dwindling hoard.

And Ardroy himself was glad of his abstention, for by this autumn of 1752 it was becoming clear that the money landed from the French ships just after the battle of Culloden, too late to be any use in the campaign, had now succeeded in setting kinsman against kinsman, in raising jealousies and even – for there were ugly rumours abroad – in breeding informers. Yes, it was dragon's teeth, after all, which Archibald Cameron had with such devotion sowed on Loch Arkaig side – seed which had sprung up, not in the guise of armed men to fight for the Stuarts, but in that of a crop of deadly poison. Even Ewen did not suspect how deadly.

In the midst of the young laird's rather absent-minded calculations Luath suddenly raised his head and growled. Ardroy laid down his papers, but he could hear nothing. The deerhound growled again, on a deep, threatening note. His eyes were fixed on the windows.

'Quiet!' said his master, and, rising, drew aside the curtains and looked out. He could see nothing, and yet he, too, felt that someone was there. With Luath, still growling, at his heels, he left the room, opened the door of the house, and going through the porch, stood outside.

The cool, spacious calm of the Highland night enveloped him in an instant; he saw Aldebaran brilliant in the south-east between two dark continents of cloud. Then footsteps came out of the shadows, and a slim, cloaked figure slipped quickly past him into the porch.

'*Est-il permis d'entrer, mon cher?*' it asked, low and half laughing. 'Down, Luath – it's a friend, good dog!'

The intruder was in the parlour now, in the lamplight, and as Ewen hastened after him he flung his hat upon the table, and advanced with both hands outstretched, a dark, slender, clear-featured young man of about five and twenty, wearing powder and a long green roquelaure.

'Hector, by all the powers!' exclaimed his involuntary host. 'What – '

'What brings me here? I'll tell you in a moment. How does Alison, and yourself, and the bairns?'

'Alison is very well,' replied Ewen to Alison's only brother, 'and will be vastly pleased to see you, as I am. But why my dear Hector – this mysterious entrance by night? 'Tis mere chance that I am not abed like the rest of the house.'

'I had my reasons,' said Hector Grant cheerfully. 'Nay, I'm no deserter' (he was an officer in French service), 'but I thought it wiser to slip in unnoticed if I could. I'll tell you why when I am less – you'll pardon me for mentioning it? – less sharp-set.'

'My sorrow!' exclaimed his host. 'Forgive me – I'll have food before you in a moment. I will tell Alison of your arrival.'

Hector caught at him. 'Don't rouse her now. The morn will be time enough, and I'm wanting a few words with you first.' He threw off his roquelaure. 'May I not come and forage with you, as we did – where was it ... at Manchester, I think – in the '45.'

'Come on then,' said his brother-in-law, a hand on his shoulder, and they each lit a candle and went, rather like schoolboys, to rifle the larder. And presently Ardroy was sitting at the table watching his midnight visitor give a very good account of a venison pie. This slim, vivacious, distinctly attractive young man might almost have passed for a Frenchman, for Hector Grant had lived abroad since he entered French service at the age of sixteen – and only during the fateful year of the Rising had he spent any length of time in Britain. It was indeed, his French commission which had saved him from the scaffold, for he had been one of the ill-fated garrison of Carlisle.

'Venison – ah, good to be back where one can have a shot at a deer again!' he presently observed. 'I envy you, *mon frère*.'

'You need not,' answered Ewen. 'You forget that I have no means of doing it – no firearms, no, not the smallest fowling-piece. We have to snare our deer or use dogs.'

'*C'est vrai*; I had forgotten. But I cannot think how you submit to such a deprivation.'

'Submit?' asked Ardroy rather bitterly. 'There is no choice: every Highland gentleman of our party has to submit to it, unless he has "qualified" to the English Government.'

'And you still have not done that?'

Ewen flushed. 'My dear Hector, how should I take an oath of fidelity to the Elector of Hanover? Do you think I'm become a Whig?'

'Faith, no – unless you've mightily changed since we marched into England together, seven years ago come Hallowmas. But, Eoghain, besides the arms which you have been forced to give up, there'll surely be some which you have contrived to keep back, as has always been done in the past when these distasteful measures were imposed upon us?'

Ewen's face darkened. 'The English were cleverer this time. After the Act of '25 no one was made to call down a curse upon himself, his kin and all his undertakings, to invoke the death of a coward and burial without a prayer in a strange land if he broke his oath that he had not, and never would have in his possession, any sword or pistol or arm whatsoever, nor would use any part of the highland garb.'

Hector whistled. '*Ma foi*, you subscribed to that!'

'I had to,' answered Ewen shortly.

'I never realized that when I was here two years ago, but then my visit was so short. I did indeed know that the wearing of the tartan in any form was forbidden.'

'That,' observed Ardroy, 'bears harder in a way upon the poor folk than upon us gentry. I had other clothes, if not, I could buy some; but the crofters, what else had they but their hamespun plaids and philabegs and gowns? Is it any wonder that they resorted at first to all sorts of shifts and evasions of the law, and do still, wearing a piece of plain cloth merely wrapped round the waist, sewing up the kilt in the hope that it may pass for breeches, and the like?'

'But that is not the only side of it,' said the young Franco-Scot rather impatiently. 'Surely you do not yourself relish being deprived by an enemy of the garb which has always marked us as a race?'

He was young, impetuous, not remarkable for tact, and his brother-in-law had turned his head away without reply, so that Hector Grant could not see the gleam which had come into those very blue eyes of his, nor guess the passionate resentment which was always smouldering in Ardroy's heart over a measure which, in common with the poorest Highlander, he loathed with every fibre of his being.

'I should have thought – ' young Grant was going on, when

Ewen broke in, turning round and reaching for the claret, 'Have some more wine, Hector. Now, am I really not to wake Alison to tell her that you are here?'

Hector finished his glass. 'No, let her sleep, the darling! I'll have plenty of time to talk with her – that is, if you will keep me a few days, Ardroy?'

'My dear brother, why ask? My house is yours,' said Ewen warmly. 'I'll see about a bed for you now.'

The young officer stayed him. 'I want a word with you, Ewen, a serious word. I'd liefer indeed say it before I sleep under your roof, I think … more especially since (for your family's sake) you have become … prudent.'

Ardroy's face clouded a little. 'Say on,' he responded rather briefly.

'*Eh bien*,' began Hector, his eyes on the empty wineglass, 'although it is quite true that I am come hither to see my sister and her children, there is someone else whom I am very anxious to have speech with.'

'And who's that?' asked Ewen uneasily. 'You are not come, I hope, on any business connected with the Loch Arkaig treasure? 'Tis not Cluny Macpherson whom you wish to see?'

Hector looked at him and smiled. 'I hope to see Cluny later – though not about the treasure. Just now it's a man much easier to come at, a man in Lochaber, that I'm seeking – yourself, in short.'

Ewen raised his eyebrows. 'You have not far to go, then.'

'I am not so sure of that,' responded young Grant cryptically. He paused a moment. 'Ewen, have you ever heard of Alexander Murray?'

'The brother of Lord Murray of Elibank, do you mean? Yes. What of him?'

'And Finlay MacPhair of Glenshian – young Glenshian – did you ever meet him in Paris?'

'No, I have never met him.'

'*N'importe*. Now listen, and I will tell you a great secret.'

He drew closer, and into Ardroy's ears he poured the somewhat vague details of a plot to surprise St James's Palace and kidnap the whole English Royal Family, by means, chiefly, of young officers like himself in the French service, aided by Highlanders, of whom five hundred, he alleged, could be raised in London. The German Elector, his remaining son and his grandsons once out of the way, England would acquiesce with joy in the *fait accompli,* and welcome her true Prince, who was to be ready on the coast. The Highlands, of course, must be prepared to rise, and quickly, for Hector believed that an early date in November had been fixed for the attempt. The Scots whom he had just mentioned were in the plot; the Earl Marischal knew of it. And Hector himself had conceived the idea of offering Ardroy a share in the enterprise, apparently hoping to induce him to go to London and enrol himself among the putative five hundred Highlanders.

'But, before we discuss that,' he finished, 'tell me what you think of the whole notion of this *coup de main*? Is it not excellent, and just what we ought to have carried out long ago, had we been wise?' And he leant back with a satisfied air as if he had no fear of the reply.

But there was no answering light on the clear, strong face opposite him. Cameron of Ardroy was looking very grave.

'You want to know what I think?' he asked slowly. 'Well, first I think that the scheme is mad, and could not succeed; and secondly, that it is unworthy, and does not deserve to.'

Hector sat up in his chair. '*Hé! qu'est-ce que tu me chantes là?*' he cried with a frown. 'Say that again!'

Ewen did not comply; instead he went on very earnestly: 'You surely do not hold with assassination, Hector! But no doubt you do not see the affair in that light ... you spoke of kidnapping, I think. O, for Heaven's sake, have nothing to do with a plot of that kind, which the Prince would never soil his hands with!'

'You are become very squeamish on a sudden,' observed his visitor. 'And somewhat behind the times, too. The Prince not only knows but approves of the plan.'

His brother-in-law's face expressed scepticism. 'I think your enthusiasm misleads you, Hector. His Royal Highness has always refused to countenance schemes of the kind.'

'You are a trifle out of date, my dear Ewen! I suppose His Royal Highness may change his mind. As it happens, it is in connexion with this enterprise that he is sending MacPhair of Lochdornie and Doctor Cameron to Scotland. They are to work the clans meanwhile, so that when the blow is struck in London by those responsible – '

But by now Ewen was interrupting him. 'Archie – Archie Cameron is connected with this plot! I'm sorry to appear to doubt you, Hector but – since at this point we had best be frank – I don't believe it.'

Hector's lips were compressed, his eyes glinting. He seemed to be making an effort to keep his temper. 'He'll tell you differently, *parbleu,* when you meet him!'

'When I meet him! He's not in Scotland.'

'He is, by this time! And I suppose, since he's your cousin, and you have always been intimate with him, that he'll come here, and mayhap you will accord him a more courteous welcome than you have me!' He pushed back his chair and got up.

Ewen did the same. 'I ask your pardon if I was uncivil,' he said with some stiffness. 'But I cannot be courteous over a scheme so ill-judged and so repugnant. Moreover Archibald Cameron will not come here. When he was over in '49 on the business of the Loch Arkaig gold he purposely kept away from Ardroy.'

'Purposely? Why? – Oh, ay, lest he should compromise you, I suppose!'

'Something of the sort,' answered Ewen without flinching.

'Yes, that's your chief preoccupation now, I see!' flared out Hector, hot as ginger. 'It were much better I had not come here either, but I'll go at once, lest *I* should commit that unpardonable sin!'

'Hector, Hector, do not be hasty!' cried Ewen, angry enough himself, but still able to control his tongue. 'You asked me what I thought – I told you. Let's leave this business till the morning, and we'll talk of it again then.'

'No, indeed we will not!' retorted the young plotter defiantly. 'I'll find some other roof to shelter me tonight – some humbler dwelling where the White Rose is still cherished. It grows no longer at Ardroy – I see that very plainly.' He flung the cloak round him with a swing. 'I'll bid you goodnight, *monsieur mon beau-frère*!'

Ewen had put his hands behind him; one gripping the wrist of the other. He had turned a little pale. 'You can say what you please to me in this house,' he answered between his teeth, 'for you know that I cannot touch you. But if you still feel minded to repeat that about the White Rose to me tomorrow, somewhere off my land – '

'The White Rose,' broke in a gentle voice from the doorway. 'Who is speaking of – O *Hector*!'

It was Lady Ardroy, in her nightshift with a shawl about her. Both men stood looking at her and wondering how much she had heard.

'Hector, dear brother, what a surprise!' She ran across the big room to him. 'Have you but just arrived? Take off your cloak – how delightful this is!' With the words she threw her arms round his neck and kissed him warmly.

But there must have been something amiss in her brother's answering salute, as in her husband's silence. 'What is troubling you?' she asked, looking from one to the other, her hand still on Hector's shoulder. 'Is there . . . ill news?'

Neither of the men answered for a moment. 'Ewen considers it ill,' said Hector at last, curtly. 'But it does not touch him – nor you, my dear. So I'll say goodnight; I must be going on my way.'

'Going on your way – *tonight*!' There was almost stupefaction in his sister's tone. 'But 'tis long past midnight; you cannot go, Hector? Ewen, make him bide here?'

'Hector must please himself,' replied her husband coldly. 'But naturally I have no desire that he should continue his journey before morning.'

Alison gazed at him in dismay. Highland hospitality – and to a kinsman – offered in so half-hearted a fashion! 'Surely you have not been . . . differing about anything?'

Again neither of them answered her at once, but they both looked a trifle like children detected in wrong-doing. 'You had better go back to bed, my heart,' said Ewen gently. 'Did you come down because you heard voices?'

'I came,' said Alison, her eyes suddenly clouding, 'because of Keithie – I don't know, but I fear he may be going to be ill.'

'You see, I had best go,' said her brother instantly, in a softer tone. 'If you have a child ill – '

'But that is neither here nor there,' replied Alison. 'O Hector, stay, stay!'

Of course the young soldier wanted to stay. But having announced in so fiery a manner that he was going, and having undeniably insulted the master of the house, how could he with dignity remain unless that master begged him to? And that Ardroy, evidently, was not minded to do.

'If Hector wishes to please you, Alison, he will no doubt bide here the night,' was all the olive-branch that he tendered. 'But I gather that he fears he will compromise us by his presence. If you can persuade him that his fear is groundless, pray do so.'

'No,' said Hector, not to Ewen but to Alison. 'No, best have no more words about it. It were wiser I did not sleep here tonight. I'll come on my return ... or perhaps tomorrow,' he added, melted by his sister's appealing face. 'I'll find a shelter, never fear. But things have changed somewhat of late in the Highlands.'

With which mysterious words he kissed Alison again, flung his cloak once more about him, and made for the door. Lady Ardroy followed him a little way, distressed and puzzled, then stopped; half her heart, no doubt, was upstairs. But Ewen left the room after the young officer, and found him already opening the front door.

'Do me the justice to admit that I am not turning you out,' said Ardroy rather sternly. 'It is your own doing; the house is open to you tonight ... and for as long afterwards as you wish, if you apologize – '

'I'll return when you apologize for calling me an assassin!' retorted Hector over his shoulder.

'You know I never called you so! Hector, I hate your going off in anger in this fashion, at dead of night – and how am I to

25

know that you will not stumble into some ill affair or other with the redcoats or with broken men?'

Hector gave an unsteady laugh. 'If I do, you may be sure I shall not risk "compromising" you by asking for your assistance! Sleep quietly!' And, loosing that last arrow, he was lost in the darkness out of which he had come.

Ardroy stood on the edge of that darkness for a moment, swallowing down the anger which fought with his concern, for he had himself a temper as hot as Hector's own, though it was more difficult to rouse. Hector's last thrust was childish, but his previous stab about the White Rose had gone deep . . . yet he knew well that the root of that flower was not dead at Ardroy, though scarce a blossom might show on it.

He went back with bent head, to find Alison saying in great distress, 'O dearest, what has happened between you and Hector? And Keithie is feverish; I am so afraid lest the cold water and the exposure . . . for you know he's not very strong . . .'

Ewen put his arm round her. 'Please God 'tis only a fever of cold he's taken. . . . And as for Hector – yes, I will tell you about it. He'll think better of it, I dare say, foolish boy, in the morning.'

Chapter 3

A FRENCH SONG BY LOCH TREIG

By three o'clock next afternoon Ewen Cameron was riding fast to Maryburgh to fetch a doctor. Little Keith was really ill, and it was with a sickening pang at his own heart that Ardroy had tried to comfort the now extremely penitent Donald.

Ardroy had to try to comfort himself, too, as he went along Loch Lochy banks, where the incomparable tints of the Northern autumn were lighting their first fires in beech and bracken. Children had fever so easily; it might signify nothing, old Marsali had said, but Alison, he could see, was terribly anxious. He wished that his aunt, Miss Margaret Cameron, who had brought him up, and still lived with them, were not away visiting. He wished that he himself could have stayed at home and sent a gillie for the doctor, but even one who spoke English might get involved in some difficulty with the military at Fort William, and the message never be delivered. It was safer to go himself.

There was also last night's unfortunate business with his brother-in-law to perturb him. High-spirited and impulsive as he was, Hector might repent and come back in a day or two, if only for his sister's sake. Ewen devoutly hoped that he would. For that same sister's sake he would forgive the young man his wounding words. It was worse to reflect that Hector had evidently mixed himself up in some way with this mad, reprehensible plot against the Elector. And he had averred that Archibald Cameron, of all men, had come or was coming to Scotland on the same enterprise.

Ewen involuntarily tightened his reins. That he did not believe. His respect and affection for Archibald Cameron were scarcely less than those he had borne his elder brother Lochiel himself. Archie had probably come over again to confer with Cluny Macpherson about that accursed Loch Arkaig gold, very likely in order to take some of it back to France with him – a risky business, as always, but a perfectly justifiable one. It was true, as Ewen had told Hector, that Archie purposely avoided coming to Ardroy, though it lay not far from the shores of Loch Arkaig, yet Ewen hoped that they should meet somehow. He had not seen his cousin for nearly three years.

On the other hand, if Archie had come over to work in any way for the Cause in the Highlands, there was certainly a good deal of ferment here at present, and a proportionately good chance of fishing in troubled waters. Yes, it might be fruitful soil, but who was to organize a new rising; still more, who was to lead it? There was only one man whom the broken, often jealous clans would follow, and he was far away . . . and some whispered that he was broken too.

Although he was not well mounted (for a good horse was a luxury which he could not afford himself nowadays) Ardroy, thus occupied in mind, found himself crossing the Spean, almost before he realized it, on that bridge which had been the scene of the first Jacobite exploit in the Rising, and of his own daring escape in the summer of '46. But he hardly gave a thought to either today. And, in order to examine one of his horse's legs, he pulled up at the change-house on the farther side without reflecting that it was the very spot where, six years ago, he had been made to halt, a prisoner with his feet tied together under a sorrel's belly.

While he was feeling the leg, suspecting incipient lameness, the keeper of the change-house came out; not a Cameron now, but a Campbell protégé, yet a decent fellow enough. Though on the winning side, he too was debarred from the use of the tartan – which was some consolation to a man on the losing.

'Good day to you, Ardroy,' he said, recognizing the stooping rider. 'You'll be for Maryburgh the day? Has the horse gone lame on you, then?'

'Hardly that yet,' answered Ewen, 'but I fear me there's a strain or something of the sort. Yes, I am going to Maryburgh, to fetch Doctor Kincaid. Can I do aught for you there, MacNichol?'

'*Dhé!* ye'll not find the doctor at Maryburgh,' observed the other. 'He's away up Loch Treig side the day.'

'Loch Treig!' exclaimed Ewen, dismayed. 'How do you know that, man – and are you very sure of it?'

MacNichol was very sure. His own wife was ill; the doctor had visited her that same morning, and instead of returning to Maryburgh had departed along the south bank of the Spean – the only practicable way – for a lonely farm on Loch Treig. It was of no use waiting at the change-house for his return, since he would naturally go back to Maryburgh along the shorter road by Corriechoille and Lianachan. There was nothing then to be done but ride after him.

Ewen's heart sank lower and lower. It would be getting dusk by the time that he had covered the twelve or fourteen miles to the nearer end of the desolate loch. Suppose he somehow missed the doctor, or suppose the latter could not or would not start back for Ardroy so late? Yet at least it would be better than nothing to have speech with him, and to learn what was the proper treatment for that little coughing, shivering, bright-cheeked thing at home.

So he went by Spean side where it hurried in its gorges, where it swirled in wide pools; by the dangerous ford at Inch, past the falls where it hurled itself to a destruction which it never met; he rode between it and the long heights of Beinn Chlinaig and finally turned south with the lessening river itself. And after a while there opened before him a narrow, steel-coloured trough of loneliness and menace imprisoned between unfriendly heights – Loch Treig. On its eastern side Cnoc Dearg reared himself starkly; on the other Stob Choire an Easain Mhoir, even loftier, shut it in – kinsmen of Ben Nevis both. The track went low by the shore under Cnoc Dearg, for there was no place for it on his steep flanks.

As there was no habitation anywhere within sight, Ewan concluded that the farm to which Doctor Kincaid had gone was probably at Loch Treig head, at the farther end of the lake, where the mountains relaxed their grip – another five or six miles. He went on. The livid surface of the water by which he rode was not ruffled today by any wind; a heavy, sinister silence lay upon it, as on the dark, brooding heights which hemmed it about. It hardly seemed surprising that after a mile and a half of its company Ewen's horse definitely went lame. But he could not spare the time to lead him; he must push on at all costs.

The halting beast had carried him but a little way farther before he was aware of distant sounds like – yes, they *were* snatches of song. And soon he saw coming towards him through the September dusk the indistinct figure of a man walking with the uncertain gait of one who has been looking upon the wine-cup. And Ewen, thinking, 'That poor fool will either spend the night by the roadside or fall into the loch,' pulled up his horse to a walk, for the drunkard was staggering first to one side of the narrow road and then to the other, and he feared to knock him down.

As he did so he recognized the air which the reveller was singing. . . . But the words which belonged to that tune were neither Gaelic, Scots nor English, so how should they be sung here, by one of the loneliest lochs in the Highlands?

> *'Aux nouvell's que j'apporte*
> *Vos beaux yeux vont pleurer . . .'*

What was a Frenchman doing here, singing 'Malbrouck'?

> *'Quittez vos habits roses,'*

sang the voice, coming nearer:

> *'Mironton, mironton, mirontaine,*
> *Quittez vos habits roses*
> *Et vos satins brochés.'*

Ewen jumped off his horse. It was not perhaps, after all, a Frenchman born who was singing that song in so lamentable and ragged a fashion along this lonely track to nowhere.

The lurching figure was already nearly up to him, and now the singer seemed to become aware of the man and the horse in his path, for he stopped in the middle of the refrain.

'Laissez-moi passer, s'il vous plât,' he muttered indistinctly, and tried to steady himself. He was hatless, and wore a green roquelaure.

Ewen dropped his horse's bridle and seized him by the arm.

'*Hector!* What in the name of the Good Being are you doing here in this state?'

Out of a very white face Hector Grant's eyes stared at him totally without recognition. 'Let me pass, if you pl – please,' he said again, but in English this time.

'You are not fit to be abroad,' said Ewen in disgust. The revelation that Hector could ever be as drunk as this came as a shock; he had always thought him a temperate youth, if excitable . . . but it was true that he had seen nothing of him for the past two years. 'Where have you been – what, in God's name, have you been doing? Answer me! I am in haste.'

'So am I,' replied Hector, still more thickly. 'Let me pass, I say, whoever you are. Let me pass, or I'll make you!'

'Don't you even know me?' demanded his brother-in-law indignantly.

'No, and have no wish to. . . . O God, my head!' And Ardroy having removed his grasp, the reveller reeled backwards against the horse, putting both hands to his brow.

'You had best sit down for a moment,' counselled Ewen dryly, and with an arm round him guided him to the side of the path. Hector must be pretty far gone if he really did not know him, for it was still quite light enough for recognition.

As he sat hunched there the back of that same head was presented to Ardroy's unsympathetic gaze. Just above the black ribbon which tied Hector's queue the powder appeared all smirched, and of a curious rusty colour. . . . Ewen uttered a sudden exclamation, stooped, touched the patch, and looked at his fingers. Next moment he was down by the supposed tippler's side, his arm round him.

'Hector, have you had a blow on the head? How came you by it?' His voice was sharp with anxiety. 'My God, how much are you hurt – who did it?' But Hector did not answer; instead, as he sat there, his knees suddenly gave, and he lurched forward and sideways on to his mentor.

Penitent, and to spare, for having misjudged him, Ewen straightened him out, laid him down in the heather and bog-myrtle which bordered the track, brought water from the burn in his hat, dashed it in the young man's face, and turning his head on one side, tried to examine the injury. He could not see much, only the hair matted with dried blood; it was even possibly the fact of its being gathered thus into a queue and tied with a stout ribbon which had saved him from more serious damage – perhaps, indeed, had saved his life.

After a moment, the young soldier gave a little sigh, and, still lying in Ardroy's arms, began to murmur something incoherent about stopping someone at all costs; that he was losing time and must push on. He even made a feeble effort to rise, which Ewen easily frustrated.

'You cannot push on anywhere after a blow like that,' he said gently. (Had he not had a presentiment of something like this last night!) 'I'll make you as comfortable as I can with my cloak, and when I come back from my errand to the head of the loch I'm in hopes I'll have a doctor with me, and he can – Don't you know me now, Hector?'

For the prostrate man was saying thickly, 'The doctor – do you mean Doctor Cameron? No, no, he must not be brought here – good God, he must not come this way now, any more than Lochdornie! Don't you understand, that's what I am trying to do – to stop Lochdornie ... now that damned spy has taken my papers!'

'What's that?' asked Ewen sharply. 'You were carrying papers, and they have been taken from you?'

Hector wrested himself a little away. 'Who are you?' he asked suspiciously, looking up at him with the strangest eyes. 'Another Government agent? Papers ... no, I have no papers! I have but come to Scotland to visit my sister, and she's married to a gentleman of these parts. ... Oh, you may be easy – he'll have naught to do now with him they name the young Pretender, so how should I be carrying treasonable papers?'

Ewen bit his lip hard. The half-stunned brain was remembering yesterday night at Ardroy. But how could he be angry with a speaker in this plight? Moreover, there was something extremely disquieting behind his utterances; he must be patient – but quick too, for precious time was slipping by, and he might somehow miss Doctor Kincaid in the oncoming darkness.

'Hector, don't you really know me?' he asked again, almost pleadingly. 'It's Ewen — Ewen Cameron of Ardroy, Alison's husband!'

His sister's name seemed, luckily, to act as a magnet to Hector's scattered wits. They fastened on it. 'Alison — Alison's husband?' Suspicion turned to perplexity; he stared afresh. 'You're uncommonly like ... why, it *is* Ardroy!' he exclaimed after a moment's further scrutiny.

'Yes,' said Ewen, greatly relieved, 'it is Ardroy, and thankful to have come upon you. Now tell me what's wrong, and why you talk of stopping MacPhair of Lochdornie?'

Relief was on Hector's strained face too. He passed his hand once or twice over his eyes and became almost miraculously coherent. 'I was on my way to Ben Alder, to Cluny Macpherson ... I fell in with a man as I went along the Spean ... he must have been a Government spy. I could not shake him off. I had even to come out of my way with him — like this — lest he should guess where I was making for ... I stooped at last to drink of a burn, and I do not remember any more. ... When I knew what had happened I found that he had taken everything ... and if Lochdornie makes for Badenoch or Lochaber now he'll be captured, for there was news of him in a letter I had on me — though it was mostly in cipher — and the redcoats will be on the alert. ... He must be warned, for he is on his way hither — he must be warned at once, or all is lost!' Hector groaned, put a hand over his eyes again, and this time kept it there.

Ewen sat silent for a moment. What a terrible misfortune! 'You mentioned Archibald Cameron's name just now,' he said uneasily. 'What of *his* movements?'

'Doctor Cameron's in Knoidart,' answered Hector. 'He'll not be coming this way yet, I understand. No, 'tis Lochdornie you must — ' And there he stopped, removed his hand and said in a different tone, 'But I am forgetting — you do not wish now to have aught to do with the Prince and his plans.'

'I never said that!' protested Ardroy. 'I said ... but no matter! I've given proofs enough of my loyalty, Hector!'

'Proofs? We have all given them!' returned the younger man

impatiently. 'Show me that I wronged you last night! You have a horse there – ride back without a moment's delay to Glen Mallie and stop Lochdornie. I'll give you directions.'

He looked up at his brother-in-law in a silence so dead, so devoid of any sound from the sullen water of the loch, that the very mountains seemed to be holding their breaths to listen.

'I cannot turn back now,' said Ardroy in a slow voice. 'But when I have found the doctor – '

'Ah, never think of me!' cried Hector, misunderstanding. 'I'll do well enough here for the present. But to save Lochdornie you must turn back this instant! Surely some good angel sent you here, Ewen, to undo what I have done. Listen, you'll find him – ' he clutched at Ardroy, 'somewhere in Glen Mallie, making towards Loch Arkaig. If he gets the length of the glen by dark it's like he'll spend the night in an old tumble-down croft there is on the side of Beinn Bhan. You'll be put to it to get there in time, I fear; yet you may meet him coming away . . . But if once he crosses the Lochy. . . .' He made a despairing gesture. 'You'll do it, Ewen?' And his unhappy eyes searched the face above him hungrily.

But Ewen turned his head aside. 'I would go willingly, if . . . Do you know why I am on this road at all, Hector? His voice grew hoarse. 'My little son is very ill; I am riding after the only doctor for miles round – and he gone up Loch Treig I know not how far. How can I turn back to warn anyone until I have found him?'

'Then I must go,' said Hector wildly ' 'Tis I have ruined Lochdornie's plans. But I shall go so slow . . . and it is so far. . . . I shall never be in time.' He was struggling to his knees, only to be there for a second or two ere he relapsed into Ewen's arms. 'My head . . . I can't stand ... it swims so! O God, why did I carry that letter on me!' And he burst into tears.

Ewen let him weep, staring out over the darkening loch where some bird flew wailing like a lost spirit, and where against the desolate heights opposite he seemed to see Keithie's flushed little face. Words spoken six years ago came back to him, when the speaker, himself in danger, was urging him to seek safety. 'God knows, my dear Ewen, I hold that neither wife, children nor home should stand in a man's way when duty and loyalty call him – and as you know, I have turned my back on all these.' He could hear Archibald Cameron's voice as if it were yesterday. Duty and loyalty – were they not calling now?

Hector had cast himself face downwards, and the scent of the bruised bog-myrtle came up strong and sweet. Ewen clenched his teeth; then he stooped and laid a hand on his shoulder.

'I will turn back,' he said almost inaudibly. 'Perhaps the child is better now. . . . If anyone passes, call out; it may be the doctor – you need him.' His voice stuck in his throat, but he contrived to add, 'And send him on to Ardroy.'

Hector raised his face and seized his brother-in-law's arm in an almost convulsive grip. 'You'll go – you'll go? God bless you, Ewen! And forgive me, forgive me! . . . Had I not been so hasty last night . . .'

'If Lochdornie be not in the croft I suppose I'll come on him farther up the glen,' said Ewen shortly. There were no words to spare for anything save the hard choice he was making. He stripped off his cloak and wrapped it round Hector as well as Hector's own; the night, fortunately, was not setting in cold.

But as Ewen pulled round his horse and threw himself into the saddle he could almost see Alison in the road to bar his return. How could he ever tell her what he had done! When he met her again he would perhaps be the murderer of his child and hers.

Soon his hoof-beats made a dwindling refrain by the dark water, and the wardens of Loch Treig tossed the sound to each other as they tossed Hector's song. Sharp, sharp, sharp, said the echo, are the thorns of the White Rose, and the hearth where that flower has twined itself is never a safe one.

Chapter 4

THE MAN WITH A PRICE ON HIS HEAD

1

THE sky was clear with morning but the hollows of the hills were yet cold and drowsy after the night; the mountain grasses, tawny and speckled like the hairs on a deerhide, stood motionless; the rust of the bracken shone with moisture. And the tiny ruined croft up the braeside, behind the old thorn which had so long guarded it from ill, seemed to slumber even more soundly than the fern and the grasses.

None the less there was life inside that abandoned shell of a building, but life which, like that outside, was scarcely yet stirring. In the half of the croft which still kept its thatch a man was lying on his back, lightly asleep; from time to time he moved a trifle, and once he opened his eyes wide and then, passing a hand over them, stared up at the sky between the rowan boughs with a little frown, as of one who is not over pleased to see daylight. The face on that makeshift pillow was that of a man in the middle forties, handsome and kindly, and not at first sight the face of one whom adventure or dubious dealings would have led to seek shelter in so comfortless a bedchamber, and whose apparent reluctance to leave it suggested that he had not, perhaps, enjoyed even that shelter very long.

Presently, however, the sleeper opened his eyes again, raised his head as if listening, then laid it back in the fern and remained very still. A slow and rather dragging footfall could be heard, though dully, coming up the hill-side, and pausing at last outside the crazy half-shut door which was all that hid the present inmate of the ruin from the outer word. The latter, however, continued to lie without moving; perhaps he hoped thus to escape notice.

A pause, then the broken door, catching in the weeds of the threshold, was pushed open. A tall man, his stature exaggerated by the little entry to proportions almost gigantic, stood there against the flushed sky, breathing rather fast. As he stood, the light behind him, his face was not clearly discernible, nor could he, coming suddenly into this half-dark place, make out more of the man in the corner than that there was a man there.

He peered forward. 'Thank God that I have found you,' he said in Gaelic. 'Give me a sign, and I will tell you why I have come.'

The man under the cloak raised himself on an elbow. 'I give you the sign of the Blackbird,' he said in the same tongue. It was the old Jacobite cant name for James Edward Stuart. 'And what do you give me, honest man?'

'I have no password,' answered the newcomer, entering. 'But in exchange for the blackbird,' he gave a rather weary little laugh – 'I give you the grouse, since it's that fowl you must emulate for a while, Lochdornie. You must lie close, and not come into Lochaber as yet; I am come in all haste to warn you of that.'

An exclamation interrupted him. The man in the corner was sitting up, throwing off the cloak which had served him for a blanket.

' 'Tis not Lochdornie – Lochdornie's in Knoidart. You have warned the wrong man, my dear Ewen!' He was on his feet now, smiling and holding out his hands in welcome.

'What! it's *you*, Archie!' exclaimed Ewen in surprise so great that he involuntarily recoiled for an instant. Then he seized the outstretched hands with alacrity. 'I did not know ... I thought it was Lochdornie I was seeking!'

'Are you disappointed, then, at the exchange?' asked Doctor Cameron with a half-quizzical smile. 'Even if you are, *Eoghain mhóir*, I am delighted to see *you*!'

'Disappointed – of course not! only puzzled,' answered Ewen, looking at him, indeed, with a light of pleasure on his tired face. 'Had I known it was you I should have come less un – have made even more haste' he substituted. 'Then is Loch-dornie here too?'

'No, he is in Knoidart, where I was to have gone. I don't

know why we laid our first plans that way, for at the last moment we thought better of it, and changed places. Hence it comes that I am for Lochaber, instead of him. But what are you saying about a grouse and a warning? From whom are you bringing me a warning?'

'From my young brother-in-law, Hector Grant. He's of your regiment.' For Doctor Cameron was major in Lord Ogilvie's regiment in the French service wherein Hector also had a commission.

'He is, but I had no notion that he was in Scotland.'

'But he knows that you and Lochdornie are; and seems, un-luckily, to have carried that piece of news about him in some letter which – '

'Sit down before you tell me, dear lad,' said his cousin, inter-rupting, 'for you look uncommon weary. ' 'Tis true I have no seat to offer you – '

'Yon fern will serve well enough,' said Ewen, going towards the heap of bracken and letting himself fall stiffly upon it. He *was* weary, for he had walked all night, and in consequence his injured leg was troubling him. Doctor Cameron sat down be-side him.

'I came on Hector,' resumed Ardroy, 'last evening by Loch Treig side, staggering about like a drunken man from a blow on the head, and with his pockets rifled. It seems that while making for Cluny's hiding-place he fell in with some man whom he could not shake off – a Government spy, he thought afterwards. When I found him Hector was trying himself to warn Lochdornie of the loss of the letter; but that was mani-festly impossible, and he implored me to take his place. Luckily I was mounted ... on a lame horse,' he added with a shrug. 'So I have come, and glad I am to be in time.'

Archibald Cameron was looking grave. 'I wonder what was in that letter, and whom it was from?'

'Hector did not tell me. He had not too many words at his command; I had enough ado at first to get him to recognize me. The letter was, I gather, mostly in cipher, which is something; but cipher can be read. And since he was so insistent that a warning should be carried, and I turn – ' He checked himself –

38

'Since he was so insistent you will pay heed, Archie, will you not, and avoid crossing the Lochy yet awhile?'

'Yes, indeed I will. I must not be captured if I can help it,' answered Doctor Cameron simply. 'But, my dear Ewen' – he laid a hand on his kinsman's arm, 'do not look so anxious over it! You have succeeded in warning me, and in preventing, perhaps, a great wreckage of hopes. The Prince owes you a fine debt for this, and some day he will be able to repay you.'

'I am already more than repaid,' said the young man, looking at him with sincere affection, 'if I have stayed you from running into special peril ... and I'm glad that 'twas for *you,* after all, that I came. But what of MacPhair of Lochdornie – should one take steps to warn him also?'

'He'll not be coming this way yet,' replied his cousin. 'We are to meet in a week, back in Glen Dessary, and since he is to await me there, there is no danger.'

'And what will you do meanwhile – where will you bestow yourself?'

'Oh, I'll skulk for a while here and in Glen Dessary, moving about. I am become quite an old hand at that game,' said Archibald Cameron cheerfully. 'And now, *'ille,* the sun's coming up, let us break our fast. I have some meal with me, and you must be hungry.' Rising, he went over to the other corner of the shelter.

Directly his back was turned Ewen leant his head against the rough wall behind him and closed his eyes, spent with the anxiety which had ridden with him to the point where the increasing lameness of his horse had forced him to abandon the beast and go on foot, and then had flitted by his side like a little wraith, taking on the darling shape of the child who was causing it. He heard Archie saying from the corner, 'And how's all with you, Ewen? Mrs Alison and the children, are they well?'

'Alison is well. The children. . . .' He could get no farther, for with the words it came to him that by sunrise there was perhaps but one child at Ardroy.

Archibald Cameron caught the break in his voice and turned

quickly, the little bag of meal in his hand. 'What's wrong, Ewen – what is it?'

Ewen looked out of the doorway. The sun was up; a hare ran across the grass. 'Little Keith is . . . very ill. I must get back home as quickly as I can; I will not stay to eat.'

Archie came quickly over to him, his face full of concern; 'Very ill – and yet you left home for my sake! Have you a doctor there, Ewen?'

Ardroy shook his head. 'I was on my way to fetch one yesterday when I came upon Hector . . . so I could not go on . . . I dare say Keithie is better by now. Children so easily get fever that it may mean nothing,' he added, with a rather heartrending air of reciting as a charm a creed in which he did not really believe. 'That's true, is it not?' And as Doctor Cameron nodded, but gravely, Ewen tried to smile, and said, getting to his feet, 'Well, I'll be starting back. Thank God that I was in time. And, Archie, you swear that you will be prudent? It would break my heart if you were captured.'

He held out his hand. His kinsman did not take it. Instead, he put both of his on the broad shoulders.

'I need not ask you if you are willing to run a risk for your child's sake. If you will have me under your roof, Ewen, I will come back with you and do my best for little Keith. But if I were taken at Ardroy it would be no light matter for you, so you must weigh the question carefully.'

Ewen started away from him. 'No, no! – for it's you that would be running the risk, Archie. No, I cannot accept such a sacrifice – you must go back farther west. Ardroy might be searched.'

'Why should it be? You must be in fairly good repute with the authorities by now. And I would not stay long, to endanger you. Ewen, Ewen, let me come to the bairn! I have not quite sunk the physician yet in the Jacobite agent.'

'It would be wrong of me,' said Ewen, wavering. 'I ought not. No, I will not have you.' Yet his eyes showed how much he longed to accept.

'You cannot prevent my coming after you, my dear boy, even if you do not take me with you, and it would certainly be more prudent if you introduced me quietly by a back door than if I presented myself at the front. ... Which is it to be? ... Come now, let's eat a few mouthfuls of drammoch; we'll go all the faster for it.'

2

That evening there seemed to be bestowed on Loch na h-Iolaire a new and ethereal loveliness, when the hunter's moon had changed the orange of her rising to argent. Yet the two men who stood on its banks were not looking at the silvered beauty of the water but at each other.

'Yes, quite sure,' said the elder, who had just made his way there from the house. 'The wean was, I think, on the mend before I came; a trifle of treatment did the rest. He'll need a little care now for the next few days, that is all. A beautiful bairn, Ewen. ... You can come back and see him now; he's sleeping finely.'

'It's hard to believe,' said Ewen in a low voice. 'But you *have* saved him, Archie; he was very ill when you got here this morning, I'm convinced. And now he is really going to recover?'

'Yes, please God,' answered Archibald Cameron. 'I could not find you at first to tell you; then I guessed somehow, that you would be by the lochan.'

'I have been here all afternoon, since you turned me out of the room; yet I don't know why I came – above all to this very spot – for I have been hating Loch na h-Iolaire, for the first time in my life. It so nearly slew him.'

'Yet Loch na h-Iolaire is very beautiful this evening,' said his cousin, and he gave a little sigh, the sigh of the exile. 'Those were happy days, Ewen, when I used to come here, and Lochiel too, we've both fished in this water, and I remember Donald's catching a pike so large that you were, I believe, secretly alarmed at it. You were a small boy then, and I but two and twenty. ...' He moved nearer to the brink. 'And what's that, pray, down there – hidden treasure?'

Ewen came and looked – the moon also. Through the crystal

clear water something gleamed and wavered. It was the Culloden broadsword hilt, cause of all these last days' happenings.

'That thing, which was once a Stewart claymore, is really why you are here, Archie.'

But the more obvious cause lay asleep in the house of Ardroy clutching one of his mother's fingers, his curls dank and tumbled, his peach-bloom cheeks wan, dark circles under his long, unstirring lashes – but sleeping the sleep of recovery. Even his father, tiptoeing in ten minutes later, could not doubt that.

Without any false shame he knelt down by the little bed and bowed his head in his hands upon the edge. Alison, a trifle pale from the position whch she was so rigidly keeping – since not for anything would she have withdrawn that prisoned finger, though it would have been quite easy – looked across at her husband kneeling there with a lovely light in her eyes. And the man to whom, as they both felt, they owed this miracle (though he disclaimed the debt) who had a brood of his own oversea, wore the air, as he gazed at the scene, of thinking that his own life would have been well risked to bring it about.

3

Since by nine o'clock that evening Dr Kincaid had not put in an appearance, it could be taken for granted that he was not coming at all. This made it seem doubtful whether he had seen Hector by the roadside, and though such an encounter was highly desirable for Hector's own sake, yet, if the doctor had missed him, it probably meant that the farmer at Inverlair had sent at once and got the injured man into shelter, as he had promised Ewen to do.

Alison was naturally distressed and increasingly anxious about her brother now that her acute anxiety over Keithie had subsided, and her husband undertook to send a messenger early next morning to get news of the stricken adventurer. But tonight nothing could be done to this end. So, while his wife remained by the child's side, Ardroy and his cousin sat together in his sanctum, and Ewen tried more fully to convey his gratitude. But once again Doctor Cameron would have none of the thanks which he averred he had not deserved. Besides, it was rather good, he observed, to be at the old trade again.

Ewen looked thoughtfully at his kinsman as the latter leant back in his chair. He could not help thinking also what strange and dangerous activities had been the Doctor's, man of peace though he was, since that July day in '45 when his brother the Chief had sent him to Borrodale to dissuade the Prince from going on with his enterprise. He had become the Prince's aide-de-camp, had taken part in that early and unsuccessful attack on Ruthven barracks during the march to Edinburgh, had been wounded at Falkirk, and shared Lochiel's perils after Culloden, adding to them his own numerous and perilous journeys as go-between for him with the lost and hunted Prince; it was he who conveyed the belated French gold from the sea-coast to Loch Arkaig and buried it there. Then had come (as for Ewen too) exile, and anxiety about employment; after Lochiel's death fresh cares, on behalf of his brother's young family as well as his own, and more than one hazardous return to the shores where his life was forfeit. If Archibald Cameron had been a soldier born and bred instead of a physician he could not have run more risks . . .

'Why do you continue this dangerous work, Archie?' asked Ewen suddenly. 'There are others who could do it who have not your family ties. Do you relish it?'

Doctor Cameron turned his head, with its haunting likeness to Lochiel's. He looked as serene as usual. 'Why do I go on with it? Because the Prince bade me, and I can refuse him nothing.'

'But have you seen him recently?' asked Ewen in some excitement.

'This very month, at Menin in Flanders. He sent for me and MacPhair of Lochdornie and gave me this commission.'

'Menin! Is *that* where he lives now?'

Archibald Cameron shook his head. 'It was but a rendezvous. He does not live there.'

'Tell me of him, Archie!' urged the younger man. 'One

hears no news ... and he never comes! Will he ever come again ... and could we do aught for him if he did?'

But Archibald Cameron, for all that he had been the Prince's companion on that fruitless journey to Spain after the 'Forty-five, for all that he was devoted to him, body and soul, could tell the inquirer very little. The Prince, he said, kept himself so close, changed his residence so often; and a cloud of mystery of his own devising surrounded him and his movements. It had been a joy, however, to see his face again; an even greater to be sent upon this hazardous mission by him. Yes, please God, his Royal Highness *would* come again to Scotland some day, but there was much to be done in preparation first.

Ewen listened rather sadly. Too many of his questions Archie was unable to answer, and at last the questioner turned to more immediate matters.

'Did the Prince send for anyone else save you and Lochdornie to meet him at Menin?'

'There was young Glenshian, the Chief's son – Finlay Mac-Phair ... Fionnlagh Ruadh, as they call him.'

'Two MacPhairs! I had not fancied you so intimate with those of that name, Archie!'

'Nor am I,' answered Archibald Cameron quickly. 'But one does not choose one's associates in a matter of this kind.'

'Or you would not have chosen them?' queried Ewen. Doctor Cameron made no answer. 'Why not?' asked Ardroy with a tinge of uneasiness. 'I thought that MacPhair of Lochdornie was beyond suspicion. Of young Glenshian I know nothing.'

'So *is* Lochdornie beyond suspicion,' answered the elder man. He got up and sought on the mantelshelf for a pine chip to light the still unlighted pipe he was holding, lit the chip at a candle and then, without using it, threw it into the fire. 'But he does not think that I am,' he ended dryly.

'*Archie!* What do you mean?'

Doctor Cameron waited a moment, looking down into the fire. 'You remember that Lochdornie and I were both over in the '49 after the Loch Arkaig gold, and that with Cluny's assistance we contrived to take away quite a deal of it?'

'Yes.'

'Six thousand pounds of that went to Lady Lochiel and her family. Lochdornie – he's an honest man and a bonny fighter, but the notion was put into his head by . . . some third person – Lochdornie accused me of taking the money for myself.'

'And after that,' said Ewen, leaning forward in his chair, his eyes burning, 'you can come over and work side by side with MacPhair of Lochdornie! Why, in your place, I could not trust my fingers near my dirk!'

Doctor Cameron looked at him rather sadly. 'It's well for you, perhaps, that you are not a conspirator, Ewen. A man finds himself treading sometimes in miry ways and slippery on that road, and he's lucky who can come through without someone calling him a blackguard. Remember, Lochdornie's a MacPhair, and our clans have so often been at variance that there's some excuse for him. And indeed I can put up with a MacPhair's doubts of me so long as our Prince does not think that any of the gold has stuck to my fingers; and that he does not, thank God! Heigh-ho, my poor Jean and the children would be going about at this moment in Lille with stouter shoes to their feet if it had!' He smiled rather ruefully. 'Lochdornie and I sink our difference, and get on well enough for our joint purpose. At any rate, I do not have to suspect him; he's as loyal as the day . . . and when all's said, he has never thought me more than mercenary. 'Tis for the Prince's sake, Ewen; *he* sent me, and I came.'

'And to think that it was on Lochdornie's account – or so I believed at the time – that I turned back yesterday!' Ewen said in a tone which suggested that he was not likely ever to repeat the action.

'No, you did it for the sake of our dear Prince,' said his cousin instantly. 'And wasn't that the best motive you could have had?'

Ardroy did not answer; he was frowning. 'Is young Mac-Phair of Glenshian in the Highlands too?'

'No, he remains in London. He is thought to be more useful there.'

'Why, what does he do there? But that brings to my mind Archie – what is this cock-and-bull story which Hector has got hold of, about a plot to kidnap the Elector and his family? He called it "kidnap", but I guessed the term to cover something worse. He coupled it, too, with the name of Alexander Murray of Elibank.'

'Hector is a very indiscreet young man,' said Doctor Cameron.

Ewen's face clouded still more. 'It is true, then, not an idle tale?'

'It is true,' said Doctor Cameron with evident reluctance, 'that there is such a scheme afoot.'

'And I refused to believe or at least approve it!' exclaimed Ewen. 'That indeed was why Hector left the house in anger. I swore that the Prince, who was so set against the idea of an enemy's being taken off, could not know of it, and that you of all men could not possibly have a share in it!'

'I have not, Ewen, and I don't approve. It is a mad scheme, and I doubt – I hope, rather – that it will never come to the ripening. It is quite another business which has brought me to Scotland, a business that for a while yet I'll not fully open, even to you.'

'I have no wish to hear more secrets,' retorted Ardroy with a sigh. 'I like them little enough when I do hear them. It's ill to learn of men who serve the same master and have notions so different. Yes, I must be glad that I don't have to tread those ways, even though I live here idly and do naught for the White Rose, as Hector pointed out to me the other night.'

He saw his cousin look at him with an expression which he could not read, save that it had sadness in it, and what seemed, too, a kind of envy. 'Ewen,' he said, and laid his hand on Ewen's knee, 'when the call came in '45 you gave everything you had, your home, your hopes of happiness, your blood. And you still have clean hands and a single heart. You bring those to the Cause today.'

'Archie, how dare you speak as if you had not the same!' began the younger man quite fiercely. 'You –'

'Don't eat me, lad! God be thanked, I have. But, as I told

you, I am not without unfriends. . . . We'll not speak of that any more. And, Ewen, how can you say that you do naught for the White Rose now when only yesternight you threw aside what might have been your child's sole chance of life in order to warn the Prince's messenger? If that bonny bairn upstairs had died I'd never have been able to look you in the face again. . . . You have named him after poor Major Windham, as you said you should. I see you still have the Major's ring on your finger.'

Ewen looked down at the ring, with a crest not his own, which he always wore, a memento of the English enemy and friend to whom he owed it that he had not been shot, a helpless fugitive, after Culloden.

'Yes, Keithie is named after him. Strangely enough Windham, in his turn, though purely English, was named for a Scot, so he once told me. Six years, Archie, and he lies sleeping there at Morar, yet it seems but yesterday that he died.' Ardroy's eyes darkened; they were full of pain. 'He lies there – and I stand here, because of him. There had been no Keithie if Windham had not rushed between me and the muskets that day on Beinn Laoigh.'

'You have never chanced upon that brute Major Guthrie again, I suppose?'

The sorrow went out of the young man's face and was succeeded by a very grim expression. 'Pray that I do not, Archie, for if I do I shall kill him!'

'My dear Ewen ... do you then resent his treatment of you as much as that?'

'His treatment of me!' exclaimed Ewen, and his eyes began to get very blue. '*Dhé!* I never think of that now! It is what he brought about for Windham. Had it not been for his lies and insinuations, poor Lachlan would never have taken that terrible and misguided notion into his head, and – have done what he did.' For it was Lachlan MacMartin, Ewen's own fosterbrother, who, misapprehending that part which the English officer had played in his chieftain's affairs, had fatally stabbed him just before Ewen's own escape to France, and had then thrown away his own life – a double tragedy for Ardroy.[1]

1. See *The Flight of the Heron*, by the same writer.

'So you charge Major Guthrie with being the real cause of Keith Windham's death?' said his cousin. ' 'Tis a serious accusation, Ewen; on what grounds do you base it?'

'Why, I know everything now,' replied Ewen. 'Soon after my return to Scotland I happened to fall in with one of Guthrie's subalterns, a Lieutenant Paton. He recognized me, for he had been in Guthrie's camp on the Corryarrick road, and in the end I had the whole story, from which it was clear that Guthrie had talked about Windham's "betrayal" of me – false as hell though he knew the notion to be – so openly in those days after my capture that it became the subject of gossip among his redcoats too. And when Lachlan went prowling round the camp in the darkness, he overheard that talk, and believed it. It was Guthrie, no other, who put the fatal dirk in Lachlan's hand. . . . And it is a curious thing, Archie, I have for some time felt a strange presentiment that before long I shall meet someone connected with Keith Windham, and that the meeting will mean much to me. For Alison's sake, and the children's – and for my own too – I hope the man is not Major Guthrie.'

'I hope so, too,' returned Doctor Cameron gravely, knowing that at bottom, under so much that was gentle, patient and civilized, Ardroy kept the passionate and unforgiving temper of the Highlander. 'But is it not more like to be some relative of Major Windham's? Did he not leave a wife, for instance?'

His cousin's eyes softened again. 'I knew so little of his private affairs. I never heard him mention any of his family save his father, who died when he was a child.' He looked at the ring again, at its lion's head surrounded by a fetterlock, and began to twist it on his finger. 'I sometimes think that Windham would have been amused to see me as the father of two children – especially if he had been present at my interview with Donald last Monday.' His own mouth began to twitch at the remembrance. 'He used to laugh at me, I know, in the early days of our acquaintance. I wish he could have seen his namesake.'

'I expect,' said Archibald Cameron, 'that he knows, in some fashion or other, that you do not forget him.'

'Forget him! I never forgot!' exclaimed Ewen, the Celt again. 'And that is why I pray God I do not meet the man who really has my friend's blood upon his hands.'

'If the Fates should bring you into collision, then I hope it may at least be in fair fight – in battle,' observed Doctor Cameron.

'What chance is there of that?' asked Ewen. 'Who's to lead us now? We are poor, broken and scattered – and watched to boot! When Donald's a man, perhaps. ...' He gave a bitter sigh. 'But for all that I live here so tamely under the eyes of the Sassenach, I swear to you, Archie, that I'd give all the rest of my life for one year – one month – of war in which to try our fortunes again, and drive them out of our glens to their own fat fields for ever! I could die happy on the banks of Esk if I thought they'd never cross it again, and the King was come back to the land they have robbed him of! ... But it's a dream; and 'tis small profit being a dreamer, without a sword.'

The exaltation and the fierce pain, flaring up like a sudden fire in the whin, were reflected in Archibald Cameron's face also. He, too, was on his feet.

'Ewen,' he said in an eager voice, 'Ewen, we may yet have an ally, if I can only prepare, as I ame here to do ... for that's my errand – to make ready for another blow, with that help.'

Ardroy was like a man transformed. 'Help! Whose? France is a thrice-broken reed.'

'I'll not tell you yet. But, when the hour strikes, will you get you a sword to your side again, and come?'

'Come! I'd come if I had nothing better than yon claymore hilt in the loch – and if your helper were the Great Sorrow himself! Archie, when, when?'

'In the spring, perchance – if we are ready. No, you cannot help me, Ewen; best go on living quietly here and give no cause for suspicion. I shall hope to find my way to Crieff by Michaelmas, and there I shall meet a good many folk that I must needs see, and after that Lochdornie and I can begin to work the clans in earnest.'

Ewen nodded. Thousands of people, both Highland and Lowland, met at the great annual cattle fair at Crieff, and under cover of buying and selling much other husiness could be transacted.

'O God, I wish the spring were here!' he cried impatiently.

Chapter 5

KEITHIE HAS TOO MANY PHYSICIANS

1

STILL rather pale and wrapped about in a voluminous shawl, little Keith was nevertheless to be seen next afternoon, sitting up in bed making two small round-bodied, stiff-legged animals of wood – known to him as 'deers' – walk across the quilt.

When the door opened and Ewen and Doctor Cameron came in, Alison asked, 'Ought he to be sitting up like this, Doctor Archibald? He seems so much better that I thought ...'

The small invalid eyed Doctor Cameron a trifle suspiciously, and then gave him his shy, angelic smile.

'He *is* much better,' pronounced his physician after a moment. 'Still and on, he must have another dose of that draught.' He got up and poured out something into a glass.

With refusals, with grimaces, and finally with an adorable sudden submission Keithie drank off the potion. But immediately after he had demolished the consolatory scrap of sugar which followed it, he pointed a minute and accusing finger at its compounder, and said, 'Naughty gentleman – naughty, to make Keithie sick!' with so much conviction that Alison began anxiously – 'Darling, do you really – '

It was precisely at that moment that the door was opened and 'Doctor Kincaid from Maryburgh' was announced.

The three adults in the room caught their breaths. None of them had ever imagined that Doctor Kincaid would come *now*. 'Tell the doctor that I will be with him in a moment,' said Alison to the servant visible in the doorway; and then in a hasty aside to Ewen, 'Of course he must not see –' she indicated Doctor Cameron on the other side of the bed.

But there was no time to carry out that precaution, for the

girl, fresh from the wilds, and ignorant of the need for dissimulation, had brought Doctor Kincaid straight up to the sick-room, and there he was, already on the threshold, a little, uncompromising, hard-featured man of fifty, overworked between the claims of Maryburgh, where he dwelt, of its neighbour Fort William, and of the countryside in general. There was no hope of his not seeing Doctor Cameron; still, the chances were heavily against his knowing and recognizing him. Yet who, save a doctor or a relative had a rightful place in this sick-room ... and a doctor was the one thing which they must not admit that guest to be.

So completely were the three taken by surprise that there was scarcely time to think. But Ewen instinctively got in front of his kinsman, while Alison went forward to greet the newcomer with the embarrassment which she could not completely hide, murmuring, 'Doctor Kincaid ... how good of you ... we did not expect ...'

'You are surprised to see me, madam?' asked he, coming forward. 'But I came on a brither o' yours the nicht before last in a sair plight by Loch Treig side, and he begged me to come to Ardroy as soon as possible. But I couldna come before; I'm fair run off ma legs.'

'How is my brother?' asked Alison anxiously. 'I heard of his mishap, but with the child so ill – '

'Ay, ye'd be thinking of yer wean first, nae doot. Aweel, the young fellow's nane too bad, having an unco stout skull, as I jalouse your good man must hae kent when he left him all his lane there.'

'But I arranged with the farmer at Inverlair – ' began Ewen.

'Ou ay, they came fra Inverlair and fetched him, and there he bides,' said Doctor Kincaid. He swept a glance round the room. 'Ye're pretty throng here. Is yon the patient, sitting up in bed?'

'Well, Doctor, he seems, thank God, so much better,' murmured Alison in extenuation of this proceeding. As she led the physician to the bedside she saw with relief that Doctor Archibald had moved quietly to the window and was looking out;

and she thought, 'After all, no one could *know* that he was a doctor!'

Doctor Kincaid examined the little boy, asked some questions, seemed surprised at the answers (from which answers it appeared that his directions had been anticipated), but said that the child was doing well.

The flower-like eyes were upraised to his. 'Then My not have no more nasty drink like that gentleman gived Keithie?' observed their owner, and again a small finger pointed accusingly to Archibald Cameron – to his back this time.

Doctor Kincaid also looked at that back. 'Ah,' he observed sharply, 'so yon gentleman has already been treating the bairn – and the measures ye have taken were of his suggesting? Pray, why did ye no' tell me that, madam?'

Ewen plunged to the rescue. He had been longing for Archie to leave the room, but supposed the latter thought that flight might arouse suspicion. 'My friend, Mr John Sinclair from Caithness, who is paying us a visit, having a certain knowledge of medicine, was good enough. ... Let me make you known to each other – Doctor Kincaid, Mr Sinclair.'

'Mr Sinclair from Caithness' – Ewen had placed his domicile as far away as possible – turned and bowed; there was a twinkle in his eye. But not in Doctor Kincaid's.

'Humph! it seems I wasna sae mickle needed, seeing ye hae gotten a leech to the bairn already! But the young man wi' the dunt on his heid begged me sae sair to come that I listened to him, though I micht hae spared ma pains!'

Alison and Ewen hastened in chorus to express their appreciation of his coming, and Ewen, with an appealing glance at his kinsman, began to move towards the door. One or other of the rival practitioners must certainly be got out of the room. And Archie himself now seemed to be of the same opinion.

'A leech? no, sir, the merest *amateur,* who, now that the real physician has come, will take himself off,' he said pleasantly.

'Nay, I'm through,' said Doctor Kincaid. 'Ye've left me nae mair to do.' And, as he seemed to be going to leave the room in 'Mr Sinclair's' company, Alison hastily appealed for more information about a detail of treatment, so that he had to stay behind.

But outside, as he put a foot into the stirrup, he said, pretty sourly, to Ewen, 'I'm glad the wean's better, Ardroy, but I'd hae been obleeged tae ye if ye hadna garred me come all these miles when ye already had a medical man in the hoose. There was nae need o' me, and I'm a gey busy man.'

'I am very sorry indeed, Doctor,' said Ewen, and could not but feel that the reproach was merited. 'The fact is that – ' He was just on the point of exonerating himself by saying that Mr Sinclair had not yet arrived on Tuesday, nor did they know of his impending visit, but, thinking that plea possibly imprudent, said instead, 'I had no knowledge that Mr Sinclair was so skilled. We . . . have not met recently.'

'Humph,' remarked Doctor Kincaid, now astride his horse. 'A peety that he doesna practise; but maybe he does – in Caithness. At ony rate, he'll be able tae exercise his skill on your brither-in-law – if ye mean tae do ony mair for that young man. For ye'll pardon me if I say that ye havena done much as yet!'

Ewen's colour rose. To have left Hector in that state on a lonely road at nightfall – even despite the measures he had taken for his removal – did indeed show him in a strange and unpleasant light. But it was impossible to explain what had obliged him to do it, and the more than willingness of Hector to be so left. 'Can I have him brought hither from Inverlair without risk to himself?' he asked.

'Ay,' said Kincaid, 'that I think ye micht do if ye send some sort of conveyance – the morn, say, then ye'll hae him here Saturday. He'll no' walk this distance naturally – nor ride it. And indeed if ye send for him he'll be better off here under the care of yer friend Sinclair, than lying in a farm sae mony miles fra Maryburgh; I havena been able to get to him syne. Forbye, Ardroy,' added the doctor, looking at him in a rather disturbing manner, 'the callant talked a wheen gibberish yon-nicht – and not Erse gibberish, neither!'

French, of course; Ewen had already witnessed that propensity! And he groaned inwardly, for what had Hector been saying in that tongue when lightheaded? It was to be hoped, if he had forsaken 'Malbrouck' for more dangerous themes, that Doctor Kincaid was no French scholar; from the epithet which he had just applied to the language it sounded as though he were not. However, the physician then took a curt farewell, and he and his steed jogged away down the avenue, Ewen standing looking after him in perplexity. He did not like to leave Hector at Inverlair; yet if he fetched him here he might be drawing down pursuit on Archie – supposing that suspicion were to fall upon Hector himself by reason of his abstracted papers.

However, by the time he came in again Ewen had arrived at a compromise. Archie should leave the house at once, which might be more prudent in any case. (For though Doctor Kincaid would hardly go and lay information against him at Fort William ... what indeed had he to lay information about? ... he might easily get talking if he happened to be summoned there professionally.) So, as it wanted yet five days to Archie's rendezvous with Lochdornie, and he must dispose himself somewhere, he should transfer himself to the cottage of Angus MacMartin, Ewen's young piper up at Slochd nan Eun, on the farther side of the loch, whence, if necessary, it would be an easy matter to disappear into the mountains.

Doctor Cameron raised no objections to this plan, his small patient being now out of danger; he thought the change would be wise, too, on Ewen's own account. He stipulated only that he should not go until next morning, in case Keithie should take a turn for the worse. But the little boy passed an excellent night, so next morning early Ewen took his guest up the brae, and gave him over to the care of the little colony of Mac-Martins in the crofts at Slochd nan Eun, where he himself had once been a foster-child.

2

The day after, which was Saturday, Ewen's plan of exchanging one compromising visitor for another should have completed itself, but in the early afternoon, to his dismay, the cart which he had sent the previous day to Inverlair to fetch his damaged brother-in-law returned without him. Mr Grant was no longer at the farm; not, reported Angus MacMartin, who had been sent in charge of it, that he had wandered away light-headed, as Ewen immediately feared; no, the farmer had said that the gentleman was fully in his right mind, and had left a message that his friends were not to be concerned on his behalf, and that they would see him again before long.

A good deal perturbed, however, on Alison's account as well, Ewen went up to Slochd nan Eun to tell Doctor Cameron the news. He found his kinsman sitting over the peat fire with a book in his hand, though indeed the illumination of the low little dwelling had not been designed in the interests of study. Doctor Cameron thought it quite likely, though sur-prising, that Hector really had fully recovered, and added some medical details about certain blows on the head and how the disturbance which they cause was often merely temporary.

'Nevertheless,' he concluded, 'one would like to know what notion the boy's got now into that same hot pate of his. You young men – '

'Don't talk like a grandfather, Archie! You are only twelve years older than I!'

'I feel more your senior than that, lad! – How's the bairn?'

'He is leaving his bed this afternoon – since both you and your colleague from Maryburgh allowed it.'

Doctor Cameron laughed. Then he bit his lip, stooped for-ward to throw peat on the fire, and, under cover of the move-ment, pressed his other hand surreptitiously to his side. But Ewen saw him do it.

'What's wrong with you, Archie – are you not well today?'

'Quite well,' answered his cousin, leaning his elbows on his knees. 'But my old companion is troublesome this afternoon – the ball I got at Falkirk, you'll remember.'

'You'll not tell me that you are still carrying that in your body!' cried Ewen in tones of reprobation, and he went down from Slochd nan Eun with an impression of a man in more discomfort than he would acknowledge, and a fresh trouble to worry over. Yet how could he worry in the presence of Keithie, to whom he then paid a visit in the nursery – Keithie, who, now out of bed, sat upon his knee, and in an earnest voice told him a sorrowful tale of how the fairies, having mistaken his 'deers' for cows, had carried them off, as all Highland children knew was their reprehensible habit with cattle. His father, holding the little pliant body close, and kissing him under the chin, said that more probably his deers were somewhere in the house, and that he would find them for him.

Which was the reason why, somewhat later, he went in search of Donald, and discovered him in his mother's room, watching her brush out her dark, rippling hair, which she had evidently been washing, for the room smelt faintly and deliciously of birch.

'Do you want me, my dear?' asked Alison, tossing back her locks.

'Do I not always want you, heart of mine?' But in the glass Ewen saw her smile abruptly die out. Her eyes had wandered away from his, reflected there, to the window, and she stood, all at once, like a statue with uplifted arms.

'What – ' he began ... and in the same moment she said breathlessly, 'Ewen – look!'

He took a step or two forward, and saw, about a quarter of a mile away on the far side of the avenue, a moving growth of scarlet: and more, two thinner streams of it, like poppies, spreading out to right and left to encircle the house. Alison's arms fell; the soft masses of her hair slipped in a coil to her shoulder. 'Soldiers!' shouted Donald, and gave a little skip of excitement.

For a second Ewen also stood like a statue. 'My God! and Archie half-disabled today! ... Have I the time to get up to him? Yes, this way.' He indicated the window at the far side of the room, which looked over the back premises. 'Listen, my heart, and you, too, Donald! If the soldiers cut me off, and I cannot get up to Slochd nan Eun to warn him – if I see that it is hopeless to attempt it, then I shall run from them. Likely enough they'll think I am the man they're after, and I shall lead them as long a chase as I can, in order to give Archie time to get away ... for some of the MacMartins may meanwhile take the alarm. Do you understand?'

'Oh, Ewen . . .' said his wife, hesitating. He took her hands.

'And should I be caught ... nay, I think I'll *let* myself be caught in the end ... and they bring me to the house, you may feign to be agitated at the sight of me, but you must not know me for who I am; you must let them think that I am the man you are hiding. But you must not call me Doctor Cameron neither – you must not name me at all! If they take me off to Fort William, all the better. By the time they have got me there Archie will be miles away. Then all Colonel Leighton can do, when he recognizes me, will be to send me back again. Heaven grant, though,' he added, 'that the officer with these men does not know me! – Dearest love,' for Alison had turned rather white, 'remember that it was for Keithie's sake – for our sakes – that Archie came here at all! I must get him safely away if ... if it should cost more than that!'

'Yes,' said Alison a little faintly. 'Yes ... go – I will do as you say.'

He held her to him for an instant and the next was throwing up the sash of the far window. 'You understand too, Donald? And, Alison, I think you will have to tell a lie, and say that I myself am away from home. – One thing more' – Ewen paused with a leg over the window-sill – 'if I fail to warn Archie, which I'll contrive to let you know somehow, you must send another messenger, provided that messenger can get away without being followed.'

He hung by his hands a moment and dropped: a loud cackling of astonished hens announced his arrival below. Lady Ardroy went back to the glass and began hastily to fasten up her hair.

'How near are they, Donald? – Run quickly to the kitchen and tell the servants to say, if they are asked, that the laird went away to Inverness ... yesterday ... and that if they see him they are to pretend not to know him. And then come back to me.'

Donald left the the room like a stone from a catapult. This was great sport – and fancy a lie's being enjoined by those authorities who usually regarded the mere tendency to one as so reprehensible!

Chapter 6

'WHO IS THIS MAN?'

1

WHEN the officer in charge of the party of redcoats, having set his men close round the house of Ardroy, went in person to demand admittance, it was no servant, out of whom he might have surprised information, who answered his peremptory knocking, but (doubtless to his annoyance) the châtelaine herself.

Captain Jackson, however, saluted civilly enough. 'Mrs Cameron, I think?' for, being English, he saw no reason to give those ridiculous courtesy titles to the wives of petty landowners.

'Yes, sir,' responded Alison with dignity. 'I am Mrs Cameron. I saw you from above, and, since I have no notion why you have come, I descended in order to find out.'

'If I may enter, madam, I will tell you why I have come,' responded the officer promptly.

'By all means enter,' said Alison with even more of stateliness (hoping he would not notice that she was still out of breath with haste) and, waiting while he gave an order or two, preceded him into the parlour. Captain Jackson then became aware that a small boy had somehow slipped to her side.

He took a careful look round the large room, and meanwhile Alison, studying his thin, sallow face, decided that she had never seen this officer before, and hoped, for the success of the plan, that neither had he ever seen Ewen. Behind him, through the open parlour door, she perceived her hall full of scarlet coats and white cross-belts and breeches.

'I am here, madam,' now said the invader, fixing her with a meaning glance, 'as I think you can very well guess, in the King's name, with a warrant to search this house, in which

60

there is every reason to believe that the owner is sheltering a rebel.'

'Mr Cameron is away, sir,' responded Alison. 'How, therefore, can he be sheltering anyone?'

'Away?' exclaimed Captain Jackson suspiciously. 'How is that? for he was certainly at home on Thursday!'

('The day of Doctor Kincaid's visit,' thought Alison. 'Then he *did* give the alarm!')

'Mr Cameron was here on Thursday,' repeated Captain Jackson with emphasis.

'I did not deny it,' said Alison, beginning to be nettled at his tone. 'Nevertheless he went away yesterday.'

'Whither?' was the next question rapped out at her. 'Whither, and for what purpose?'

Alison's own Highland temper began to rise now, and with the warming uprush came almost a relief in her own statement. 'Does "the King" really demand to know that, sir? He went to Inverness on affairs.'

By this time Captain Jackson had no doubt realized that he had to do with a lady of spirit. 'Perhaps, then, madam,' he suggested, 'Mr Cameron deputed the task of hiding the rebel to you? I think you would do it well. I must search the house thoroughly. Are any of the rooms locked?'

'Yes, one,' said Lady Ardroy. 'I will come with you and unlock it if you wish to see in.'

'No, you'll stay where you are, madam, if you please,' retorted the soldier. 'I will trouble you for your keys – all your keys. I do not wish to damage any of your property by breaking it open.'

Biting her lip, Alison went in silence to her writing-desk. Captain Jackson took the bunch without more ado, and a moment later Alison and her eldest son were alone ... locked in.

And when she heard the key turned on her the colour came flooding into her face, and she stood very erect, tapping with one foot upon the floor, in no peaceable mood.

'Mother,' said Donald, tugging at her skirt, 'the redcoat has not locked *this* door!' For Captain Jackson had either overlooked or chosen to disregard that, in the far corner of the room, which led into the kitchen domain.

Alison hesitated for a moment. No, better to stay here quietly, as if she had no cause for anxiety; and better not as yet to attempt to send another messenger to Slochd nan Eun who, by blundering, might draw on Doctor Cameron just the danger to be averted. So for twenty minutes or more she waited with Donald in the living-room, wondering, calculating, praying for patience, sometimes going to the windows and looking out, hearing now and then heavy footsteps about the house and all the sounds of a search which she knew would be fruitless, and picturing the havoc which the invaders were doubtless making of her household arrangements. Perhaps, in spite of Morag's presence, they were frightening little Keith – a thought which nearly broke her resolution of staying where she was.

Yet, as the minutes ticked away with the slowly fading daylight outside, and nothing happened, her spirits began to rise. Ewen had evidently not been stopped; indeed, if he once got safely beyond the policies it was unlikely that he would be. He had probably reached Slochd nan Eun unmolested. Surely, too, he would remain there until the soldiers had gone altogether? And feeling at last some security on that score, Alison sat down and took up a piece of sewing.

But she had not even threaded her needle before there was a stir and a trampling outside the house, and she jumped up and ran to the window. More soldiers . . . and someone in the midst of them, tightly held – her husband!

And in that moment Alison knew, and was ashamed of the knowledge, that she must at the bottom of her heart have been hoping that if anyone was captured. . . . No, no, she had not hoped that! For Doctor Cameron's life was in jeopardy, while nothing could happen to Ewen save unpleasantness. In expiation of that half-wish she braced herself to the dissimulation which Ewen had enjoined. She drew the boy beside her away from the window.

'The soldiers have caught your father, Donald, after all. Remember that you are to pretend not to know who he is, nor what he is doing here.'

The little boy nodded with bright eyes, and held her hand rather tightly.

'Will they do anything to me, Mother, for – saying what is not true?'

'No, darling, not this time. And if they take Father away to Fort William, it is only what he hopes they will do; and he will soon come back to us.'

By this time the door of the parlour was being unlocked, and in another moment Captain Jackson was striding into the room.

'Bring him in,' he commanded, half-turning, and the redcoats brought in a rather hot, dishevelled Ardroy, with a smear of blood down his chin, and with four soldiers, no less, holding him firmly by wrists and arms and shoulders. It was not difficult for Alison to show the agitation demanded; indeed there was for an instant the risk that it might exceed its legitimate bounds; but she had herself in hand again at once. Her husband gave her one glance and shook his head almost imperceptibly to show that he had not succeeded in his attempt. Then he looked away again and studied the antlers over the hearth while the sergeant in charge of him made his report, the gist of which was that the prisoner, coming unexpectedly upon them near the lake up there, had led them the devil of a chase; indeed, had he not tripped and fallen, he might have escaped them altogether.

'Tripped!' thought Alison scornfully – as if Ewen with his perfect balance and stag's fleetness, ever tripped when he was running! He had thrown himself down for them to take, the fools! and that this really was the case she knew from the passing twitch of amusement at the corner of her husband's blood-stained mouth. But, seeing him standing there in the power of the *saighdearan deary* – oh, she wished he had not done it!

'Well, have you anything to say, "Mr Sinclair"?' demanded Captain Jackson, planting himself in front of the prize. And at the mention of that name both Ewen and his wife knew for certain that they owed this visitation to Doctor Kincaid.

'Not to you, sir. But I should wish to offer my apologies to Lady Ardroy,' said Ewen, with an inclination of the head in Alison's direction, 'for bringing about an ... an annoying incident in her house.'

Captain Jackson shrugged his shoulder. 'Very polite of you, egad! But, in that case, why have you come here in the first instance?' He moved away a little, got out a paper, and studied it. Then he looked up, frowning.

'Who are you?' he demanded.

'Does not your paper tell you that?' asked Ewen pleasantly.

Alison wondered if the officer thought that he was Lochdornie; but Lochdornie was, she believed, a man between fifty and sixty, and Doctor Cameron in the forties. Surely this officer could not take Ewen for either? Her heart began to lift a little. Captain Jackson, after looking, still with the frown from Ewen to the paper, and from the paper to Ewen, suddenly folded it up and glared at her.

'Madam, who is this man?'

'If I have sheltered him, as you state, is it likely that I should tell you?' asked Alison quietly.

'Call the servants!' said Captain Jackson to a soldier near the door. 'No, wait a moment!' He turned again and pointed at Donald, standing at his mother's side, his eyes fixed on the captive, who, for his part, was now looking out of the window. 'You, boy, do you know who this man is?'

'Must you drag in a small child – ' began Alison indignantly.

'If you will not answer, yes,' retorted the Englishman. 'And he is quite of an age to supplement your unwillingness, madam. Come, boy' – he advanced a little on Donald, 'don't be frightened; I am not going to hurt you. Just tell me now, have you ever seen this man before?'

The question appeared to Donald extremely amusing, and, since he was not at all frightened, but merely excited, he gave a little laugh.

'Oh yes, sir.'

'How often?'

His mother's hand on his shoulder gave him a warning pressure. 'I . . . I could not count.'

'Six times – seven times? More? He comes here often, then?

Donald considered. One could not say that Father *came* here; he *was* here. 'No, sir.'

'He does not come often, eh? How long has he been here this time?'

Donald, a little perplexed, glanced up at his mother. What was he to say to this? But Captain Jackson now took steps to prevent his receiving any more assistance from that source. He stretched out a hand.

'No, thank you, Mrs Cameron! If you won't speak you shan't prompt either! Come here, boy.' He drew Donald, without roughness, away, and placed him more in the middle of the room, with his back to his mother. 'Have you ever heard this gentleman called "Sinclair"?' he asked. 'Now, tell the truth!'

Donald told it. 'No, never!' he replied, shaking his golden head.

'I thought as much! Well now, my boy, I'll make a guess at what you *have* heard him called, and you shall tell me if I guess right, eh?' And Captain Jackson, attempting heartiness, smiled somewhat sourly.

'I'll not promise,' said the child cautiously.

'The young devil has been primed!' said the soldier under his breath. Then he shot his query at him as suddenly as possible. 'His name is the same as yours – *Cameron!*'

Taken aback by this, Donald wrinkled his brows and said nothing.

'With "Doctor" in front of it – "Doctor Cameron"?' pursued the inquisitor. 'Now, have I not guessed right?'

'Oh no, sir,' said Donald, relieved.

Ewen was no longer looking out of the window, and he was frowning more than Captain Jackson had frowned. He had never foreseen Donald's being harried with questions. 'Do you imagine,' he broke in suddenly, 'that a man in my shoes is like to have his real name flung about in the hearing of a small child?'

Captain Jackson paid no heed to this remark. 'Now, my boy, you can remember the name quite well if you choose, of that I'm sure. If you don't choose . . .' He paused suggestively.

'Take your hand off that child's shoulder!' commanded Ardroy in a voice so dangerous that, though he had not moved, his guards instinctively took a fresh grip of him.

T - c
65

'Oho!' said Captain Jackson, transferring his attention at once from the little boy, 'is that where the wind blows from? This young mule is a relative of yours?'

'Is that the only reason a man may have for objecting to see a small child bullied?' asked Ewen hotly. ' 'Tis not the only one in Scotland, I assure you, whatever you English may feel about the matter.'

But Captain Jackson declined to follow this red herring. 'It lies entirely with you, "Mr Sinclair", to prevent any further questioning.'

'No, it does not!' declared Ewen. 'I have told you once, sir, that a man in my position does not have his real name cried to all the winds of heaven. Lady Ardroy herself is ignorant of it: she took me in knowing only that I was in need of rest and shelter. I do not wish her to learn it, lest Mr Cameron, when he returns, be not best pleased to find whom she has been housing in his absence. But I will tell you my name at Fort William – if, indeed, your commanding officer there do not find it out first.'

This excursion into romance – a quite sudden inspiration on its author's part – really shook Captain Jackson for a moment, since he was well aware that there were divisions, and sharp ones, among the Jacobites. Yet from Doctor Kincaid's account Ewen Cameron himself, two days ago, had answered for "Mr Sinclair". As he stood undecided, enlightenment came to him from a most unexpected quarter.

'Father,' suddenly said a high, clear little voice, 'Father, has you finded them?'

'What's this?' The English officer swung round – indeed, every man in the room turned to look at the small figure which, quite unobserved, even by Alison, had strayed in through the open door. And before anyone had tried to stop him Keith had pattered forward and seized his father round the legs. 'My comed down to look for mine deers,' he announced, smiling up at him. 'Who is all these peoples?'

It was the last query about identity asked that evening. Ewen saw that the game was up, and, the soldiers who held him having, perhaps unconsciously, loosed their hold at this gentle and unexpected arrival, he stooped and caught up the wrecker of his gallant scheme. 'No, my wee bird, I have not found your deers ... I have been found myself,' he whispered, and could not keep a smile from the lips which touched that velvet cheek.

But the implications of this unlooked-for greeting had now burst upon Captain Jackson with shattering force. Half-inarticulate with rage, he strode forward and shook his fist in the prisoner's face. 'You ... you liar! You are yourself Ewen Cameron!'

'Pray do not terrify this child also,' observed the culprit coolly, for Keithie, after one look at the angry soldier, had hidden his face on his father's shoulder. 'He is only three years old, and not worthy of your attentions!'

Captain Jackson fairly gibbered. 'You think that you have fooled me – you and your lady there! You'll soon find out at Fort William who is the fool! Put that child down!'

'Please make that red gentleman go away!' petitioned a small voice from the neighbourhood of Ardroy's neck.

'That's out of my power, I fear, my darling,' replied the young man. 'And you had better go to Mother now.' Since, with the child in his arms, not a soldier seemed disposed to hinder him, he walked calmly across the room and put Keithie into Alison's, whence he contemplated Captain Jackson with a severe and heavenly gaze.

'Well, now that this charming domestic interlude is over,' snapped that officer, 'perhaps, sir, you will vouchsafe some explanation of your conduct in leading my men this dance, and in striving to hide your identity in your own house in this ridiculous fashion? "When Mr Cameron returns", forsooth!'

Again Ewen, usually a punctiliously truthful person, was inspired to a flight of imagination. 'I admit that it was foolish of me,' he replied with every appearance of candour. 'But I saw you and your men coming, and having been "out", as you probably know, in the Forty-five, I thought it better to instruct my wife to say that I was from home, and left the house by a back window. I see now that I should have done better to show more courage, and stay and face your visit out.'

During this explanation Captain Jackson, his hands behind

his back, was regarding the self-styled coward very fixedly. 'Do you think that you can gull me into believing that you led my men that chase because of anything you did six or seven years ago, Mr Ewen Cameron? No; you were playing the decoy – and giving the man you are hiding here a chance to get away!'

Ardroy shrugged his shoulders. 'Have it your own way, sir,' he said indifferently. 'I know that a simple explanation of a natural action is seldom believed.'

'No, only by simpletons!' retorted Captain Jackson. 'However, you can try its effects upon Lieutenant-Governor Leighton at Fort William, for to Fort William you will go, Mr Cameron, without delay. And do not imagine that I shall accompany you; I have not finished looking for your friend from Caithness, and, when you are no longer here to draw the pursuit, it may be that I shall find him.'

It was true that Ewen had contemplated being taken to Fort William, but not exactly in his own character and upon his own account. This was a much less attractive prospect. However, there was no help for it, and the only thing that mattered was that Archie should get safely away. If only he could be certain that he had! Surely the MacMartins. . . . His thought sped up to Slochd nan Eun.

'Take two file of men, sergeant,' said Captain Jackson, 'and set out with Mr Cameron at once. You can reach High Bridge by nightfall, and lie there.'

At that Alison came forward; she had put down Keithie and was holding him by the hand; he continued to regard the English officer with the same unmitigated disapproval. 'Do you mean, sir, that you are sending my husband to Fort William at once – this very evening?'

'Yes, madam. I have really no choice,' replied the soldier, who appeared to have regained control of his temper. 'But if he will give me his word of honour to go peaceably, and make no attempt to escape by the way, I need not order any harsh measures for the journey. Will you do that, Mr Cameron?'

Ewen came back to his own situation, and to a longing to feel Keithie in his arms again for a moment. 'Yes, sir, I pledge you my word as a gentleman to give no trouble on the road. Indeed, why should I?' he added. 'I am innocent.'

'But if Mr Cameron is to go at once,' objected Alison, 'pray allow me time to put together a few necessaries for him, since however short a while he stays at Fort William he will need them.'

Instant departure was not so urgent that Captain Jackson could reasonably refuse this request. 'Yes, you may do that, madam,' he replied a trifle stiffly, 'provided that you are not more than a quarter of an hour about the business; otherwise the party may be benighted before they can reach High Bridge.' And he went quite civilly to hold the door for her.

As Alison passed her husband she looked at him hard with a question in her eyes; she wanted to be sure. Again he gave an almost imperceptible shake of the head. She drew her brows together, and with a child on either side of her, the elder lagging and gazing half-frightened, half-admiringly, at his captive father, went out of the room. Captain Jackson did the same; but he left four men with muskets behind him.

Of these Ewen took no notice, but began walking slowly up and down the room dear to him by so many memories. Now that the moment of being taken from his home was upon him he did not like it. But he would soon be back, he told himself. How heavily would he be fined by the Government for this escapade? However little, it would mean a still harder struggle to make both ends meet. But no price was too high to pay for Archie's life – or for Keithie's. Both of them were tangled up somehow in this payment. He wondered too, with some uneasiness, how and why the redcoats whom he had allowed to capture him had been right up by Loch na h-Iolaire when he came upon them. *Dhé!* that had been a chase, too – he was young enough to have enjoyed it.

The door was opened again; there was Alison, with a little packet in her hand, and Captain Jackson behind her. 'You can take leave of your wife, Mr Cameron,' said he, motioning him to come to her at the door.

But only, it was evident, under his eyes and in his hearing.

So nothing could be said about Archie; even Gaelic was not safe, for it was quite possible that the Englishman had picked up a few words. Under the officer's eyes, then, Ardroy took his wife in his arms and kissed her.

'I shall not be away for long, my dear. God bless you. Kiss the boys for me.'

She looked up into his eyes and said with meaning, 'I will try to do all you wish while you are away,' a wifely utterance to which Captain Jackson could hardly take exception.

And three minutes later, with no more intimate leave-taking than that, she was at the window watching her husband being marched away under the beeches of the avenue with his little guard.

'I am sorry for this, madam,' said the voice of Captain Jackson behind her. 'But, if you'll forgive me for saying so, Mr Cameron has brought it upon himself. Now understand, if you please, that no one is to leave the house on any pretext; I have not finished yet. But you are free to go about your ordinary occupations, and I'll see that you are not molested – so long as my order is observed.'

For that Alison thanked him, and went upstairs to solace her loneliness by putting little Keith to bed. She had already tried to send Morag – the easiest to come at of the servants – up the brae, and had not found it feasible. And surely, surely Doctor Cameron must have taken the alarm by now and be away? Still, there was always her promise to Ewen – a promise which it began to seem impossible to carry out.

2

Yet, in a sense, that promise was already in process of being kept, though in a manner of which Alison was fortunately ignorant. At the very moment when she had finally succeeded in satisfying her younger son's critical inquiries about 'the gentleman downstairs that was so angry', her eldest born, whom she had last seen seated on the stairs gazing down through the rails with deep interest at the group of soldiers in the hall, was half-way between the house and Loch na h-Iolaire, his heart beating rapidly with excitement, triumph, and another less agreeable emotion.

Both in courage and intelligence Donald was old for his years. He knew that his mother had tried in vain to send Morag out of the house while she was making up the packet for Father. The resplendent idea had then come to him of himself carrying out Father's wish, and warning Doctor Cameron of the presence of the soldiers, of which he partially at least grasped the importance. As for getting out of the house, perhaps the soldiers at the various doors would not pay much attention to him, whom they probably considered just a little boy – though it was scarcely so that he thought of himself. Perhaps also they would not be aware that never in his life before had he been out so late alone. He could say that he had lost a ball in the shrubbery, and that would be true, for so he had, about a month ago; and even if it had not been true, lies seemed to be strangely permissible today.

As it happened, Donald did not have to employ the plea about the lost ball, for in wandering round the back premises he came on a door which was not guarded at all. Its particular sentry was even then escorting his father towards Fort William, and by some oversight had not been replaced. A moment or two afterwards Donald was looking back in elation from the edge of the policies on the lighted windows of the house of Ardroy.

That was a good ten minutes ago. Now ... he was wishing that he had brought Luath with him. ... It was such a strange darkness – not really dark, but an eerie kind of half-light. And the loch, which he was now approaching ... what an odd ghostly shine the water had between the trees! He had never seen it look like that before. This was, past all doubt, the hour of that dread Thing, the water-horse.

And Donald's feet began to falter a little in the path as he came nearer and nearer to the Loch of the Eagle, so friendly in the day, so very different now. No child in the Highlands but had heard many a story of water-horse and kelpie and *uruisg*, however much his elders might discourage such narratives. It was true that Father had told him there were no such things as these fabled inhabitants of loch and stream and mountain-side, but the awful fact remained that Morag had a second cousin in Kintail who had been carried off by an *each uisge*.

Donald's steps grew slower still. He was now almost skirting Loch na h-Iolaire in the little track through the heather and bracken, where the pine branches swayed and whispered and made the whole atmosphere, too, much darker and more alarming. Then he thought of those who had fought at the great battle before he was born, of cousin Ian Stewart and the broken claymore, of his father, of the dead Chief whose name he bore, and went onwards with a brave and beating heart. But there were such strange sounds all round him – noises and cracklings which he had never heard in the day, open-air little boy though he was; and once he jumped violently as something shadowy and slim ran across his very path.

And then Donald's heart gave a bound and seemed to stop altogether. Something was trampling through the undergrowth on his right. There broke from him a little sound too attenuated for a shriek, a small puppy-like whimper of dismay.

'Who's there?' called out a man's voice sharply. 'Who's there – answer me!'

At least, then, it was not a water-horse. 'I'm ... I'm Donald Cameron of Ardroy,' replied the adventurer in quavering tones, his eyes fixed on the dark, dim shape now visible, from the waist upwards, among the surging waves of bracken.

'Donald!' it exclaimed. 'What in the name of the Good Being are you doing here at this hour? Don't be frightened, child – 'tis your uncle Hector.' And the apparition pushed through the fern and bent over him. 'Are you lost, my boy?'

Immensely relieved, Donald looked up at the young man. He had not seen him for nearly two years, but he had often heard of the uncle who was a soldier of the King of France. Evidently, too, Uncle Hector had lately been in some battle, for he wore round his head a bandage which showed white in the dusk.

'No, Uncle Hector, I'm not lost. I am going up to Slochd nan Eun to tell Doctor Cameron that there are some soldiers come after him, and that he must go away quickly.'

'Doctor Cameron!' exclaimed his uncle in surprise. 'What on earth is *he* doing at Ardroy? I thought he never came here now. You are sure it was Doctor Cameron, Donald – and not Mr MacPhair of Lochdornie?'

'No, I know it was Doctor Cameron. He stayed in our house first; he came because – because Keithie was ill.' His head went down for a second. 'He made him well again. The other doctor from Maryburgh came too. Then Doctor Cameron went up to stay with Angus MacMartin. And if you please I must go to Slochd nan Eun at once.'

But his young uncle was staring down at him, and saying as though he were speaking to himself, 'Then it was *he* who is just gone away from Slochd nan Eun with Angus, only they were so discreet they'd not name him to me! – No, my little hero, there's no need for you to go any farther. I have just come from Angus's cottage myself, and they told me the gentleman was gone some time since, because of the soldiers down at the house. And, by the way, are the soldiers still there?'

'Yes, and some of them have taken Father away to Fort William. They ran after him – he got out of a window – and they caught him and thought at first he was Doctor Cameron. Father wanted them to think that,' explained Donald with a sort of vicarious pride.

Hector Grant's brow grew blacker under the bandage. *'Mon Dieu, mon Dieu, quel malheur!* – I must see your mother, Donald. Go back, *laochain*, and try to get her to come up to me here by the loch. I'll take you a part of the way.'

'You are sure, Uncle Hector,' asked Donald anxiously, 'that Doctor Cameron is gone away?'

'Good child!' said Uncle Hector appreciatively. *'Yes, foi de gentilhomme,* Donald, he is gone. There is no need for you to continue this nocturnal adventure. Come along.'

'I don't think, Uncle Hector,' Donald said doubtfully, as they began to move away, 'that the soldiers will let Mother come out to see you. Nobody was to leave the house, they said. They did not see me come out. But perhaps they would let you go in?'

Uncle Hector stopped. 'They'll let me in fast enough, I

warrant – but would they let me come out again? . . . Perhaps after all I had better come no nearer. Can you go back from here alone, Donald – but indeed I see you can, since you have such a stout heart.' (The heart in question fell a little at this flattering deduction.) 'By the way, you say Keithie is better – is he quite recovered?'

'Keithie? He is out of bed today. Indeed,' said Keithie's senior rather scornfully, ' 'tis a pity he is, for he came downstairs by his lane when the soldiers were here and did a very silly thing.' And he explained in what Keithie's foolishness had consisted. 'So 'twas he that spoilt Father's fine plan . . . which *I* knew all about!'

' "Fine plan" – I wonder what your mother thought of it?' once more commented Hector Grant half to himself. 'Well, Donald, give her a kiss for me, and tell her that I will contrive somehow to see her, when the soldiers have gone. Meanwhile I think I'll return to the safer hospitality of Meall Achadh. Now run home – she'll be anxious about you.'

He stooped and kissed the self-appointed messenger, and gave him an encouraging pat.

'Good night, Uncle Hector,' said Donald politely. 'I will tell Mother.' And he set off at a trot which soon carried him out of sight in the dusk.

'And now, what am I going to do?' asked Lieutenant Hector Grant in French of his surroundings. 'This is a pretty coil that I have set on foot!'

Chapter 7

A GREAT MANY LIES

1

It is undoubtedly easier to invite durance than to get free of it again. So Ewen found after his interview next day with old Lieutenant-Governor Leighton, now in command at Fort William, who was rather querulous, declaring with an injured air that, from what he had been told about Mr Cameron of Ardroy, he should not have expected such conduct from him. 'However,' he finished pessimistically, 'disloyalty that is bred in the bone will always out, I suppose; and once a Cameron always a Cameron.'

Since Ewen's captor and accuser, Captain Jackson, was still absent, the brief interview produced little of value either to Colonel Leighton or himself, and Ardroy spent a good deal of that Sunday pacing round and round his bare though by no means uncomfortable place of confinement, wishing fervently that he knew whether Archie had got away in safety. Never, never, if any ill befell him, would he forgive himself for having brought him to the house The next day Colonel Leighton had him in for examination again, chiefly in order to confront him with Captain Jackson, now returned empty-handed from his raid, and it was Ewen's late visitor who took the more prominent part in the proceedings, either questioning the prisoner himself or prompting his elderly superior in a quite obvious manner. The reason for this procedure Ewen guessed to lie in the fact that Leighton was a newcomer at Fort William, having succeeded only a few months ago the astute Colonel Crauford, an adept at dealing with Highland difficulties, and one on whom Captain Jackson seemed to be desirous of modelling himself, if not his colonel.

Ewen steadily denied having had any doubtful person in his house, 'Mr Sinclair', whose presence he could not entirely explain away, being, as he had already stated, a friend on a visit, which visit had ended the day before the arrival of the military. He stuck to his story that when he himself had seen the soldiers approaching his courage had failed him, and he had dropped from a window and run from them.

'If that is so, Mr Cameron,' said the Lieutenant-Governor (echoing Captain Jackson), 'then you must either have had a guilty conscience or you were playing the decoy. And I suspect that it was the latter, since you do not look the sort of man who would get out of a window at the mere approach of danger.'

So Ewen declared that appearances were deceitful, and again pointed out his exemplary behaviour since his return to Scotland. He desired no more, he said, than to go on living quietly upon his land. It was no doubt very tame and unheroic thus to plead for release, but what was the use of remaining confined here if he could avoid it? And for a while after that he sat there – having been provided with a chair – hardly listening to Colonel Leighton as he prosed away, with occasional interruptions from his subordinate, but wondering what Alison was doing at this moment, and whether Keithie were any the worse for his fateful excursion downstairs; and scarcely noticing that the Colonel had ceased another of his homilies about disloyalty to listen to a young officer who had come in with some message – until his own name occurring in the communication drew his wandering attention.

The Colonel had become quite alert. 'Bring him up here at once,' he said to the newcomer, and, turning to the listless prisoner, added, 'Mr Cameron, here's a gentleman just come and given himself up to save you, so he says, from further molestation on his behalf.'

He had Ewen's attention now! For one horrible moment Ardroy felt quite sick. He had the wild half-thought that Archie . . . but no, Archie was incapable of so wrong and misguided an action as throwing away his liberty and wrecking his mission merely to save him from imprisonment.

Then through the open door came the young officer again, and after him, with a bandage about his head and a smile upon his lips, Hector.

Ewen suppressed a gasp, but the colour which had left it came back to his face. He got up from his chair astounded, and not best pleased at this crazy deed. Hector Grant did not seem to find *his* situation dull; he had about him an air which it would have been unkind, though possible, to call a swagger; which air, however, dropped from him a little at the sight of his brother-in-law, in whose presence he had evidently not expected so soon to find himself.

Colonel Leighton, however, glanced hopefully at the voluntary captive. 'Well, sir, and so you have come to give yourself up. On what grounds, may I ask.'

'Because,' Hector answered him easily, 'I heard that my brother-in-law, Mr Cameron of Ardroy here present, had been arrested on the charge of having entertained a suspicious stranger at his house. Now as I was myself that supposed stranger – '

'Ah,' interrupted Colonel Leighton, shaking his head sagely, 'I knew I was right in my conviction that Mr Cameron was lying when he asserted that he had sheltered nobody! I knew that no one of his name was to be trusted.'

'He was not "sheltering" me, sir,' replied Hector coolly. 'And therefore I have come of my own free will to show you how baseless are your suspicions of him. For if a man cannot have his wife's brother to visit him without being haled off to prison – '

' "His wife's brother". Who are you, then? You have not yet told us,' remarked Captain Jackson.

'Lieutenant Hector Grant, of the régiment d'Albanie in the service of His Most Christian Majesty the King of France.'

'You have papers to prove that?'

'Not on me.'

'And why not?' asked the other soldier.

'Why should I carry my commission with me when I come to pay a private visit to my sister?' asked Hector. (Evidently, thought Ewen, he was not going to admit the theft of any of his papers, though he himself suspected that the young man did, despite his denial, carry his commission with him. He wondered, and was sure that Hector was wondering too, whether the missing documents were not all the time in Colonel Leighton's hands.)

'And that was all your business in Scotland – to visit your sister?'

'Is not that sufficient?' asked the affectionate brother. 'I had not seen Lady Ardroy for a matter of two years, and she is my only near relative – '

But here Captain Jackson interrupted him. 'If it was upon your behalf, Mr Grant, that Mr Cameron found it necessary to run so far and to tell so many lies on Saturday, then he must be greatly mortified at seeing you here now. I doubt if it was for you that he went through all that. But if, on the other hand, you *were* the cause of his performances, then your visit cannot have been so innocuous as you pretend.'

Hector was seen to frown. This officer was too sharp. He had outlined a nasty dilemma, and the young Highlander hardly knew upon which of its horns to impale himself and Ewen.

The Colonel now turned heavily upon Ardroy.

'*Is* this young man your brother-in-law, Mr Cameron?'

'Certainly he is, sir.'

'And he did stay at your house upon a visit?'

Awkward to answer, that, considering the nature of Hector's 'stay' and its exceeding brevity. Hector himself prudently looked out of a window. 'Yes, he did pay me a visit.'

'And when did he arrive?'

Ewen decided that the whole truth was best. 'Last Monday evening.'

'I should be glad to know for what purpose he came.'

'You have heard, sir. He is, I repeat, my wife's brother.'

'But that fact, Mr Cameron,' said Colonel Leighton weightily, 'does not render him immune from suspicion, especially when one considers his profession. He is a Jacobite, or he would not be in the service of the King of France.'

'You know quite well, sir,' countered Ewen, 'that the King of France has by treaty abandoned the Jacobite cause.'

'*Was* it on Mr Grant's account that you behaved as you did on Saturday?' pressed the Colonel.

But Ewen replying that he did not feel himself bound to

answer that question, the commanding officer turned to Hector again. 'On what day, Mr Grant, did you terminate your visit to Mr Cameron?'

'On the day that your men invaded his house – Saturday,' answered Hector, driven to this unfortunate statement by a desire to give colour to Ewen's 'performances' on that day.

'But Mr Cameron has just told us that "Mr Sinclair" left the previous day – Friday,' put in Captain Jackson quickly, and Hector bit his lip. Obviously, it had a very awkward side, this ignorance of what Ewen had already committed himself to.

Captain Jackson permitted himself a smile. 'At any rate, you were at Ardroy on Thursday, and saw Doctor Kincaid when he went to visit the sick child.'

This Hector was uncertain whether to deny or avow. He therefore said nothing.

'But since you are trying to make us believe that you are the mysterious "Mr Sinclair" from Caithness who was treating him,' pursued Captain Jackson, 'you must have seen Doctor Kincaid.'

'I see no reason why I should not have done what I could for my own nephew,' answered Hector, doubling off on a new track.

'Quite so,' agreed Captain Jackson. 'Then, since your visit was purely of a domestic character, one may well ask why Mr Cameron was at such pains on that occasion to pass you off, not as a relation, but as a friend from the North? . . . And why were you then so much older, a man in the forties, instead of in the twenties, as you are today?'

'Was there so much difference in my appearance?' queried Hector innocently. 'I was fatigued; I had been sitting up all night with the sick child.'

'Pshaw – we are wasting time!' declared Captain Jackson. 'This is not "Mr Sinclair"!' And the Colonel echoed him with dignity. 'No, certainly not.'

'Is not Doctor Kincaid in the fort this morning, sir?' asked the Captain, leaning towards him.

'I believe he is. Go and request him to come here at once, if you please, Mr Burton,' said the Colonel to the subaltern who had brought Hector in. 'And then we shall settle this question once for all.'

By this time Ewen had resumed his seat. Hector, his hands behind his back, appeared to be whistling a soundless air between his teeth. It was impossible to say whether he were regretting his fruitless effort – for plainly it was going to be fruitless – but at all events he was showing a good front to the enemy.

Doctor Kincaid hurried in, with his usual air of being very busy. 'You sent for me, Colonel?'

'Yes, Doctor, if you please. Have you seen this young man before – not Mr Cameron of Ardroy here, but the other.'

'Perhaps Doctor Kincaid does not greatly care to look at me,' suggested Ewen.

The doctor threw him a glance. 'I had ma duty to do, Ardroy.' Then he looked, as desired, at the younger prisoner. 'Losh, I should think I had seen him before! God's name young man, you're gey hard in the heid! 'Tis the lad I found half-doited on Loch Treig side Tuesday nicht syne wi' a dunt in it of which yon's the sign!' He pointed to the bandage.

'Tuesday night, you say, Doctor?' asked Captain Jackson.

'Aye, Tuesday nicht, I mind well it was. I was away up Loch Treig the day to auld MacInnes there.'

Captain Jackson turned on Hector. 'Perhaps, Mr Grant,' he suggested, 'you were light-headed from this blow when you thought you were at Ardroy till Saturday.'

'And what's to prevent me having been carried there at my brother-in-law's orders?' queried Hector.

' 'Tis true that Ardroy spoke of doing that,' admitted Doctor Kincaid. 'He speired after the young man the day I was at his hoose. But yon was the Thursday.'

'Mr Cameron says that Mr Grant came to Ardroy on the Monday, and Mr Grant himself states that he stayed there until Saturday. Yet on Tuesday, Doctor, you find him twenty miles away with a broken head. And he has the effrontery to pretend that he was the "Mr Sinclair" whom you saw in the sick child's room at Ardroy on the Thursday!'

'Set him up!' exclaimed the doctor scornfully. 'The man I

saw then, as I've told you, Colonel, was over forty, a tall, comely man, and fair-complexioned to boot. And I told you who that man was, in my opeenion – Doctor Erchibald Cameron, the Jacobite, himself – and for this callant to seek to pretend to me that *he* was yon "Sinclair" is fair flying in the face of such wits as Providence has given me. Ye'd better keep him here for treatment of his ain!' And on that, scarce waiting for dismissal, Doctor Kincaid took himself off again.

'Come, come,' said Colonel Leighton impatiently, 'One thing is quite plain: Mr Cameron and his kinsman here are both in collusion to shield someone else, and that person has probably been correctly named by Doctor Kincaid. Have Mr Cameron taken back. You can put Mr Grant in the same room with him, for the present at any rate.'

2

'My dear Hector!' began Ardroy, half-laughing, half-sighing, when the door of that locality was shut on them.

'Oh, I know what you are going to say, Ewen!' Hector did not let him say it in consequence. 'Yes, I've done no good – I may even have done harm – but I could not stay a free man when I had brought all this trouble upon you . . . as I have done – don't shake your head! But I had a faint hope that I could gull them into some sort of an exchange. At any rate, I have brought you all kinds of messages from Alison.'

'You saw her? How is Keithie? And – most important of all – did Archie get safely away?'

' 'Tis "Yes" to all of your questions. I did see Alison; Keithie, I understand, is as well as ever he was – and Doctor Cameron was clear away from the MacMartins before I myself arrived there on Saturday evening. Nor has he been captured since, or one would have heard it in the neighbourhood.' Here Hector looked at the windows. 'I wonder how much filing those bars would need?'

Ewen could not help laughing. 'You go too fast, Eachainn! I hope shortly to be invited to walk out of the door in the ordinary way, and against you – since I do not believe that they have your stolen papers – they can prove nothing. It was self-sacrificing of you in the extreme to come here and give yourself up, but my arrest, I feel sure, was due in the first instance to Doctor Kincaid's sense of duty, of which he made mention just now, and not to any information about Doctor Cameron rifled from your pockets.'

His hand at his chin, Hector looked at him. 'I wish I could believe that. Yet it is my doing, Ewen, for this reason: if I had not been so damnably ill-tempered at Ardroy the other evening I'd not have come upon that spy where I did next day, and have lost my papers; my loss was the direct cause of your going to warn Lochdornie and hence meeting Doctor Cameron in his stead; and if you had not met him he could not have come back to Ardroy with you, and have been seen by that curst interfering physician of yours. You see I know all about that from Alison, with whom I contrived a meeting through your little hero of a son; I came upon him trotting up to Slochd nan Eun in the dark to carry a warning.'

'*Donald* went up to Slochd nan Eun! Did Alison choose *him* as the messenger?'

'Not a bit of it. 'Twas his own notion, stout little fellow. I found him by the loch and sent him back, since I knew that whoever was sheltering with Angus MacMartin was already gone. It was from Donald that I first learnt who it was. He's a brave child, Ewen, and I congratulate you on giving me such a nephew!'

And yet, thought Ewen all at once, it is really Donald who is the cause of everything; if he had not pushed Keith into the loch I should never have ridden for Doctor Kincaid and come upon Hector. . . . Nay, it goes further back: if Keithie had not first thrown in that treasure of Donald's. . . . Perhaps in justice I ought to blame my cousin Ian for giving it to him!

Hector meanwhile was looking round their joint prison. The room stood at the corner of the block of buildings in the fort nearest to the loch, and was actually blessed with a window in each of its outer walls. It was therefore unusually light and airy, and had a view across and down Loch Linnhe.

'This place might be worse,' now pronounced the newcomer.

'I doubt this room was not originally intended to keep prisoners in.' Going to one of the windows he shook the bars. 'Not very far to the ground, I should suppose, but there seems to be a considerable drop afterwards down that bastion wall on the loch side.'

But Ewen, scarcely heeding, was murmuring that he ought never to have brought Doctor Cameron to Ardroy.

Hector turned round from his investigations. 'Yet he's clear away now, Ewen, that's certain.'

'But the authorities must guess that he is in Scotland.'

' 'Tis no more than a guess; they do not know it. Even from that unlucky letter of mine I do not think they could be sure of it.'

'Hector, what *was* in that letter?' asked his fellow-captive. 'And why were you carrying it? On someone else's account, I suppose? It was very unfortunate that you were charged with it.'

Lieutenant Grant got rather red. He stuffed his hands into his breeches pockets and studied the floor for a moment. Then he lifted his head and said with an air of resignation, 'I may as well make a clean breast of it. Ever since my mishap I have been wondering how I could have been so misguided, but I had the best intentions, Ewen, as you'll hear. I wrote the letter myself.'

'Wrote it yourself! and carried it on you! To whom was it then?'

'To Cluny Macpherson.'

'But you were on your way to Cluny Macpherson – or so I understood!'

'Yes, I was. But you know, Ewen, how jealously the secret of his hiding-place in Badenoch is kept, and how devilish hard it is to come at him, even when one is accredited as a friend. So, thinking over the problem that morning, it occurred to me that I would write him a short letter, in case I found difficulty in gaining access to his person. You will ask me why in Heaven's name I wrote it beforehand and carried it on me, but it was really my caution, Ewen, that was my undoing. I saw that it would not be wise to write it in a shape which any chance person could read, and that I must turn most of it into cipher. But I could not write my letter and then turn portions of it into cipher – a laborious process, as you know – sitting on a tussock of heather in a wind on Ben Alder, with an impatient gillie of Cluny's gibbering Erse at me. So I wrote down my information as shortly as I could and turned it into cipher before setting out, in order to have it ready to hand over should need arise. And I still believe that the cipher may defy reading, though when you came upon me by Loch Treig, knowing that the letter was gone from me, with the Doctor's and Lochdornie's names in it, I – ' He made one of his half-French gestures.

'Yes,' said Ewen meditatively, 'as things turned out, your notion was not a fortunate one. Was the letter directed to Cluny?'

'No; that foolishness at least I did not commit, since I meant to give it, if at all, straight into the hands of one of his men.'

'That's something, certainly. And if the man who took it was a spy – and not an ordinary robber, which is always possible – I should say the letter had been sent straight to Edinburgh or to London.'

'Why not to the old fellow here? 'Tis true that if he had it he could not read the cipher, but that Captain Jackson might.'

'I think the letter was never brought here, because, if it had been, even though neither of them could read a word of it, they would know that it had been taken from you on Tuesday, and would hardly have wasted their time in allowing you to pretend that you were at Ardroy until Saturday, nor have sent for Doctor Kincaid to testify that you were not the "Mr Sinclair" whom he saw there, worse luck, on Thursday.'

'Unless they wished to give me more rope to hang myself in,' commented Hector, with a slight access of gloom. 'But as to that,' he added after a moment, more cheerfully, 'I'm more like to be shot as a deserter by the French than hanged as a conspirator by the English.'

'You should have thought of that before coming here and giving yourself up!' exclaimed Ewen. 'Are you serious, Hector?'

'No,' confessed Lieutenant Grant with a grin. 'Lord Ogilvie will see to it that he does not lose one of his best officers in that manner. I'll report before my leave's up, never fear. By the way, I *was* carrying my commission on me, as a safeguard, though I denied it; and the scoundrel who took my papers has that too, a bad meeting to him!'

'I thought you were lying to those officers just now,' observed Ardroy. 'But again, had your commission been brought here, I am sure that Captain Jackson could never have resisted the temptation of clapping it down in front of you when you denied that you had it.'

'I wonder,' remarked Hector rather irrelevantly, 'who has done the more lying of late, you or I? Nay, you, past a doubt, for you have had vastly more opportunity. And you don't enjoy it, more's the pity!'

Chapter 8

ON CHRISTMAS NIGHT

1

No more scope for lying, however, was to be afforded to either of the captives, nor were they invited to walk out of Fort William, though for a week, ten days, a fortnight, this was their waking hope every morning. Ewen began to think that Colonel Leighton was not, perhaps, so happy an exchange as some had fancied for the astute but determined Crauford, that he was keeping them there because he knew that he was incompetent and wanted to disguise the fact by a show of severity. Of course it was quite possible that he was only obeying orders from Edinburgh, or, as time went on, from London, but that they could not find out. 'At any rate,' declared Hector, 'he is stupid; *bête comme une oie*, a man one cannot reason with. I saw that at once.'

Stupid or clever, Colonel Leighton was the master of the situation. As the October days crawled by, shortening a little, so that one saw the glow from the sunset – when there was one – fall ever a little less far round on the wall, Lieutenant Grant's temper grew shorter also. What right had Colonel Leighton to keep him imprisoned here, an officer of a foreign power against whom he had no producible evidence? He kept sending messages to that effect, and getting the invariable reply that since the Lieutenant-Governor had only his word that he possessed this status, Mr Grant must produce his commission or something equivalent if he hoped to be believed.

November set in, cold and very windy, and with it came a sinister reminder that there are even worse fates than bondage. There lay in Fort William a prisoner, brought thither from Inveraray, tied on a horse, at the beginning of October, for whom the sands of captivity were running out. On the seventh of November, a day of tempest, an armed procession set out down the side of Loch Linnhe, and in the midst was James Stewart of Acharn. Next morning, in the same high wind, he was taken across Loch Leven and hanged at Ballachulish in Appin, the scene of the murder of Campbell of Glenure, meeting his unjust fate with composure and with the psalm destined ever after to be associated in that country with his name, the thirty-fifth.

November was to have seen that attempt on the liberty of George II over which Ewen and his brother-in-law had come to loggerheads that night at Ardroy. But no news of any such attempt filtered through to the captives. Ewen was very glad, and Hector, presumably, sorry. It was a subject not mentioned between them, although the breach which it had made was healed.

And so another five or six weeks trailed by. James Stewart's chain-encircled body, still guarded by soldiers, rattled and froze on the hillock by Ballachulish ferry, and Hector by this time could think or talk of nothing but escape. Every day his denunciations of Ewen for his passivity became more fervid. He told him among other things that he was like a cow which stays in a byre merely because the farmer has put it there. In vain Ewen pointed out the small advantages to be reaped by escape, at least in his own case, since he could not possibly return to Ardroy; he would be rearrested at once.

But at last Ewen's own patience, not natural to him, but painfully acquired in the difficult years since his return from exile, was completely exhausted. For one thing, it fretted him more with every day that dawned that he knew nothing of Archie's doings, nor had he even learnt whence that aid was to come on which Doctor Cameron was building. So, one day about mid-December, when he and Hector had been discussing the various unsatisfactory plans for escape which the latter had concocted, he considerably startled that youth by saying, 'Let us fix on Christmas Day, then, for the garrison will be more or less drunk, and we may have some small chance of walking out in the manner you propose.' (For the great obstacle to evasion in the orthodox way, by sawing through the bars of a window and letting themselves down, was the by now established impossibility of procuring a file or anything like it.)

Hector leaped up from his chair. '*Enfin!* You mean it, Ewen – you are at last converted? *Dieu soit loué!* And you suggest Christmas Day. You do not think that Hogmanay would be better?'

'No, for the garrison is English. It is on the evening of Christmas Day that we must look for the effect of their potations.'

'Christmas Day be it, then! Now we can plan to better purpose!'

2

During those weary weeks Ewen had written as often as he was allowed to his wife, and had received replies from her, all correspondence of course passing through the hands of the authorities at Fort William, so that only personal and domestic news could be conveyed. But Alison had all along been determined to come and visit him, should his release be delayed, and wrote a few days after this that she believed she should succeed in getting permission to do so before Christmas.

'Faith, if she do not come before, 'twill be of little use, or so I hope, coming after,' declared her brother. 'Indeed, if one wished to throw dust in the eyes of that Leighton creature, it might have been well had she said that she was coming at the New Year.'

'But I, at least, desire to be here when she comes,' objected Ewen. In his heart of hearts he thought that the New Year would probably find them still in Fort William, but he did not wish to dash Hector's optimism, and proceeded with his occupation of making a sketch map of Loch Linnhe and its neighbourhood from memory on a clean pocket-handkerchief.

And four days before Christmas Alison came. A message from the Lieutenant-Governor had previously apprised the captives of the event, and they trimmed each other's hair and shaved with great particularity. Lady Ardroy had written that she would bring them some Christmas fare; this, the two agreed, would prove a most useful viaticum for the subsequent journey.

She brought something else, more unexpected. The young and courteous officer who escorted her up himself carried the big basket of provisions, for, to the captives' amazement, Alison's two hands were otherwise engaged. One held the small hand of Keith, so wrapped about in furs that he looked a mere fluffy ball, the other rested on Donald's shoulder. The officer deposited the basket on the table and swiftly closed the door on the family re-union – but not before Alison was in her husband's arms. It was over three months since she had seen him marched away down the avenue at Ardroy.

And then, while Hector and his sister embraced, Ewen could attend to the claims of his offspring. 'Keithie, you look for all the world like a fat little bear!' he exclaimed. Nor was the small person at all abashed by his surroundings, remarking that he had seen a great many red gentlemen downstairs, and why was Father living with them? He would prefer him to come home. The fairies had restored his 'deers' unharmed, and he now had in addition a *damh-feidh* with horns, which he had put in the large, large basket so that Father could see it. Meanwhile Donald, who appeared grown, and did seem a trifle overawed by the place in which he found himself, rather shyly told him that Angus had recovered the claymore hilt from the Loch of the Eagle; and he too asked, not so cheerfully as Keith, even reproachfully, why his father did not return, as Mother had said he would.

But it was the prisoners who had most questions to put. Chief among Ewen's was, what had become of Doctor Cameron? Alison knew nothing of his movements, less still, as of what success or failure he had met with in his mission. It was said that he had left the West altogether.

'Then it is well known to the English that he is in the Highlands,' said Ewen despondently, 'and it is my fault!'

'No,' said Alison with decision, 'the knowledge seems too widespread for that. But enough of Doctor Archibald for the moment; I have to speak of something which concerns you both more nearly at this time – and it would be better to speak

French, because of the children,' she added, plunging into that tongue, which they all three spoke with ease.

And, beckoning them close to her Lady Ardroy, to their no small astonishment, unfolded a plan of escape which it seemed had been devised in conjunction with young Ian Stewart of Invernacree, her husband's cousin, and the rest of his Stewart kin in Appin. If he and Hector could succeed in getting out of the fort, and would be on the shore of Loch Linnhe at a given spot and hour on the night of Christmas Day –

'*What* night?' exclaimed both her hearers together.

Alison looked a little startled. 'We had thought of Christmas night for it, because the garrison – What are you both laughing at?'

At that Hector laughed the more, and Ewen seized and kissed her.

'Because, *mo chridhe,* you or Ian must have the two sights, I think. That is precisely the night that Hector and I were already favouring, and for exactly the same reason. Go on!'

Flushed and eager, Alison went on. Under the fort a boat would be waiting, manned by Stewarts; this, with all possible speed would convey them down Loch Linnhe to Invernacree in Appin, where old Alexander Stewart, Ewen's maternal uncle, proposed that the fugitives should remain hid for a while. Some twenty miles would then lie between them and Fort William, while in any case the pursuit would probably be made in the first instance towards Ardroy.

To all the first part of the plan Ewen agreed without demur. The presence of a boat waiting for them would solve their greatest difficulty, how to leave the neighbourhood of the fort. For the previous part of the programme, the actual breaking out of their prison, they must as before rely upon themselves – and upon the effects of the garrison's Christmas celebrations.

But to taking refuge with his uncle and cousin Ewen would not agree. 'If I succeed in getting free, darling, it's more than enough that I shall owe them. But I am not going to risk bringing trouble on folk who are now at peace, particularly after what took place in Appin last spring, for which an Appin man has paid so dearly. My plan is to reach Edinburgh somehow,

and there secure the legal aid for which I have been vainly trying by letter. The English know the justice of my case, or they
would not have denied me the services of an advocate. After
all, if all goes well, I shall be able to return to you and the
bairns in quiet . . . and be ready for the call to arms when it
comes,' he added internally, for not even to Alison had he revealed what Archibald Cameron had told him.

After this Alison set the children to unpack the basket and
to range its contents on the table. 'I must keep them occupied
at a distance for a few moments,' she explained, as she came
back. 'Now, first for your escape from this room. Since there
are bars to your windows . . . Hold out a hand, one of you!'

'Not . . . a file!' exclaimed Hector, almost snatching from his
sister the little key to freedom. 'Oh, you angel from heaven!'

Alison smiled. ' 'Twas Ian Stewart thought of that. There's
something further. You may be wondering why I have not
taken off my cloak all this while. If I had, you would certainly
be thinking I had lost my figure.' And, smiling, she suddenly
held her mantle wide.

'Faith, no,' admitted Hector, 'that's not the jimp waist I've
been accustomed to see in you, my sister.'

'Wait, and you shall know the reason for it . . . Look out
of the window, the two of you, until I bid you turn.'

The two men obeyed. From the table came the chatter of
the children, very busy over the basket. 'My want to see
what's in that little pot!' 'Keithie, you'll drop that if you are
not more careful; oh, here's another cheese!'

'Now,' said Alison's voice, 'lift up my cloak.'

Husband and brother turned round, and, deeply puzzled,
each raised a side of it. In her arms Lady Ardroy held, all huddled together, the coils of a long, thin, strong rope.

'Take it – hide it quickly . . . don't let the weans see it; Keithie
might go talking of it before the soldiers below. I thought you
might find it of service.'

Nevertheless, some half-hour later, two men, each wind-
ing half a rope round their bodies beneath their clothes, would
have given a good deal had those indiscreet and innocent eyes

still been upon them. The room seemed so empty now; only among the provisions on the table stood, very stiffly, Keithie's ridiculous new wooden stag, with one of its birch-twig horns hanging down broken, Keithie at the last having left the animal there for his father's consolation.

3

One may arrange an escape with due regard for sheltering darkness and the festive preoccupation of one's jailers, may have accomplices in readiness, may join them undiscovered and get a certain distance away from one's prison – only to find that Nature is not in a mood to lend her assistance, that she has, in fact, definitely resolved to hinder one's flight. And in the Highlands at midwinter this lack of cooperation on her part may lead to serious consequences.

In other words, young Ian Stewart's boat, with its four rowers, was having an increasingly rough and toilsome journey down Loch Linnhe this Christmas night. The party had waited undetected in the boat on the upper reach of the loch near the fort, the same luck had attended their reception of the two fugitives, on whose descent from their window and down the counterscarp to the shore fortune had also smiled, and, amid mutual congratulations, rescuers and rescued had started on the twenty miles' homeward pull. The wind, as they knew, was dead against them, hence they could not help themselves by a sail, and the tide would shortly be against them also, but these were circumstances which had for some time been anticipated. What, however, was dismaying, was the rapidity with which this contrary wind was rising in strength, and lashing up the waters of the loch to anger.

The boat itself was heavy and solid, and there was little risk of its being swamped. The real danger lay in the fact that its progress was being so retarded that dawn might be upon them before they had covered nearly as much distance from Fort William as was desirable. At the helm Ian Stewart, more and more uneasy, watched the pallid light spreading in the east. In front, about a mile away, a single light in some small cottage on the shore indicated the Narrows, where the long spit of land from the Ardgour side pushed out till, in that one place, Loch Linnhe was only a quarter of a mile across instead of a mile and a quarter. Young Invernacree looked at the set faces of his men as they tugged at the oars, and turned to his cousin beside him.

'I had hoped to be through the Narrows before the tide made there, but I fear it is too late. You know with what force the flood rushes up through them at first, and with this wind and the men so spent I doubt we shall be able to pass for a while.'

Ewen nodded; he was beginning to have the same doubt. 'Then let us pull in near the Ardgour shore, out of the tide rip, until the first force of it is over. Shall I relieve one of your gillies? Ay, you'd best let me – look there!'

For the bow rower at that very moment was showing signs of collapsing over his oar. Before Ian Stewart could prevent the substitution, even had he wished, Ewen was clambering carefully forward past the other oarsmen in the rocking craft, all unconscious on what a journey that change of place was to launch him.

He got the exhausted rower off the thwart to the bottom of the boat, and seized the oar, finding himself glad to handle it after three months of enforced inaction. Slowly but rather more steadily now the boat drew near to comparative shelter, and away from the oncoming flood racing through the neck of the Narrows. Nevertheless, the water was still far from smooth, for gusts of wind came tearing over the low-lying point of the spit. Had they ceased rowing they would have been blown back, or, worse still, got broadside on to the wind. 'We had much better pull right in to land,' thought Ewen, 'lest another man should collapse.' And the thought had not long formulated itself before the leader of the expedition came to the same conclusion, and, after vainly trying to shout it to his cousin, sent down by word of mouth from man to man the information that he was going to make straight for the shore near the cottage and beach the boat there.

Ewen nodded his head vigorously to show his approval, and, since he was the bow oar and must jump ashore with the rope, reached about behind him with one hand until he found it, realizing as he did so that in such rough weather it would be no easy matter to perform this operation neatly. Preoccupied with seizing the right moment, he pulled on with the rest, glancing now and then over his shoulder to see how near they were getting to the dim grey beach with its line of foam. And the moment had come, for there was Ian waving his arm and shouting something which he could not catch, Hector also.

Rapidly shipping his oar, Ewen clutched the rope and jumped over the gunwale into cold and yeasty water above his knees, which sucked heavily at him as he waded hastily into shallower, trailing the rope with him. Braced for the strain, he was hauling in the slack of this when that – or rather those – fell upon him of which his kinsman's shout had been intended to warn him. Two men in great coats, appearing (so it seemed to him) from nowhere, had dashed into the water with offers of help. Bewildered at first, Ewen was beginning to thank them, when, to his extreme dismay, he caught the gleam of scarlet under their coats. 'No, no!' he shouted almost unconsciously, his one thought being that the whole boatload were delivering themselves into an ambush, for somehow he was aware that the door of the lighted cottage behind him had opened and was emitting more soldiers. And obviously Ian's gillies had the same idea, for instead of pulling in to shore they were now vigorously backing water to keep off. What their young laird was shouting to them was probably furious orders to go on and land; but the receding and tossing boat itself tore the rope alike through Ewen's hands and those of the soldiers. He himself made a desperate effort to reach the bows and scramble on board again, but it was too late; this could only be done now by swimming, and moreover one of the soldiers had by this time closed with him, and they were soon struggling up to midthigh in icy, swirling water.

At last Ewen tore himself from the man's clutches with a push which sent his assailant under, spluttering. In front of him was the boat which he could not reach, with Ian standing up in the stern gesticulating and shouting something of which the wind carried away every syllable, while Ardroy on his side shouted to the rowers to keep off, and that he would fend for himself. Then, the better to show his intention, he turned his back on the boat, his face to the shore on which he was left. The ducked redcoat had arisen, dripping like a merman and cursing like the proverbial trooper; his companion was dodging to and fro in a few inches of water, waiting to intercept the marooned fugitive on his emergence from the swirl on the beach. Two more were hurrying down from the open door of the cottage; and Ewen was unarmed, half-drenched and hampered by the breaking water in which he stood. It looked like prison again. He set his teeth, and began to plunge stumblingly through the foam towards the shore but away from the reinforcements.

And some three-quarters of an hour later, rather to his own astonishment, he was crouching, wet, exhausted, but free, behind a boulder on the slope of Meall Breac, at the entrance to Glen Clovulin. He had been favoured by the bad light and by the high, broken ground, an outcrop of the height of Sgurr nan Eanchainne, for which he had made at full speed, and which, by falling again into a sort of gulley, had made something of a wall between him and his pursuers – who never, in fact, pursued him so far.

The wind was dropping now, and the mist crawling lower; he was safe enough from the soldiers at any rate. Presumably the boat had got through the Narrows; he had not had time to look. He could not help wondering what were the present feelings of his cousin Ian, who had undertaken this exploit, involving a good deal of risk, for him, a kinsman, and had in the end only carried off a young man with whom he had no ties of blood at all. Still, from Ewen's own point of view, this braeside, though windy and destitute of food, was greatly to be preferred to the room with the barred windows in Fort William. 'Better peace in a bush than peace in fetters,' as the Gaelic proverb had it. But what he really wanted was peace at Ardroy.

Chapter 9

THE WORM AT THE HEART

1

ALTHOUGH in the weeks to come it never occurred to Ewen – who was besides well able to look after himself – that he had been abandoned to his fate on Ardgour beach (he was only to wish sometimes that he had not been quite so precipitate in leaping ashore with the rope), Hector Grant was often to feel remorse for the safety which had been bestowed on him while his brother-in-law had been left to fend for himself.

It was true that the Stewarts had kept the boat hanging about on the other side of the Narrows as long as they dared, but no figure had appeared to claim their help. Yet since, by the last he had seen of the drama on the shore, Ardroy appeared to be outdistancing his pursuers, Ian had every confidence that he would make his way down the farther side of Loch Linnhe into Morven, and thence across to Invernacree, for which the rowers had then made with what speed was left in them. At Invernacree Hector was sheltered for a night or two, during which he gave up his former project of crossing to Ireland, and so to France, for the desire to know what had happened to wreck the scheme for kidnapping the Elector was drawing him, in spite of the hazards, to London. And so here he was, this cold January evening, actually in the capital, a refuge much less safe, one would have thought, than his unlucky relative's in the wilds of Ardgour. But he argued that he was less likely to be looked for in London than anywhere else.

Perhaps this was true, but Lieutenant Grant, after a couple of days in the capital, found himself facing other problems which had not previously weighed upon him: first, the problem of getting back to France from England without papers of any kind; second, the problem of remaining in London without money, of which he had exceedingly little left; and third, the

problem of his reception by his colonel, Lord Ogilvie, when h
did rejoin his regiment. Indeed, Hector foresaw that the sooner
he returned to France the less likely would he be to find a
court-martial awaiting him there.

So it was, for him, a trifle dejectedly that he walked this
evening along the Strand towards his lodging in Fleet Street,
wondering whether after all he could contrive to slip through
at the coast without the papers which he saw no means of ob-
taining. He had just come from the 'White Cock' tavern, a
noted Jacobite resort, where converse with several English adherents of that cause had neither impressed him nor been of
any service. No one seemed to be able to tell him exactly why
the plot had failed to mature; they had all talked a great deal,
to be sure, but were obviously the last persons to help him.

He glanced up. The winter moon, half-eaten away, sailed
eerily over the shrivelled harvest on the spikes of Temple Bar.
Townley's head, he knew, was one of the two still left there,
the commander of the doomed garrison of Carlisle. Hector's
own might well have been there too.

Yes, London was a hostile and an alien town. He had not
met one Scot there, not even him whom he had thought certainly to meet, young Finlay MacPhair of Glenshian, the old
Chief's son, who had been in the plot. Did he know where to
find him, he reflected now, he might bring himself to appeal
in his present strait to a fellow Gael where he would not sue to
those spiritless English Jacobites. And at the 'White Cock' they
would know young Glenshian's direction.

Hector turned at that thought, and began quickly to retrace
his steps, lifting his hat again, half-defiantly, as he passed the
heads of the seven years' vigil, and soon came once more to
the narrow entry off the Strand in which the 'White Cock' was
situated. There were still some customers there, drinking and
playing cards, and as he came down the little flight of steps inside the door an elderly Cumberland squire named Fether-
stonhaugh, with whom he had played that evening, looked up
and recognized him.

'Back again, Mr Grant? God's sake, you look as though you
had received bad news! I trust it is not so?'

'There is nothing amiss with me, sir,' replied Hector, annoyed that his looks could so betray him. 'But I was foolish enough to go away without inquiring the direction of my compatriot, Mr Finlay MacPhair of Glenshian, and I have returned to ask if any gentleman here could oblige me with it.'

At first it seemed as if no one there could do this, until a little grave man, looking like an attorney, got up from an equally decorous game of picquet in the corner, and volunteered the information that Mr MacPhair lodged not far from there, in Beaufort Buildings, opposite Exeter Street, the second house on the right.

Hector could not suppress an exclamation. He lowered his voice. 'He lives in the Strand, as openly as that? Why, the English Government could put their hands on him there any day!'

'I suppose,' replied the little man, 'that they do not wish to do so. After all, bygones are bygones now, and Mr MacPhair, just because he was so promptly clapped into the Tower, never actually bore arms against the Elector. But he keeps himself close, and sees few people. Perhaps, however, as you come from the Highlands, he will receive you, sir.'

2

Ten o'clock next morning saw Lieutenant Grant outside Beaufort Buildings, and knocking, as directed, at the second house on the right-hand side. The woman who opened told him to go to the upper floor, as the Scotch gentleman lodged there. Up, therefore, Hector went, and, knocking again, brought out a young, shabbily dressed manservant.

'Can I see Mr MacPhair of Glenshian?'

'Himself is fery busy,' replied the man, frowning a little. He was obviously a Highlander too.

'Already?' asked Hector. 'I came early hoping to find him free of company.'

'Himself is not having company; he is writing letters.'

Hector drew himself up. 'Tell Mr MacPhair,' he said in Gaelic, 'that his acquaintance Lieutenant Hector Grant of the régiment d'Albanie is here, and earnestly desires to see him.'

At the sound of that tongue the frown left the gillie's face, and, after seeking and apparently receiving permission from within, opened wide the door of the apartment.

Hector, as he entered, received something of a shock. To judge from his surroundings, Finlay MacPhair, son and heir of a powerful chief, was by no means well-to-do. A small four-post bed with dingy crimson hangings in one corner, together with an ash-strewn hearth upon whose hobs sat a battered kettle and a saucepan, showed that his bedchamber, living apartment and kitchen were all one. In the middle of the room stood a large table littered with a medley of objects – papers, cravats, a couple of wigs, a plate, a cane, a pair of shoes. The owner himself, in a shabby flowered dressing-gown, sat at the clearer end of this laden table mending a quill, a red-haired young man of a haughty and not over agreeable cast of countenance. A half-empty cup of coffee stood beside him. He rose as Hector came in, but with an air a great deal more arrogant than courteous.

'At your service, sir; what can I do for you?'

'It's not from *him* I'll ever borrow money!' resolved Hector instantly. But Finlay MacPhair's face had already changed. 'Why, 'tis Mr Grant of Lord Ogilvie's regiment! That stupid fellow of mine misnamed you. Sit down, I pray you, and take a morning with me. Away with that cold filth, Seumas!' he added petulantly, indicating the coffee cup with aversion.

'Well, Mr Grant,' said he, when the 'morning' had been tossed off, 'and on what errand do you find yourself here? I shall be very glad to be of assistance to you if it is within my power.'

He put the question graciously, yet with all the air of a chief receiving a not very important tacksman.

'I have had a misfortune, Mr MacPhair, which, if you'll permit me, I will acquaint you with,' said Hector, disliking the prospect of the recital even more than he had anticipated. And he made it excessively brief. Last September a spy had treacherously knocked him on the head in the Highlands, and abstracted the pocket-book containing all his papers. Since then he had been confined in Fort William.

'Lost all your papers in the Highlands, and been shut up in Fort William!' said Finlay MacPhair, his sandy eyebrows high. 'I might say you've not the luck, Mr Grant! And why, pray, do you tell me all this?'

Hector, indeed, was almost wondering the same thing. He swallowed hard.

'Because I don't know how the devil I'm to get out of England without papers of some kind. Yet I must rejoin my regiment at once. And it occurred to me –'

'*I* can't procure you papers, sir!' broke in young MacPhair, short and sharp.

'No, naturally not,' agreed Hector, surprised at the sudden acrimony of the tone. 'But I thought that maybe you knew someone who –'

He stopped, still more astonished at the gaze which his contemporary in the dressing-gown had fixed upon him.

'You thought that I – *I* – knew someone who could procure you papers!' repeated Finlay the Red, getting up and leaning over the corner of the untidy table. 'What, pray, do you mean by that, Mr Grant? Why the devil should you think such a thing? I'd have you remember, if you please, that Lincoln's Inn Fields are within convenient distance of this place ... and I suppose you are familiar with the use of the small-sword!'

Hector, too, had leapt to his feet. He had apparently met with a temper more inflammable than his own. Yet he could imagine no reason for this sudden conflagration. He was too much taken aback for adequate anger. 'Mr MacPhair, I've no notion what I have done to offend you, so 'tis impossible for me to apologize. ... Not that I'm in the habit of apologizing to any man, Highland or Lowland!' he added, with his head well back.

For a moment or so the two young Gaels faced each other like two mutually suspicious dogs. Then for the second time Finlay MacPhair's demeanour changed, and the odd expression went out of his eyes. 'I see now it's I that should apologize, Mr Grant, and to a fellow-Highlander I can do it. I misjudged you; I recognize that you did not intend in any way to insult me by hinting that I was in relations with the English Government, which was what I took your words to mean. Sit down again, if you please, and let us see whether our two heads cannot find some plan for you to get clear of England, without the *tracasserie* at the ports which you anticipate.'

Rather bewildered, Hector complied. And now his fiery host had become wonderfully friendly. He stood with his hands in his breeches pockets and said thoughtfully, 'Now, couldn't I be thinking of someone who would be of use to you? There are gentlemen in high place of Jacobite leanings, and some of the City aldermen are bitten that way. Unfortunately, I myself have to be so prodigious circumspect, lest I find myself in prison again . . .

'Yes,' he resumed after a moment, 'there's an old gentleman in Government service who is under some small obligation to me, and he chances to know Mr Pelham very well. I should have no scruples about approaching him; he'll remember me – and as I say, he is in my debt. I'll do it . . . ay, I'll do it!' He threw himself into his chair again, and in the same impulsive manner pulled towards him out of the confusion a blank sheet of paper which, sliding along, revealed a half-written one beneath.

At that lower sheet young Glenshian looked and smiled. 'I was about writing to Secretary Edgar at Rome when you came, as you see.' He pushed the page towards his visitor, and Hector, who had no wish to supervise Mr MacPhair's correspondence, but could not well avert the eyes which he was thus specifically invited to cast upon it, did see a few scraps of Finlay MacPhair's ill-spelt if loyal remarks to that trusted servant of their exiled King's, something about 'constant resolucion to venture my owne person', 'sincer, true and reale sentiments', and a desire to be 'laid at his Majesty and Royal Emenency's feet'. But he could not think why he should be invited to peruse them.

The letter upon which he was now engaged on his compatriot's behalf Finlay did not offer to show the latter, though had Hector looked over the writer's shoulder he would certainly have found its contents more arresting than those of the loyal epistle to Rome.

'Dear Grandpapa,' wrote Finlay MacPhair of Glenshian with a scratching quill to the old gentleman in Government service whom, since he was no relation of his, he must have known very well thus playfully to address 'Dear Grandpapa, Get *our* ffrind to writ a pass for a Mr Hector Grant to go to France without delai. Hee's harmlesse, and my oblidging an oficer of Lord Ogilby's regt. in this maner will not faile to rayse my creditt with the party, which is a matter I must now pay particular atention tow. Besides, I am in hopes to make some litle use of him leater. And let me know, if you please, when we shall meet to talk of the afair I last wrot of, otherwise I must undow what I have begun. Excuse my ansiety, and beliv me most sincerly, with great estime and affection, You most oblidged humble servt, Alexander Jeanson.'

And this was addressed, in the same independent spelling, to 'The Honble Guin Voughan at his house in Golden Square,' but Hector did not see the direction, for the writer folded and sealed the letter in an outer sheet on which he wrote, 'To Mr Tamas Jones, at Mr Chelburn's, a Chimmist in Scherwood Street.'

'That is not the real name of my acquaintance, Mr Grant,' said the scribe with great frankness, handing him the missive. 'And yon is the address of an apothecary at whose shop you should leave this letter with as little delay as possible. Call there again by noon tomorrow, and I'll engage there'll be somewhat awaiting you that will do what you wish.'

Hector thanked him warmly, so genuinely grateful that he failed to perceive that he had not wronged the punctilious Mr MacPhair after all, for he did know someone who could procure useful papers for a Jacobite in difficulties. The benefactor, however, cut short his thanks by asking him a question which somewhat allayed his gratitude.

'I hope, Mr Grant,' he said, looking at him meaningly, 'that there was nothing of a compromising nature among the papers which were taken from you in the Highlands?'

Hector reddened, having all along desired to obscure that fact. He fenced.

'No papers lost in such a manner, Mr MacPhair, but must, I fear, be regarded as compromising.'

'But naturally,' replied young Glenshian somewhat impatiently. 'As you no doubt found when you were in Fort William. Did they question you much there about them?'

'No. My papers were not in their hands, as far as I know.'

'Then why were *you*?'

'Oh, 'tis a long story, not worth troubling you with. But the gist of it is that I gave myself up.'

He had succeeded in astonishing Mr MacPhair. 'Gave yourself up!' exclaimed the latter. 'In God's name, what for? Gave yourself up at Fort William! I fear the knock on your head must have been a severe one!'

'Perhaps it was,' said Hector shortly. 'At any rate I accomplished nothing by doing it, and on Christmas Day I escaped.'

'My dear Mr Grant, you astonish me more and more! I took it that you had been released. And after escaping you come to London, of all places!'

'It was on my way to France,' said the adventurer, sulkily. And he then added, in a not very placatory manner, 'If you wish to give me to understand that on this account you prefer to withdraw the letter you have written, here it is!' He drew it out of his pocket.

Finlay MacPhair waved his hand. 'Not for worlds, not for worlds! It is the more needed; and your escape shall make no difference, even though it was unknown to me when I penned that request. But I should like to know, Mr Grant, why you gave yourself up. You must have had some extraordinary reason for so extraordinary a proceeding.' And, as Hector hesitated, foreseeing to what a truthful answer might lead, he added, in a tone which very plainly showed offence, 'I have surely earned the right to a little more frankness on your part, Mr Grant!'

The claim could not be gainsaid. Hector resigned himself, and in as few words as possible gave that reason. Even then he somehow contrived to keep out Doctor Cameron's name.

Glenshian threw himself back in his chair, and looked at the narrator under lowered lids. 'So you played this heroic rôle because you considered that you had compromised your brother-in-law by the loss of your papers. Then there *was* something compromising in them?'

'No, not to him. . . . I see I had best explain the whole matter,' said Hector in an annoyed voice, and being tired of cross-examination came out bluntly and baldly with everything – the loss of his prematurely written letter to Cluny Macpherson (mostly unintelligible, he hoped, owing to its cipher), Ardroy's going back to warn Lochdornie, his finding instead Doctor Cameron and bringing him to his house, the search there and Ewen's arrest. To all this the young chief listened with the most unstirring attention, his hand over his mouth, and those curiously pale hazel eyes of his fixed immovably on the speaker.

'*Dhé,* that's a tale!' said he slowly at the end. 'And this letter of yours, with its mention of the arrival of Lochdornie and Doctor Cameron – you never discovered what had become of it?'

'No. But I am pretty sure, as I say,' replied Hector, 'that it never found its way to Fort William. I was, I confess, in despair lest harm should come to either of them through its loss, but I cannot think that any has. 'Tis now more than three months since it was stolen from me, and by this time the Government has probably learnt from other sources of their presence in Scotland.'

Frowning over his own confession, and remembering too at that moment how Alison that day at Fort William had spoken of searches made by the military after the Doctor, he did not see the sharp glance which was cast at him.

'Ay, 'tis very probable they know it,' said Mr MacPhair dryly. 'What part your lost letter may have played in their knowledge. . . .' He shrugged his shoulders. 'And indeed,' he went on, with an air of disapproval, 'I cannot anyways commend this mission of my kinsman Lochdornie's and Doctor Cameron's. Had the Prince taken my advice on the matter when he made it known to me – as, considering my large interests and influence in the Western Highlands, he had done well to – they would not have been sent upon so risky an undertaking. However, since it has been set on foot, I hope my cousin Lochdornie will find means to report to me on his proceedings there; which indeed,' added the future Chief, 'it is not less than his duty to do. And yet I have had no word from him. It would be well did I hear from the Doctor also. I only trust he may not be engaged in damping down the ardour of the clans, as he did three years ago.'

'Doctor Cameron damp down the clans!' exclaimed Hector, thinking he had not heard aright. 'My dear Mr MacPhair, he's more like, surely, to inflame them with too little cause. . . . And how should the Prince have selected him for this mission if that were his habit?'

Finlay shrugged his shoulders. 'Archie Cameron has always had the Prince's ear since the day when Lochiel sent him to Arisaig to dissuade His Royal Highness from his enterprise. Moreover, 'twas to the Doctor's own interest to come to Scotland again. There's always the treasure of Loch Arkaig, about which he knows even more than Cluny – more than any man alive.' The half-sneering expression habitual to his face leapt into full life as he went on, 'That gold is like honey to a bee in his case. He dipped pretty deeply into it, did the immaculate Doctor Archibald, when we were in Lochaber together in the '49!'

'But not upon his own account!' cried Hector. 'Not for himself, Mr MacPhair! That I'll never believe!'

'Your sister's married to a man that's akin to the Doctor, you told me,' was Glenshian's retort to this. 'Unfortunately, I was there with Archibald Cameron at the time. . . . Well, there's many a man that's true enough to the Cause, but can't keep his fingers from the Cause's money. I don't blame him overmuch, with that throng family of young children to support. I've known what it is to be so near starving myself, Mr Grant, that I have had to sell my shoe-buckles for bread – 'twas when I was released from the Tower. So I'm aware why Archie Cameron finds it suits him to go back to the Highlands at any cost.'

Hector stared at him, incredulous, yet conscious of a certain inner discomfort. For it was quite true that young Glenshian had accompanied Doctor Cameron and his own kinsman Lochdornie to the Highlands in 1749, and rumours had run among the Scottish exiles over the water that since that date the two latter were scarcely on speaking terms. But when Hector had learnt that these two were going over again together, he had supposed the report much exaggerated. Still, he who spoke with such conviction was the future Chief of Glenshian, and deeper, surely, in the innermost councils of Jacobitism than he, a mere landless French officer.

'Mr Grant, I am going to ask you a favour in my turn,' here said Finlay the Red, with an air of having dealt conclusively with the last subject. 'I expect you know Captain Samuel Cameron of your regiment?'

'Crookshanks, as we call him?' answered Hector a little absently, being engaged in dissipating the momentary cloud of humility by the reflection that as one Highland gentleman he was the equal of any other, Chief or no. 'The brother of Cameron of Glenevis – that's the man you mean?'

'That is the man. They say that one good turn deserves another; will you then take him a letter from me? I'm wanting a messenger this while back, and since you are returning to the regiment, here is my chance, if you will oblige me?'

Only too pleased to confer some obligation, as a species of set-off against his own, Hector replied that he would be delighted, so Finlay once more seized paper and took up his pen. For a few seconds he nibbled the quill reflectively, the fraction of a smile at the corner of his mouth; then he dashed off a few lines, sealed the missive carefully, and handed it to its bearer. 'You'll not, I hope, be robbed again, Mr Grant!' he observed, and yet, despite the little laugh which accompanied the words, Hector felt that after what had passed he could not well take offence at them. He accepted the gibe and the letter with meekness, and prepared to take his leave. Young Glenshian rose too.

'Your visit, Mr Grant,' he said agreeably, 'has been of this advantage to me, that I know now from a first-hand source that my kinsman and Doctor Cameron did really make their appearance in the Highlands this autumn. In the absence of news from either of them I have sometimes wondered whether the plan had not fallen through at the last. Though even at that,' he added, smiling, 'the evidence is scarcely first hand, since you did not actually set eyes on either of them.'

'But my brother-in-law, with whom I was imprisoned –' began Hector.

'Ay, I forgot – a foolish remark of mine that! I'll pass the testimony as first hand,' said Finlay lightly. 'But where, I wonder, did the Doctor go after he had evaded capture at your brother-in-law's house?'

'That I never knew,' responded Hector. 'In Fort William neither Ardroy nor I had much opportunity for learning such things.'

'He'll have made for Loch Arkaig as usual, I expect,' commented young MacPhair. He looked at the table. 'Mr Grant, you'll take another dram before you leave?'

'No, thank you, Mr MacPhair,' replied Hector with a heightened colour.

And then Hector remembered the question which, during these days in London, no Englishman had satisfactorily answered for him. Striving to banish the resentment from his voice and look, he said, 'May I venture to ask a question in my turn, Mr MacPhair? Pray do not answer if it be too indiscreet. But, as I have told you, it was the proposed scheme for . . . a certain course of action in London which brought me over the sea last September. Why did that scheme come to naught?'

Mr MacPhair did not seem to find the question indiscreet, nor did he pause to consider his answer. 'Why, for the same reason that the Rising failed in '46,' he replied with prompt scorn. 'Because your English Jacobite is a man of fine promises and no performance, and as timid as a hare! Well, a good journey to you, Mr Grant; commend me to my friends over there.'

In his worn dressing-gown, surrounded by that clamorous disorder, Fionnlagh Ruadh nevertheless dismissed his visitor with an air so much *de haut en bas* that a sudden heavy strain was thrown on the cord of Hector's gratitude. He bowed, biting his lip a little.

'I hope I may be able to repay you one day, Mr MacPhair,' he said formally, and thought, 'May the Devil fly with me to the hottest corner of hell if I don't . . . somehow!'

'Seumas,' called the young chief, raising his voice, 'show this gentleman downstairs.'

And the gillie, who was peeling potatoes on the landing, hastened to obey.

'Arrogant, touchy, and vain as a peacock!' was Hector's summary of his late host as he walked away from the Strand in the direction of the 'chimmist' in Sherwood Street. But the peacock had done him a real service, and in mere gratitude he ought to try to forget that today's impression of Finlay MacPhair of Glenshian had not been a pleasant one.

3

When Seumas returned to his potato-peeling, his master, on the other side of the door, was already resuming his correspondence. But not the letter to Secretary Edgar which he had shown to Hector. From a locked drawer he extracted another sheet of paper, headed simply 'Information', and underneath the few lines already there he wrote:

'Pickle has this day spoken with one from the Highlands who says that Doctor Cameron and MacPhair of Lochdornie were certainly there at the end of September, and Doctor Cameron was then come into Lochaber, by which it may be seen that the information sent by Pickle in November last was very exact. But where the Doctor then went the informant did not know. It would not dow for Pickle to goe himself into those parts, for the Doctor distrusts him, hee knowing too much about the Doctor, and besids the risque is too great, Pickle being of such consequence there; but if hee had more mony at his disposal he cou'd employ it very well in finding a person who would goe, and undertakes hee'd find out more in a day than any government trusty in a week, or souldier in a moneth; or Pickle would be apt to corespond with persons not suspected by the disaffected, who cou'd be on the Watch for these men, if it were made worth their while. But Pickle's jants have already cost him a deal of mony, and hee has never receaved more than his bare exspences, and is at this moment in debte to severall persons in this town, in spite of the great promasis made to him, and the great services he hath already performed, both in regard to afairs in the Highlands, and among the Pretender's party in England. If something be not paid imediatly Pickle is not dispos'd to –

He broke off, hastily covering the paper. 'Damn you, Seumas, what do you want?'

The gillie might have entered upon a stage cue. 'If I am to buy flesh for dinner – ' he began timidly in his native tongue.

His master sprang up in wrath. 'Do you tell me that you have spent all I gave you? Death without a priest to you! Here, take this, and see you make it last longer!'

He really was poor – still. Yet, for all his pretence to Hector, no one stood in less danger than he of being again confined by the English Government, and well he knew it. But though that Government left him at large to continue his services it paid them chiefly in promises; and it is galling to have sold your soul, to betray your kin, your comrades, and, as far as in you lies, your Prince, and to get so few of the thirty pieces in return. Perhaps the paymasters thought but poorly of what they obtained from the informer.

Did the letter-writer himself suspect that, as he sat there now, his chin on his hand, and that scowl darkening his face? It did not seem likely, for no services that Finlay MacPhair of Glenshian could render, however base, would ever appear to him other than great and valuable.

Chapter 10

'AN ENEMY HATH DONE THIS'

1

THE snow gave no signs of ceasing. It had never been blinding, yet this steady and gentle fall had contrived to obliterate landmarks to a surprising degree, and to make progress increasingly difficult. Ewen began to think that he might possibly be benighted before he reached the little clachan for which he was bound.

Although it was the second week in February, Ardroy was still west of Loch Linnhe – in Sunart, in fact. At first, indeed, he had wandered from croft to croft, seeking shelter at each for no more than a night or two; he had known that it would be folly on his part to attempt to cross the loch, since all the way southward from Fort William the soldiers must be on the look-out for him. Yet he had not gone far up Glen Clovulin when he heard that those whom he had so unluckily encountered that morning at Ardgou were a party on their way from Mingary Castle to relieve the guard quartered at Ballachulish over the body of James Stewart. They could not possibly have known at that time of his and Hector's escape; perhaps, even, in their ignorance, they might not have molested the boat's crew had they landed.

But five weeks had elapsed since that episode, and it might be assumed that even Fort William was no longer keeping a strict look-out for the fugitives. Ewen was therefore working his way towards the Morven district, whence, crossing Loch Linnhe into Appin, he intended to seek his uncle's house at Invernacree, and once more get into touch with his own kin. To Alison, his first care, he had long ago despatched a reliable messenger with tidings of his well-being, but his own wandering existence these last weeks had cut him off from any news of her.

Pulling his cloak – which from old habit he wore more or less plaid-fashion – closer about him, Ewen stopped now for a moment and took stock of his present whereabouts. The glen which he followed, with its gently receding mountains, was here fairly wide, so wide in fact that in this small, close-falling snow and fading light he could not see across to its other side. He could not even see far ahead, so that it was not easy to guess how much of its length he still had to travel. 'I believe I'd be wiser to turn back and lie the night at Duncan MacColl's,' he thought, for, if he was where he believed, the little farm of Cuiluaine at which, MacColl being an Appin man and a Jacobite, he had already found shelter in his wanderings, must lie about two miles behind him up the slope of the farther side of the glen. He listened for the sound of the stream in the bottom, thinking that by its distance from the rack he could roughly calculate his position.

But while he thus listened and calculated he heard, in that dead and breathless silence, not only the faint far-off murmur of water, but the murmur of human voices also. Hardly believing this, he went on a few steps and then paused again to listen. Yes, he could distinctly hear voices, but not those of persons talking in an ordinary way, but the speakers seemed rather to be repeating something in antiphon, and the language had the lilt of Gaelic. Once more Ardroy went forward, puzzled as to the whereabouts of the voices, but now recognizing the matter of their recitation, for there had floated to him unmistakable fragments about the snare of the hunter, the terror by night, and the arrow by day. A snow-sprinkled crag suddenly loomed up before him, and going round it he perceived, somewhat dimly at first, who they were that repeated Gaelic psalms in the darkening and inhospitable landscape.

A little below the track, on the flatter ground which was also the brink of the bog, rose two shapes which he made out to be those of an old man and a boy, standing very close together with their backs to him. A small lantern threw a feeble patch of light over the whitened grass on which it stood; beside it lay a couple of shepherd's crooks and two bundles.

Ewen was too much amazed to shout to the two figures, and

the snow must have muffled his approach down the slope. The recitation went on uninterrupted:

' "*There shall no evil happen unto thee,*" ' said the old man's voice, gentle and steady.

' "*Neither shall any plague come nigh thy dwelling,*" ' repeated the younger, more doubtfully.

' "*For he shall give his angels charge over thee.*" '

' "*To keep thee in all –* " ' The lad who had turned his head, broke off with a shrill cry, 'Sir, sir, he has come – the angel!'

' "*To keep thee in all thy ways,*" ' finished the old man serenely. Then he too looked up and saw Ewen standing a little above them, tall, and white all over the front of him with snow.

'I told you, Callum, that it would be so,' he said, looking at the boy; and then, courteously, to Ewen, and in the unmistakable accents of a gentleman, 'You come very opportunely, sir, to an old man and a child, if it be that you are not lost yourself, as we are?'

Ewen came down to their level, and, in spite of the falling snow, removed his bonnet. 'I think I can direct you to shelter, sir. Do you know that you are in danger of becoming bogged also?'

'I was beginning to fear it,' said the old man, and now there was a sound of weariness, though none of apprehension, in his voice. 'We are on our way to Duncan MacColl's at Cuiluaine, and have lost the path in the snow. If it would not be delaying you overmuch, perhaps you would have the charity to put us into it again.'

'You are quite near the track, sir,' replied Ardroy. 'But I will accompany you to Cuiluaine. Will you take my arm?'

The old man took the proffered support, while the boy Callum, who had never removed his soft, frightened gaze from the figure of the 'angel', caught a fold of Ewen's wet cloak and kissed it, and the rescuer began to guide both wayfarers up the whitened hillside.

'But, sir,' protested the old traveller, breathing a little hard, when they were all back upon the path, 'we are perhaps taking you out of your own road?'

They were, indeed, since Ewen's face was set in the opposite direction. But there was no question about it; he could not leave the two, so old and so young, to find their doubtful way to Cuiluaine alone. 'I shall be glad enough to lie at Mr Mac-Coll's myself tonight,' he answered. 'I was almost on the point of turning back when I heard your voices. Do I go too fast for you, sir?'

'Not at all; and I hope I do not tire this strong arm of yours? We were just coming in our psalm a while ago to "*And they shall bear thee in their hands, that thou hurt not thy foot against a stone.*" ' He turned round with a smile to the boy following behind. 'You see how minutely it is fulfilled, Callum! – Are you of these parts, sir?'

'No,' answered Ewen. 'I am a Cameron from Lochaber.'

'Ah,' observed the old man, 'if you are a Cameron, as well as being the Lord's angel to us, then you will be of the persecuted Church?'

'An Episcopalian, do you mean, sir? Yes,' answered Ewen. 'But not an angel.'

'*Angelos,* as you are no doubt aware, Mr Cameron, means no more in the original Greek than a messenger.' He gave the young man the glimpse of a beautiful smile. 'But let us finish the psalm together as we go. You have the Gaelic, of course, for if we say it in English, Callum will not be able to join with us.'

And, going slowly, but now more securely, on the firmer ground, they said the remaining four verses together. To Ewen, the whole episode was so strange as to be dreamlike. Who was this saintly traveller, so frail looking and so old, who ventured himself with a boy of sixteen or so through bogs and snow in a Highland February?

Ere they reached Duncan MacColl's little farm up the other side of the glen he had learnt his identity. His charge was a Mr Oliphant, formerly an Episcopal minister in Perthshire, who had been moved by the abandoned condition of 'these poor sheep' in the Western Highlands to come out of his retirement (or rather, his concealment, for he had been ejected from his own parish) to visit them and administer the Sacraments. He was doing this at the risk of his liberty, it might be said of his life, for transportation would certainly kill him – and of his health for he was not of an age for this winter travelling on foot. When he had learnt his name Ewen was a little surprised at Mr Oliphant having the Gaelic so fluently, but it appeared that his mother was Highland, and that for half his life he had ministered to Highlanders.

The light from the little farmhouse window on the hillside above them, at first a mere glow-worm, cheered them through the cold snowy gloom which was now full about the three. Nearer, they saw that the door, too, stood open, half-blocked by a stalwart figure, for Duncan MacColl was expecting Mr Oliphant, and in considerable anxiety at his delay. He greeted the old man with joy; he would have sent out long before this to search for him, he said, but that he had no one of an age to send – he was a widower with a host of small children – and was at last on the point of setting forth himself.

'But now, thank God, you are come, sir – and you could not have found a better helper and guide than Mr Cameron of Ardroy,' he said warmly, ushering them all three into the living-room and the cheerful blaze. 'Come ben, sirs, and you, little hero!'

' 'Twas not I found Mr Cameron,' said Mr Oliphant, with his fine, sweet smile. 'He was sent to us in our distress.'

'Indeed, I think it must have been so,' agreed MacColl. 'Will you not all sit down and warm yourselves, and let the girl here dry your cloaks? You'll be wise to take a dram at once.' He fussed over the old priest as a woman might have done, and, indeed, when Ewen saw Mr Oliphant in the light he thought there could hardly be anyone less fitted for a rough journey in this inclement weather than this snowy-haired old man.

But there was for the moment no one but the boy Callum with them in the kitchen when Mr Oliphant turned round from the fire to which he had been holding out his half-frozen hands.

'*Angelos,* will you take an old man's blessing?'

'I was about to ask for it, sir,' said Ewen, bending his head; and the transparent hand was lifted.

So Ardroy had a private benediction of his own, as well as

that in which the house and all its inmates were included, when Mr Oliphant read prayers that night.

Ewen was up betimes next morning, to find the snow gone from the ground, and a clear sky behind the white mountain-tops.

'Ay, I was surprised to see that fall,' observed Duncan Mac-Coll. 'We have had so strangely mild a winter; there were strawberries, they say, in bloom in Lochiel's garden at Achna-carry near Christmas Day – though God knows they can have had little tending. Did ye hear that in Lochaber, Mr Cameron? 'Twas a kind of a portent.'

'I wish it may be a good one,' said Ewen, his thoughts swinging regretfully back to forfeited Achnacarry and his boyish rambles there. 'By the way, you have no news, I suppose, of someone who owns a very close connexion with that name and place – you know whom I mean?'

' "Mr Chalmers"?' queried the farmer, using the name by which Dr Cameron often passed. 'No, I have heard nothing more since I saw you a few weeks syne, Mr Cameron, until last Wednesday, when there was a cousin of mine passed this way and said there was a rumour that the Doctor was in Ardna-murchan again of late.'

'Do you tell me so?' exclaimed Ewen. 'To think that all this time that I have been in Ardgour and Sunart I have never heard a whisper of it, though I know he was there before Christmas. Yet it is possible that he has returned, mayhap to his kinsman Dungallon.' For Doctor Cameron's wife was a Cameron of Dungallon, and there were plenty of the name in Ardnamur-chan.

'I think it will likely be no more than a rumour,' said Mr MacColl. 'Forbye, from what he told me last night, there will soon be another man in Ardnamurchan who'll need to walk warily there, though not for the same reason.'

'You mean Mr Oliphant? Yes, I know that he is set on go-ing there, despite the presence of the garrison at Mingary Castle. And 'tis an uncommon rough journey for a man of his age and complexion. He should have someone with him besides that lad. Could not some grown man be found to accompany him?'

Duncan MacColl shook his head. 'Not here, Mr Cameron. I would offer to go myself, but that I have the whole work of the farm on my hands just now, for my herdsman is ill. Yet it's true; he needs a stronger arm than young Callum's.'

Ewen stood in the doorway reflecting, the idea which had come to him needed weighing. He did greatly long to get back across Loch Linnhe, and if he offered himself as Mr Oliphant's escort he would be turning his back upon Appin and all that it meant, even if it were but for a short time. On the other hand, supposing Archie were in Ardnamurchan after all ... As so often, two half-motives coalesced to make a whole. And when Mr Oliphant had breakfasted he made his proposal.

'But, my dear Mr Cameron, you admitted last night that you were already on your way towards Appin!'

Ewen replied that this morning, because of some news which Mr MacColl had just given him, he was, on the contrary desirous of going into Ardnamurchan. 'And if you would allow me to be your escort, sir,' he added, 'I should account it a privilege.'

'You make a sacrifice, however, Mr Cameron,' said the old priest, looking at him with eyes as keen as they had ever been. 'Be sure that it will be repaid to you in some manner.'

'I want no repayment, sir, other than that of your company. To what part of Ardnamurchan do you propose to go?'

Mr Oliphant told him that his plan was to visit, in that remote and most westerly peninsula of Scotland (and indeed of Britain) the hamlet of Kilmory on the north and of Kilchoan on the south. But Ewen and Duncan MacColl succeeded in dissuading him from going to the latter because of its dangerous proximity to Mingary Castle with its garrison. The inhabitants of Kilchoan could surely, they argued, be informed of his presence at Kilmory, and come thither, with due precautions against being observed.

2

So they set out on their journey together, the young man and the old, on this tolerably fine February day, and travelled over bad tracks and worse roads towards Ardnamurchan while the boy Callum returned from Cuiluaine to his father's croft, to tell for the rest of his life the story of a rescue in the snow by an archangel.

The distance which the two wayfarers had to traverse was not great, but Ewen was so afraid of pushing on too quickly for Mr Oliphant's strength that he probably went slower than they need have done. However, after a night spent with some very poor people who gave them of their best and refused the least payment, they came with twilight on the second day to Kilmory of Ardnamurchan and the thatched dwellings of fisher-folk who looked perpetually upon mountainous islands rising from an ever-changing sea, and knew scarcely a word of English. By them Mr Oliphant was received as if he had come straight from heaven, and the tall gentleman, his escort, the *duine uasal mór*, with the respect due to a celestial centurion. And word went instantly round to all the scattered crofts, to Swordle, to Ockle, to Plocaig, to Sanna, and in particular to Kilchoan on the southern shore.

Next day Mr Oliphant was hard at work, baptizing, catechizing, visiting. It was pathetic to see the eagerness and reverence of these poor and faithful people, who once had been under the care of a zealous Episcopal minister, now torn from them, so that they were left shepherdless, save when the Presbyterian intruder, as they considered him, came there on his rare visits to this portion of his vast parish; and his ministrations they naturally did not wish to attend.

Fortunately, it appeared that the soldiers had for the moment something else to occupy them than hunting out Episcopalians. The colonel of the garrison had been missing since the previous day, when he had gone out alone, taking a gun, and had not returned. The inhabitants of Kilmory said uncompromisingly that if he never came back it would be a good day for them, for he was a very evil and cruel man whom the soldiers themselves hated. But they had this consolation in his temporary disappearance, that the military, if they were still searching for him, would hardly trouble Kilmory or the coast round it, where there was nothing to be shot save gulls.

Nevertheless, when Mr Oliphant held a service that afternoon in the largest of the cottages, it was thought well to place a few outposts, and Ewen, though he would have liked to hear the old man preach, offered to be one of these. So about sunset he found himself walking to and fro on the high ground above the hamlet, whence he could survey the beginning of the road which dipped and wound away southwards over the moorland towards Mingary Castle and Kilchoan. But northward the island peaks soared all blue and purple out of the sea like mountains of chalcedony and amethyst, headland upon headland stretched against the foam, and the eye travelled over the broken crests of that wild land of Moidart, pressing after each other as wave follows wave, to the lovely bay where the Prince had landed seven and a half long years before, and whence he had sailed away ... into silence. Farther still the coast swept round to an unseen spot, both bitter and sacred in memory, where Ewen's murdered English friend slept under some of the whitest sand in the world.

And miles away to the north-west lay his own home and the Eagle's Loch. Ewen sighed. When should he see his wife and children again? Soon now, please God. But spring, too, would soon be come, and with the spring his sword was promised – if the time were ripe. But would it be? He knew nothing, the dwellers in these remote parts knew less, and, from what he had already heard from them, his hopes of finding Archibald Cameron in Ardnamurchan and learning of the prospects of an uprising were little likely to be fulfilled.

With the fall of twilight the momentary afterglow faded rapidly, and the strange, jagged heights of Skye began to withdraw into the magic region whence they had emerged. Voices came up from the hamlet, and the sentry saw that the service must be over, for men and women were streaming away. They would reassemble in the morning, for next day early Mr Oliphant was to celebrate the Eucharist.

Ewen's watch was ended. As he turned to go, still gazing,

half-unconsciously, towards Loch nan Uamh, he struck his
foot against some slight obstacle. Glancing down, he saw that
it was a little shrivelled bush – scarcely even a bush – no more
than eighteen inches high. There was nothing on its meagre
stem but very fine, thickly set thorns; not even a rag of the
delicately cut leaves which, with those thorns and its delicious,
haunting fragrance, mark off the little wild rose of Scotland,
the burnet rose, from every other, and especially from its
scentless sister of English hedgerows in June. Ewen stood looking down at it. Yes, this rose was ill to pluck, and ill to wear . . .
but no other grew with so brave a gesture in the waste, and none
had that heart-entangling scent.

3

Next morning had come. There was not a sound from the men
and women kneeling in the cold light upon the sand and grass;
nothing but the indrawn breath of the sea, now and then a gull's
cry, and that old, clear, steady voice. It was at the Epistle that
some intense quality in it first riveted Ewen's attention: *'and
forgiving one another, if any man have a quarrel against you;
even as Christ forgave you, so also do ye'*. Had not these simple,
reverent people much to forgive their oppressors?

The altar stood in the doorway of a cottage; it was only the
rough table of common use covered with a coarse, clean cloth.
A fisherman's lantern had been placed at either end, for it was
not yet very light. Mr Oliphant wore the usual preacher's black
gown and a stole, nothing else of priestly vestment: there were
no accessories of any kind, nothing but what was poor and
bare and even makeshift – nothing but the Rite itself.

Just before the consecration the sun rose. And when, with
the rest, Ewen knelt in the sand before that rude, transfigured
threshold, he thought of Bethlehem; and then of Gennesaret.
And afterwards, looking round at the little congregation,
fisher-folk and crofters all, he wondered when these deprived
and faithful souls would taste that Bread again. Not for years,
perhaps. And when would he, scarcely in better case – and in
whose company?

He was to remember this strange and peaceful Eucharist when that day came and brought one still stranger.

Ardroy could not help Mr Oliphant in his ministrations, so he went out fishing with some of the men on that sea which for once had none of the violence of winter. Gleams of sunshine chased each other on the peaks of Rum, and all day seemed to keep the serenity of its opening. That evening, his last there, Mr Oliphant preached on the Gospel for the day, on the parable of the tares, and this time Ewen was among the congregation. Yes, one had to be denied the exercise of one's religion truly to value it, to listen hungrily as he found himself listening. He had not so listened to Mr Hay's discourses, good man though he was, in the days when Episcopalian worship was tolerated.

Next morning, after a moving scene of leave-taking, the old priest left Kilmory under Ewen's escort. Many of his temporary flock would have desired to come part of the way with him, but it was judged wiser not to risk attracting attention. Mr Oliphant now meaning to visit Salen, on Loch Sunart, and Strontian, Ardroy intended to go with him as far as Salen; and he had a further plan, which he developed as he walked, that after he had visited Sunart and Ardgour Mr Oliphant should follow him into Appin, staying with Mr Stewart of Invernacree, where, all Stewarts of that region being, as their religious and political opponents put it, 'madly devoted to the Episcopal clergy' he would be sure of a most ready welcome.

They were discussing this plan as they went along the side of Loch Mudle, where the road led above the little lake in wild, deer-haunted country. The water had a pleasant air this morning, grey winter's day though it was, and the travellers stopped to look at it.

'To tell the truth,' said Mr Oliphant, 'I was not aware that Ardnamurchan possessed any loch of this size. It minds me a little of – '

He stopped, for Ewen had gripped his arm. 'Forgive me, sir; but I heard just then a sound not unlike a groan. Could it be?'

They both listened intently. For a while there was nothing but silence which, in very lonely places, seems itself to have the quality of noise. Then the sound came again, faint and despairing, and this time Mr Oliphant too heard it. It was not easy to be sure of its direction, but it appeared to come from the tree-covered slope above them, so Ewen sprang up this and began to search among the leafless bushes, helped after a moment or two by catching sight of a gleam of scarlet. That colour told him what he was going to find. He climbed a little higher, parted the stems, took one look at the figure sprawled in a tangle of faded bracken, and called down to his companion.

'Mr Oliphant – here he is ... and it must be the missing officer from Mingary Castle.' Then he pushed his way through and knelt down by the unfortunate man.

It seemed a marvel that he was still alive. One arm was shattered, the white facings of his uniform were pierced and blood-stained, and half his face – not a young face – was a mask of blood. Yet he was semi-conscious, his eyes were partly open, and between the faint moans which had drawn attention to him he uttered again and again the word 'water'.

'Is this murder, think you?' asked Mr Oliphant in a horrified voice. 'Ah, you have some brandy with you; thank God for that!'

But Ewen had by now caught sight of something lying a little way off. 'No, sir, not murder; nor has he been gored by a stag, as I thought at first. 'Tis a burst fowling-piece has done it – there it lies. And he has been here, poor wretch, nearly two days!'

They wetted the dried, blackened lips with brandy and tried to get a little down the injured man's throat, but he seemed unable to swallow, and Mr Oliphant feared that the spirit might choke him. 'Try water first, Mr Cameron,' he suggested, 'if you can contrive to bring some in your hands from the burn there.'

Holding his hollowed palms carefully together, Ewen brought it.

'We must, by some means or other, inform the garrison of

Mingary at once,' said the old priest, carefully supporting the ghastly head. 'I wish we had Callum with us; speed is of the first importance. Shall I lower his head a little?'

'Yes, it would be better. But I can reach Mingary as quickly as the lad would have done,' said Ewen, without giving a thought to the undesirability of approaching that stronghold. 'I'm spilling this; he's past drinking, I fear. Certainly if help is not soon – ' He gave a sudden violent exclamation under his breath, and, letting all the rest of the water drain away, sank back on his heels staring as though he had come on some unclean sight. For under the trickles of water and brandy the dried blood had become washed or smeared off the distorted face, sufficiently at least to make it recognizable to a man who, even in the mists of fever, and seven years ago, had during twenty-four hours seen more than enough of it.

'What is wrong, then?' asked Mr Oliphant, but he did not glance up from the head on his arm, for he had began cautiously to try the effect of brandy again.

Ewen did not answer for a moment. He was rubbing one wet hand upon the ground as though to cleanse it from some foul contact.

'I doubt it is worth going for help,' he said at last in a half-strangled voice. 'If one had it, the best thing would be to finish this business . . . with a dirk.'

And at that Mr Oliphant looked up and saw his face. It was not a pleasant sight.

'What – what has come to you?' he exclaimed. 'You said a moment ago that if assistance were not brought – '

'I had not seen then what we were handling,' said Ewen fiercely. He got to his feet. 'One does not fetch assistance to . . . vermin!'

'You are proposing that we should leave this unfortunate man here to die!'

Ewen looked down at him, breathing hard. 'I will finish him off if you prefer it. 'Tis the best thing that can happen to him and to all the inhabitants of Ardnamurchan. You have heard what his reputation is.' And turning away he began blindly to break a twig off the nearest birch-tree.

Mr Oliphant still knelt there for another second or two, silent, perhaps from shock. Then he gently laid down the head which he was supporting, came round the prostrate scarlet figure and over to his metamorphosed companion.

'Mr Cameron, it is not the welfare of Ardnamurchan which you have in your mind. This man has done you some injury in the past – is it not so?'

Ewen was twisting and breaking the birch twig as though it were some sentient thing which he hated.

'But for God's mercy he had made a traitor of me,' he said in a suffocated voice. 'Yet that I could forgive ... since he failed. But he has my friend's blood on his hands.'

There was a silence, save for the faint moaning behind them.

'And for that,' said Mr Oliphant sternly, 'you will take his blood on yours?'

'I have always meant to, if I got the chance,' answered Ewen, with dreadful implacability. 'I would it had been in fair fight – this is not what I had desired. But I am certainly not going to save his worse than worthless life at the expense, perhaps, of your liberty and mine ... I am not going to save it in any case. He slew my best friend.'

'You made mention just now, Mr Cameron, of God's mercy.'

'Ay, so I did,' said Ewen defiantly. 'But God has other attributes too. This,' he looked for a moment over his shoulder, 'this, I think, is His justice.'

'That is possible! but you are not God. You are a man who only yesterday received the greatest of His earthly gifts with, as I believed, a humble and thankful heart. Today you, who so lately drank of the cup of salvation, refuse a cup of cold water to a dying enemy.'

Ewen said nothing; what was there to say? He stood looking down through the trees on to the loch, his mouth set like a vice.

'Are you going to Mingary, my son?' asked Mr Oliphant after another brief and pregnant silence.

'No, I am not.'

'Very well then, I must go.' But his voice was not as steady as heretofore when he added, 'I would to God that it were you!'

In the grim white face before him the blue eyes darkened and blazed. Ardroy caught hold of the old man's arm. 'There's one thing that's certain, Mr Oliphant, and that is, that *you* are not going to enter the lion's den for the sake of that scoundrel!'

'The lion's den? Is that what is keeping you back – a natural distaste for endangering yourself? I thought it had been something less of man's weakness . . . and more of the devil!'

'So it is,' retorted Ewen stormily. 'You know quite well that I am not *afraid* to go to Mingary Castle!'

'Then why will you not let me go? I am only an old, unprofitable man whose words are not heeded. If I do not come out again what matter? It is true, I shall not get there near as quick as you, and every minute' – he glanced back – 'the faint chance of life is slipping farther away. But one of us has to go, Mr Cameron. Will you loose my arm?' His worn face was infinitely sad.

Ewen did not comply with his request. He heard Mr Oliphant say under his breath, in accents of the most poignant sorrow, '*Then appeared the tares also*. Such tall, such noble wheat! Truly the Enemy hath done this!' He understood, but he did not waver. He *would* not go for help.

'Mr Cameron, time is very short. Let me go! Do not lay this death on my conscience too. Loose me, in the name of Him Whom you are defying!'

Ewen dropped the speaker's arm, dropped his own hand. It was bleeding. He turned a tempest-ridden face on Mr Oliphant.

'It shall not be the better man of us two who goes to Mingary,' he said violently. 'I will go – you force me to it! And even though he be carrion by the time help comes, will you be satisfied?'

Mr Oliphant's look seemed to pierce him. 'By the time you get to Mingary, Highlander though you are, your vengeance will be satisfied.'

'As to that – ' Ewen shrugged his shoulders. 'But you, how will you ever reach Salen alone?'

'Salen? I shall not start for Salen until help has come; I shall stay here.' And as Ewen began a fierce exclamation he added, 'How can I, a priest, leave him lying at the gate and go away?'

'And then they will take you? – No. I will not go to Mingary ... I will not go unless you give me your word to withdraw yourself as soon as you hear the soldiers coming. That might serve, since I shall not say that any is with him, and they will not think of searching.'

Mr Oliphant considered a moment. 'Yes, I will promise that if it will ease your mind. And later, if God will, we may meet again on the Salen road, you overtaking me. Now go, and the Lord Christ go with you ... *angelos*!'

For an instant his hand rested, as if in blessing, on Ewen's breast. The young man snatched it up, put it to his lips, and without a word plunged down the slope to the track below, so torn with rage and shame and wild resentment that he could hardly see what he was doing.

Chapter 11

THE CASTLE ON THE SHORE

THE ancient stronghold of the MacIans of Ardnamurchan, where James IV had held his court, which had repulsed Lachlan Maclean with his Spanish auxiliaries from the wrecked Armada galleon, and had surrendered to Colkitto's threat of burning in Montrose's wars; which had known Argyll's seven weeks' siege and Clanranald's relief, stood on the very verge of the shore gazing over at Mull. At high tide the sea lapped its walls – or at least the rocks on which those walls were built – save on the side where a portion of the fortress had its footing on the mainland. It looked very grim and grey this winter morning, and the runner, drawing breath at last, felt exceedingly little inclination to approach it.

And yet air, flag, garrison, were all unstirring; Mingary seemed a fortress of the dead, staring across dull water at a misty shore. No one was visible save the sentry on the bridge crossing the fosse which guarded the keep on the landward, its most vulnerable side. As Ewen approached, the man brought his musket to the ready and challenged him in the accents of the Lowlands.

Ardroy made his announcement from a distance of some yards. 'I am come to tell you that your missing colonel is found. He is lying in sore straits on the slopes of Loch Mudle, and if you want him alive you must send without a moment's delay to fetch him.'

The sentry shook his head. 'I canna tak messages. Ye maun come ben and see an officer.'

'I cannot wait to do that,' replied Ewen impatiently. 'I am in great haste. I tell you your colonel is very badly hurt; his fowling-piece must have burst and injured him.'

'Man, ye suld ken that I couldna leave ma post if King Geordie himsel' was deein',' said the sentry reproachfully, and

126

suddenly uplifting his voice, bellowed to someone within, 'Sairgeant, sairgeant!' and motioned vehemently to Ewen to pass him.

Most unwillingly Ardroy crossed the bridge, and at the end of the long narrow entry into the fortress found himself confronted by a stout sergeant who listened, with no great show of emotion, to his tale. 'I'll fetch the captain – he'll wish tae see ye, sir.'

The wish was by no means reciprocal; and Ewen cursed inwardly at the recognition of his social status, from which he had hoped that his shabby clothes, worn for so long in bad weather, would have protected him.

'I am in great haste,' he asserted once more. 'Surely you could give the captain my message?'

But even as the last word left his lips two officers, talking together, suddenly appeared from he knew not where under the archway. Yet once again Ewen made his announcement, and this time it had an immediate effect. A few questions were asked him, he described the spot in detail, hasty orders were given for a party to set forth instantly with a litter and restoratives, and then the captain asked Ewen if he would be good enough to guide them to the place, which after a second or two of hesitation he agreed to do. Indeed, provided he were not asked questions of too searching a nature on the way, the arrangement would suit him well.

But he was not destined to profit by it. He had noticed the other officer, a young lieutenant whose face seemed vaguely familiar, looking at him closely; now, when this latter could gain the attention of his superior, he drew him aside and whispered to him.

The captain swung round to Ewen again, looking at him with a gaze which the Highlander did not at all appreciate. 'By the way, you have not told us your name, sir?' he remarked. 'We are so much in your debt that we should be glad to learn it.'

Ewen helped himself to that of the good tenant of Cuiluaine. He was, he announced, a MacColl, originally of Appin.

'Well, Mr MacColl,' said the captain, 'obliged as we are to

you for your information, I don't think we will trouble you to accompany us to Loch Mudle.'

'Then I'll bid you good day,' responded Ewen, making as if to go. But he had known instantly the subaltern's whisper meant he would not be allowed to walk out of Mingary Castle.

The officer took a step forward. 'Not so fast, if you please. I'll ask you to await our return here, Mr MacColl.'

'In God's name, why?' demanded Ewen, playing astonishment. But he was not really astonished; this was what came of running into a hornet's nest!

'That I shall be able to tell you when I return,' said the officer. 'For one thing, I think you have made a mistake in your name. Sergeant, a guard!'

'My name! What is wrong with my name? You are not proposing to keep me here illegally when I have just saved your colonel's life for you!'

'Believe me, I regret it, Mr ... Mr MacColl,' returned the captain suavely. 'I doubt if there is much illegality about it; but, since there is such great need of haste at the moment, we cannot possibly discuss the matter now. Sergeant, have this gentleman safely bestowed.'

'And how do you suppose that you are going to find your injured officer without me?' asked Ewen sarcastically, as a guard came trooping under the archway.

'Easily, if the details you have furnished are correct. And I shall be the first to apologize to you, Mr MacColl, for this detention ... if there is cause for apology. Come, Burton.' He swung on his heel and hurried off.

Resistance were foolish. Grinding his teeth, Ewen went whither he was taken, and three minutes later found himself in a dusky place with oozing stone walls and a floor of solid rock. There was a barred window just out of his reach, a worm-eaten table, a rough bench and a broken pitcher – nothing else. As Mingary Castle was of thirteenth-century construction, this spot might well have been even more disagreeable, but Ewen in his present temper would have found a boudoir intolerable if he could not leave it at will. He was furiously angry – angry even with Mr Oliphant. One might have known that this would happen! Here he was, caged up again, and all for rendering, as much against his will as a good action had ever been done in the history of the world, a service to a man whom he hated and had sworn to kill! He sat down upon the bench and cursed aloud.

When he ceased it was to become conscious of fresh details of his prison, notably the rustiness of the iron bars across the window, and to hear, faint but distinct, the sound of waves not very far away. He might be here for weeks in this seagirt hole! ... Or Guthrie, if he recovered sufficiently, might recognize what he had done for him, and let him go out of gratitude.

That would be the most intolerable consequence of all – that Guthrie should know he had played the Good Samaritan! Ewen jumped up. Out of this place he would be before Guthrie was brought into it! He felt capable of tearing down the stones with his nails, of wrenching the iron bars of the window out of their sockets with his bare hands.

But ... that was not necessary! In his pocket, surely, was still the file which had won his and Hector's freedom from Fort William. What great good fortune that no orders had been given to search him! Without a moment's delay he pushed the crazy table under the window, and, mounted rather precariously upon it, began to file feverishly at the middle bar.

Ardroy had worked away for perhaps an hour, his hands red with rust, hoping that no one would hear the noise of scraping, when it came to him where he had seen the face of the subaltern who had whispered about him to the captain. It was the lieutenant who had brought up Hector the day that youth had surrendered himself at Fort William. He had without doubt recognized the other ex-captive. There was more need of haste than ever; his case was worse than he had supposed, and even if Guthrie, distasteful as the notion was, should be smitten with gratitude, he would hardly dare to let an already escaped prisoner go free.

By three o'clock the first bar was through. It was half-worn away, or it would not have yielded to the file in the time. The second was eaten too, and when in about three-quarters of an hour that also parted, and could be wrenched aside, by cautiously thrusting his head out Ewen was able to ascertain where he was – only a matter of ten feet or so above the basaltic rock on which the castle was built. At the base of this rock leapt the waves, not an encouraging sight; but if, as he judged, it was now high tide or thereabouts, he guessed that by half-tide the rock, and indeed a good part of the little bay to the west of the castle, would be clear of these invaders. He thought this probable because to his left he could see that a stone causeway, now slapped by the waves, had been constructed for use when the tide was low.

Ardroy drew his head in again and resumed his filing, debating, while he worked, where he should aim for when he got out. He certainly must not immediately go back in the direction whence he had come. Then should he make across the peninsula to its northern shore, or should he strike out for its extreme end?

Suddenly he thought of the two Coll fishermen in Kilchoan bay. If they had not yet sailed for their island he might induce them to take him in their boat back up Loch Sunart, and, even if they were gone, he could perhaps find someone else at Kilchoan willing to do this for him. It would be a good plan to get clear off the peninsula before he had the whole garrison of Mingary searching for him. It might no doubt be better, for the purpose of getting away unseen from the castle, to wait until nightfall, but by then, who knew, the sawn bars might be discovered, and he removed to another dungeon. Moreover, the detestable Guthrie, living or dead, would have been brought in, and be under the same roof with him. He must be gone before either of these things could happen.

And at length the last bar, a very thin one, gave. The daylight was now beginning to fade a trifle, and the waves were no longer washing against the rock below; as Ewen had anticipated, a considerable segment of the little bay was free of water altogether. Once down on the shore he had only to cross this and climb the low, grassy cliff at some convenient spot, and he would be well away from Mingary, even, perhaps, out of sight of it. It seemed, indeed, a good deal to hope that before he got as far as that he should not have been seen and shot at, but he reflected that only a very few of the garrison could possibly have observed his entrance or know of his being made prisoner, that a number, including two officers at least, had gone off to Loch Mudle, and that the rest would surely not fire without reason at an unknown individual making his way, not too fast, along the shingle below them.

It required, in the end, more muscular effort to pull himself from the shaky table entirely up to the level of the little window and to get himself through this, than to lower himself the other side. At last, with a good deal of strain and wriggling, he was through, dropped on to the shelf of rock at the bottom of the masonry, and crouched there a moment or two, holding his breath, for men's voices and laughter had all at once drifted ominously to his ears. But he could not make out whence they came, and in any case must go on.

There was a place on the side of the shelf nearest to the sea which was much wider, and which seemed to overhang the shore; but this end of it Ewen naturally avoided, creeping along in the opposite direction pressed as close as possible to the grey stones of the keep. But soon he could do this no longer, for the shelf had narrowed until it ceased altogether; on which, finding foothold with some difficulty, he clambered down the rock itself to the beach.

But when the fugitive was there he instantly stood motionless, for he saw, only too clearly, what the overhanging shelf had hidden from him. Above him towered Mingary, with who knew what observers on its battlements, but between him and the sea, at no great distance, was worse – a party of about a dozen soldiers uproariously washing their feet in a pool left by the tide. It was their voices which he had heard on the ledge.

One moment of sharp dismay and Ardroy turned, quick as a fox, and began to tiptoe away over the shingle. If he could only reach the low cliff over there unobserved, he would soon be up that. He did not think that he had been seen; his impression was that the men mostly had their backs turned in his direction, or were absorbed in their chilly ablutions. And their talk and guffaws might cover the scrunch of the shingle under his feet.

But to get away from so many eyes without being seen by any was too much to ask for. A minute later cries of 'Halt, you there – halt and tell your business!' reached him, and he knew that measures were on foot to enforce the command. Ewen did not look back; he took to his heels, a pretty certain means, he knew, of ensuring a bullet's being sent after him. But he was too desperately set upon escape to weigh that risk. Instant pursuit, of course, there would be; he heard the cries with which it started, and the sound of men scrambling to their feet over stones – yet not a single shot.

Two facts, indeed, were in the Highlander's favour, though he knew it not; no redcoat had committed so unheard-of a folly as to burden himself with his musket when off duty, and not a single man of the party at the pool happened to be fully shod when he took the alarm. Those with one boot paused to pull on the other, those with none, less cautious or more zealous, began the chase as they were – and, over shingle and edges of bare rock, did not get very far. Meanwhile, therefore, Ewen had quite a respectable start, and made the very best of it. In a few minutes he had reached the slope, part grass, part rock, part bare earth, and had hurled himself up it. For one instant he thought that a patch of earth over which he had to pull himself was going to give way and slide with his weight, but his muscles carried him to a securer spot before this could happen. And, once on the top, he found a stretch of rough but not precipitous going between him and the hamlet of Kilchoan, which now seemed his best goal. To turn the other way was to pass the fortress again.

A glance showed him that no one had yet topped the cliff. He ran like a deer through heather stems and bog-myrtle, up slopes and down them, and when his track was crossed by a tangled hollow with a burn at the bottom he plunged gratefull down, for it meant cover, and he could work along it unseen for a little. When he was obliged to come up again on the other side he saw with thankfulness the forms of only three pursuers running stumblingly towards the ravine which they had yet to cross, and he took fresh breath and sped still faster over the moorland.

Soon, as he went, Kilchoan bay with its string of white cottages round the shore was fully visible, under the remains of a smouldering sunset. He could see only one sailing-boat at anchor; was that the Macleans', the Coll men's? In another three minutes he was near enough to see figures moving about in her. Perhaps she was about to sail with the ebb. He came, still running very fast, though the pace was distressing him, through a little cluster of fishermen's huts at the edge of the strand. 'Is that boat out yonder from Coll?' he shouted to an old man at his door, and understood the ancient to pipe after him as he passed that it was, and just upon sailing.

Ewen pulled up breathless. 'I want a boat ... take me to her!' But he could see without being told that there was no boat within easy reach. He threw a look behind him; two scarlet-clad forms were doggedly pounding along towards the cottages, and would be on the shore in another couple of minutes. He must do without a boat. Shouting and waving to the Coll men, who seemed to have been attracted by what was going on, he ran out along a wet spit of rock and, pausing only to remove his shoes, plunged into the water.

The sea was as calm as a summer's day and colder than anything he had ever imagined. The yellow-bladdered fingers of the low-tide seaweed slid gropingly round him, but in a moment he was clear of them, and, gasping for breath, was striking out furiously for the fishing-boat. ... Then he was underneath her counter, and the Macleans, with exclamations which showed that they recognized him, were helping him over the side. And as by now the two persistent soldiers could be heard shouting, with gesticulations, for a boat, there was no need for the dripping fugitive to explain from whom he was escaping.

'Will you take me with you?' he got out, panting. It was folly now even to suggest their putting about and passing Mingary to go up Loch Sunart, as he had once thought of doing.

'Ay, will we,' said the elder Maclean. 'Ye'll please give my brother a hand with the sails, then.' He ran forward to the anchor.

The pursuers had not even got hold of a boat before the little fishing vessel was moving up the top of the Sound of Mull towards the open sea and the flat mass of the isle of Coll, vaguely discernible about eight miles away; while Ewen, after making fast the last halyard, had sunk drenched and exhausted on a thwart.

An hour and a half later he was sitting on a heap of nets in the bows of the *Ròn*, the Seal, clad in an odd assortment of garments. His own were hanging up to dry. For a February night in these latitudes the air was remarkably warm, as he had already noticed, thinking, not of himself, but of the old man to whom he had lent his arm for so many miles. But surely Mr Oliphant had gained some kind of shelter for the night . . . only Ewen prayed that shelter were not Mingary Castle.

Though darkness would soon shroud the little boat from Mingary, the Macleans were not willing to put about because, other considerations apart, they were carrying meal to their families in Coll, where it was needed immediately; and Ewen had to acquiesce in this reluctance, feeling, as he did, that they had already rendered him a much greater service than he could have expected of them, in thus taking him off under the very eyes of the redcoats.

The *Ròn* rolled before the following wind, and the sail flapped; the younger Maclean was singing under his breath some air of the Outer Isles full of cadences at once monotonous and unexpected. A hidden moon was tingeing the heavy clouds over Mull and at last Ewen had time to think. But thought was tumbled and broken, like those clouds. He had met his enemy, after all these years, and . . . well, what had he done with him? Saved him, or tried to, at another's bidding, and with a reluctance which amounted to abhorrence. Small credit could he take to himself for that deed!

The wind freshened, and seemed to be changing too; it ran cool over Ewen's damp hair. The *Ròn* was feeling the Atlantic swell; blessed little boat, which had cheated his pursuers! And where was now his heat of baffled revenge – a mere cinder in his breast. Certainly it burnt with flame no longer; quenched, perhaps, as the half-fantastic thought whispered, by the cold waves of Kilchoan bay. And was he glad of it, or did he miss the purpose which had lain buried in his heart so long, the purpose which he had avowed to Archibald Cameron that evening at Ardroy, but which he could never again take out and finger over, like a treasure? Ewen did not know.

Time passed; Ardroy lay still without moving, half-propped against the gunwale, his head on his arm, seeing more clearly, with every wave that heaved, dimly frothing, past the boat's nose, from what Mr Oliphant had saved him; beginning indeed to have shuddering glimpses of a deep and very dark place in himself full of horrible things. Well did the Gaelic name the Enemy 'the One from the Abyss'! . . . But that very deliverance had parted him from the old man, it might be for ever, and he could not say to him now what he longed to say. Perhaps he would never be able to.

'Will you sleep, sir?' came a voice in his ear. One of the Macleans was bending over him. 'We'll not make Coll till morning now; the wind's gone round, and we must take a long tack to the northward. I have brought a sail to cover you.'

Ewen looked up. The moon was gone, the clouds too; the sky was velvet dark, and sown with myriad points of light. 'Thank you, Maclean; yes, I'll sleep awhile.'

And to himself he said, as he stretched himself on the brine-scented nets, 'Thank God – and a saint of His – that I can!'

Chapter 12

AFTER SUNSET

1

'My dear Ewen,' said old Invernacree, and he reached across and replenished his nephew's glass, 'my dear Ewen, have you not had your fill of wandering, that you cannot bide with us a few days?'

But Ewen shook his head. 'I would that I could, for I have, indeed, had my fill of wandering – near three months of it. But I must push on to Edinburgh tomorrow, to consult an advocate, as I told you, sir.'

Mid-March had come and passed ere he finally sat at his uncle's board, not sorry to see silver and napery again, and to look forward to a comfortable bed. And now, supper being over, he was alone with his uncle, the ladies having withdrawn – the middle-aged daughter, by his first wife, who kept house for the twice-widowed Alexander Stewart of Invernacree, and the pretty girl who was Ian's own sister. Ian himself, to Ewen's regret, was from home.

The candlelight fell on Ewen's auburn head and air of content and shabby clothes – no others in the house would fit him – and on Invernacree's silver hair and deeply furrowed face. To Ewen it had seemed almost more strange, these last few years, to see his uncle, so essentially a Highlander and a Jacobite of the old breed, in Lowland garb and without a scrap of tartan, than to see himself thus clad. Looking thoughtfully at him now, he saw how greatly the death of his elder son at Culloden Moor had aged him. But at the moment there was content on the old man's face also, though tempered by his nephew's refusal to contemplate a longer stay.

'Yes, I fear I must lose no more time,' resumed Ewen. 'I had thought to be in Edinburgh, as you know, soon after Christmas, and now it is close upon Lady Day.'

'Ay,' said Invernacree. 'Ay, I doubted from what he told me at the time that Ian somehow mismanaged that affair at the Narrows – either he or that young Frenchified brother-in-law of yours.'

'No, sir, I assure you that he did not!' protested his nephew warmly. 'Neither Ian nor Hector was a whit to blame for what happened. If there was a blunder it was mine. I owe Ian more than I can easily repay, and if Hector had had his wish we should have broken out of Fort William long before we did.'

'But it was young Grant, nevertheless, who brought trouble upon you in the first instance; he told me so himself.'

Ewen could not repress a smile. 'Hector is indiscreet,' he said, thinking of someone else who had remarked that of him. 'Yet I suppose he told you the whole story, so that you have not truly been without news of me for centuries, as my cousins have just been complaining.'

'Why, we have had much more recent news of you than Hector Grant's,' exclaimed his uncle. 'They must have been teasing you, the jades, for they cannot have forgotten who brought it. Can you guess who it was, Ewen?'

'I think so. Mr Oliphant did make his way here, then, sir?' Ewen's face had lit up.

'He did,' said the old man with an air of satisfaction. 'It was from him that we learnt of the truly Christian deed of charity to an enemy which was the cause of your separation from him. But he feared – and justly, it seems – that you might have become a prisoner in Mingary Castle on account of it.'

Ewen had coloured vividly and turned his head away. 'I escaped the same day from Mingary,' he said hurriedly. And then, after a second or two, 'Mr Oliphant should have told you how unwillingly I was brought to that act.'

'Then, my dear Ewen, I honour you the more for having done it,' was his uncle's reply. 'But Mr Oliphant said not a word of that. He left a letter for you. If you will come into my room I will give it to you now.' He rose, helping himself up by the table. 'Fill your glass, nephew!'

Ewen rose and lifted it. 'The King!' said Alexander Stewart, and they drank. In that house there was no need to pass their glasses over water-jug or finger bowl, since there was no other King than James the Third and Eighth to avoid pledging by that consecrated subterfuge.

A tall, upright old man, though moving stiffly, Invernacree opened the door of his own study for his nephew. 'Sit there, Ewen, under your mother's picture. It is good to see you there; and I like to remember,' he added, looking him up and down, 'that Stewart blood went to the making of that braw body of yours. I sometimes think that you are the finest piece of manhood ever I set eyes on.'

'My dear uncle,' murmured the subject of this enconium, considerably embarrassed.

'You must forgive an old man who has lost a son not unlike you – No matter; sit down, *Eoghain mhóir*, while I fetch you good Mr Oliphant's letter. He, I assure you, could not say enough of you and what you had done for him.'

'I cannot say enough of what he did for me,' murmured Ewen as he took the letter and put it in his pocket. 'And in truth I went with him into Ardnamurchan half in hopes of meeting Doctor Cameron there. Do you know aught of the Doctor's recent movements, Uncle Alexander?'

'Nothing whatever. Ian, though he alleged some other motive, has gone, I believe, to try to learn some news; the boy is made very restless by the rumours which go about. But rumours will not help us. I doubt our sun went down upon Culloden Moor, Ewen.'

'A man might have thought,' objected his nephew, 'that the sun of the Stuart cause went down at Worcester fight; yet nine years afterwards Charles Stuart was riding triumphantly into London. 'Tis not yet nine years since Culloden.'

Old Alexander Stewart shook his head. He was silent, sitting perfectly still, so that the leaping flames might have been casting their flicker on the chin and brow of a statue.

'I have sometimes wondered,' began Invernacree again, 'whether the Almighty does not wish us to learn that His Will is changed, and that for our many unfaithfulnesses He does not purpose at this time to restore the kingdom unto Israel.'

With the older school of Jacobites religious and political

138

principles were so much one that it was perfectly natural to them to speak of one hope in terms of the other, and his language held no incongruity for Ewen. In moments of depression he had himself harboured the same doubt and had given voice to it, as that evening with Archibald Cameron – but he was too young and vigorous to have it as an abiding thought, and he tried to comfort the old man now, pointing out that a new door had opened, from what Doctor Cameron had told him; that if France would not and could not help there were others willing to do so.

'Yes,' admitted his uncle, 'it may be that all this long delay is but to try our faith. But I can recall Killiecrankie, the victory that brought no gain; I fought at Sheriffmuir nearly forty years ago, and I remember the failure at Glenshiel the year you were born – the failure which drove your father into exile. If this spring do not bring the assistance which I hear vaguely spoken of on all sides since Doctor Cameron's arrival, then our sun has truly set; we shall never see the White Rose bloom again. The hope of it is perhaps no more than the rainbow which spans the loch here so constantly between storms, or those streamers which you see in the northern sky at night – we have been seeing them of late, very bright. But they mean nothing ... if it be not ill weather next day. They come too late – after sunset.'

'But before dawn!' suggested Ewen.

'If you like, my dear boy, if you like, yes. You are young, and may yet see a dawn. Get you to bed now, and do not let an old man's faithlessness make you despond. . . . Good night, and God bless you!'

Up in the room which had been his mother's as a girl, and which he always occupied when he visited Invernacree, Ewen broke the seal of Mr Oliphant's letter.

'My dear son,' wrote the old man, 'I think you will guess how often I have thought of you and blessed you and prayed for you, even as David prayed, "Deliver my darling from the power of the dog." And I am sure that you were delivered, if not without scathe; and I hope, my dear son, that you had not to pay by an unjust captivity for your good deed, which *was* good even though it were done in the spirit of the man who said "I go not," and went. For you will remember that, for all his first refusing, it was he who was justified, and not the other.

'The unfortunate officer, your enemy, was still alive when the soldiers reached the place. I had written upon a piece of paper, which I then placed in his pocket, these words: "If you recover, you owe it to a man whom you greatly injured." I would not mention your name lest it brought harm upon you, and I thought, too, that you would not have wished it. But I wrote what I did for the man's own sake; it was right that he should know it – if indeed he would ever know anything again in this world. I had concealed myself, as I promised you, and I was not searched for. Moreover, I found help and shelter upon my road to Salen; yet I greatly missed my son's strong arm and his heartening company.

'Yet I have the hope, *angelos,* that before long you will reach this house of your good uncle's, which has been so kind a haven to me, and where it has been my delight to speak of you.

'The Lord bless and keep you, and lead you back safely to your own!'

Ewen put the letter carefully away in his breast, and going to the window stood looking out into the clear March night. Over the mountains facing him, though it was after ten at night, the sky was irradiated with a soft, white glow. As Ewen stood there it grew in intensity and widened; a faint, perfectly straight shaft of the same unearthly light shot up into the sky, then another. But Ardroy was thinking of other things: of the old priest's letter; of how his presentiment about meeting one who had to do with Keith Windham had been fulfilled; and of how strangely – it was not a new thought now – he had resembled his own small son in his desire that vengeance should be meted out to the evil-doer who had wrought him such an injury. "He was wicked – it was right that he should be punished!" had been Donald's cry of justification on that September evening. The idea still had power to raise in Ewen some of the rueful dismay which had swept over him when it had first presented itself, one morning when he was pacing the sandy shores of Coll, half-deafened by the green Atlantic surges, and praying for the wind to change. . . . But all reflections were merged now into an impatience to begin tomorrow's journey to Edinburgh, the next milestone on the road which was to bring him back to his wife and home. He turned away from the window, and began to make ready for bed.

Yet when, after blowing out his candle, he went for a last look over the loch, he gave a smothered exclamation. The moon was gone, vanquished, and the whole of the sky from north-west to north-east was pulsing with light, with great eddying rivers and pools of that magic radiance. The miraculous glow was no longer a background to the dark mountains of Morven, nor did it now send forth those straight pencils of light; it streamed and billowed, as it seemed for miles, right over the house-top; and it was never still for an instant. It shimmered across the sky like ethereal banners, for ever changing their shape; like the swirling draperies of a throng of dancers. Ewen had often seen the Aurora Borealis, but he could not remember ever having seen it so fine at this time of year. For a while he lay and watched from his bed what he could see of those bright and soundless evolutions; they were a commentary on his uncle's words this evening; but he was too tired, and the bed, after three months of hard and varied lying, too seductive, for him to stay awake and ponder the matter.

When he woke some hours later and turned over, the night was quite dark; all the wonderful white dance of flame in the heavens was gone as if it had never been.

2

Next day Ewen set out from Invernacree on his journey to Edinburgh, a gillie of his uncle's carrying his modest valise – not his, in truth, but one of Ian's. He meant to go on foot through Benderloch to the ferry on the curve of Loch Etive at Bonawe, and there, in the little inn on the farther side, hoped to hire a horse. If he failed in this he would have to trudge on for another twelve or thirteen miles to the next hostelry at Dalmally, beyond the Pass of Brander and Loch Awe.

The proud mass of Ben Cruachan, monarch of all the heights around, with a wreath of cloud veiling the snow upon his summit, frowned at the Cameron as he came along the northern shore of beautiful Etive towards the heart of Lorne. Ewen dismissed the gillie, took his valise and was rowed across the wind-rippled blue water.

'Is it true that the innkeeper here has horses for hire?' he asked, as he paid the ferryman on the farther side.

'Ay, he has, though but the one now. The beast will not be hired out the day, however, for I saw him no later than noon.'

The tiny inn under the three wind-bent pines looked as if it could scarcely provide a decent meal, still less a horse, yet, somewhat to Ewen's surprise, there was a very well-appointed chaise standing outside it. But there seemed something wrong with this equipage, for one of the horses was out of the shafts, and the middle-aged postilion was talking earnestly to an elegantly dressed young man, presumably the traveller. Various ragged underlings of the hostelry, possessing no knowledge of English, vociferated round them.

Ewen called one of these, told him he wanted a saddle-horse, and entered the inn to pay for its hire. He had some difficulty in finding the innkeeper, and the man had finally to be summoned.

'You have a saddle-horse for hire, I believe,' said Ardroy. 'For how many stages are you willing to let it out?'

The Highlander seemed embarrassed. 'I fear that I cannot let you have it at all, sir. I have but the one horse for hire, and the young gentleman out there, who is returning from Dunstaffnage Castle of Edinburgh, requires it for his chaise, for one of his own horses has suddenly gone lame.'

With instant resentment Ewen thought, 'From Dunstaffnage? A Campbell, of course, who thinks all belongs to him in Lorne! I would like to show him that he is wrong. ... But *I* need the horse, to carry me,' he said aloud with an unwonted haughtiness, 'and this sprig of Clan Diarmaid must make shift with his remaining horse, and go the slower.'

'He is not a Campbell, sir,' returned the innkeeper quickly. 'It is a Sassenach, a young English lord returning from a visit to Dunstaffnage.'

Ewen was slightly mollified. Even an Englishman was preferable, on the whole, to a Campbell. 'Perhaps,' he suggested, 'if he is told that this horse of yours is the only means of my getting on my way he will have the grace to relinquish it.'

Like the innkeeper he had used the Gaelic. The sentence was scarcely finished when a voice behind him made him start, he did not know why. 'It seems that there is now some difficulty about this horse of yours,' it said, addressing the landlord with some impatience, 'but I am unable to understand what your people say. Why cannot I hire the horse, since it is for hire?'

Ewen had turned, and saw a very handsome youth clad in what he, somewhat cut off of late from such vanities, guessed to be the latest mode. 'I am myself the difficulty, I fear, sir,' he said civilly. 'I had hoped to hire the horse to ride as far, at least, as Dalmally.'

'The horse iss for the saddle,' explained the innkeeper to the young Englishman. 'Though, inteet, he iss going fery well in harness too.' He looked from one client to the other in evident perplexity.

'In that case it would seem that I must ride postilion,' observed Ardroy with a recrudescence of annoyance.

The young traveller – English nobleman, if the innkeeper were correct – came forward to the elder. He was not only extremely good-looking, but had a delightfully frank and boyish expression; and, indeed, he was not very much more than a boy. 'Sir, could we not come to some arrangement, if we take the same road, and if I have unwittingly disappointed you of a horse? There is plenty of room in my chaise if you would do me the honour of driving in it.'

The offer was made so spontaneously, and speed was so desirable, that Ewen was tempted by it.

'You are too kind, sir,' he said, hesitating. 'I should be incommoding you.'

'Not in the least, I assure you,' declared the agreeable young traveller. 'There is ample room, for I left my man behind in

Edinburgh, and it would be a pleasure to have a companion. My name is Aveling – Viscount Aveling.'

'And mine is Cameron,' replied Ewen; but he did not add 'of Ardroy'. It flashed through his mind as ironical that a young English Whig – for Lord Aveling must be of Whig sympathies, or he would not have been visiting Campbell of Dunstaffnage – should propose to take the road with a man who not three months ago had escaped from Government hands at Fort William.

'Then you will give me the honour of your company, sir?' asked the young man eagerly. 'Otherwise I shall feel bound to surrender the horse to you, and I will not disguise that I am anxious to reach Edinburgh with as little delay as possible.' He said this with something of a joyous air, as though some good fortune awaited him at his journey's end. 'I hope to lie tonight at Dalmally,' he went on, 'and I think that even on horseback you would hardly go beyond that, for the next stage is, I am told, a long one.'

'No, that is quite true,' admitted Ewen, 'and so, my lord, I will with gratitude take advantage of your very obliging proposal. And if we are to be fellow travellers, may I not propose in my turn that before taking the road in company you should join me in a bottle of claret?'

So they sat down to some indifferent claret, and over it this suddenly blossoming acquaintance ripened as quickly to a very unlooked-for harvest. Lord Aveling seemed to Ardroy a really charming and attractive young man, unspoilt, so far as he could judge, by the fashionable world of routs and coffee-houses in which he probably moved – for it transpired after a while that he was the only son of the Earl of Stowe, whose name was known even in the Highlands. It appeared, also, that he was really visiting Edinburgh, and had only gone to Dunstaffnage on a short stay, from which he was now returning. He had never been in Scotland before, he said, and, but for a very particular circumstance, would not have come now, because the country, and especially the Highlands, held a most painful association to him, he having lost a brother there in the late rebellion.

Ewen said that he was sorry to hear it. 'He was a soldier, I presume?'

The young man nodded. His bright face had saddened, and looking down, he said as though to himself, 'I am ashamed now that I did not attempt the pilgrimage when I was at Dunstaffnage – I suppose, sir,' he went on rather hesitatingly, 'that you do not chance to know a wild spot on the coast, farther north, called Morar?'

Ewen put down his wine-glass very suddenly, the colour leaving his face. He tried to speak and could not. But his companion went on without waiting for an answer, 'It was there that my brother met his death, Mr Cameron. And he was not killed in fair fight, he was murdered. That is why I do not like the Highlands . . . yet I wish time had permitted of my going to Morar.'

A moment Ewen stared as though the handsome speaker were himself a ghost. Keith Windham's brother – could it be true? The tiny inn-parlour was gone, and he was kneeling again in the moonlight on that bloodstained sand. He did not know that he had put his hand over his eyes.

And then the voice that was – he knew it now – so like Keith's, was asking him breathlessly, fiercely, 'Where did you get that ring – my God, where did you get it?'

Ewen dropped his hand and looked up almost dazedly at the young Englishman, who was on his feet, leaning over the table, with a face as white as his own, and eyes suddenly grown hard and accusing.

'He gave it to me . . . it was in my arms that he died at Morar . . . the victim of a terrible mistake.'

'A mistake, you say? He was killed, then, in the place of another?'

'No, no – not that kind of mistake. My unfortunate foster-brother – '

'Your foster-brother was the murderer! And by whose orders? Yours?'

Ewen gave a strangled cry, and leapt to his own feet, and faced this stern, almost unrecognizable young accuser.

'God forgive you for the suggestion! I wished that day that

Lachlan's dirk had been in my own breast! Major Windham was my friend, Lord Aveling, my saviour ... and yet he came to his death through me – And you are his brother! I felt ... yes, that was it – you have his voice.'

'I am his brother of the half-blood,' said the young Viscount, standing very still and looking hard at him. 'My mother was his mother too. ... And so you wear his ring. But if you have not his blood upon your hands, what do you mean by saying that he came to his death through you?'

Ewen caught his breath. 'His blood on *my* hands! If it is on anyone's – besides poor deluded Lachlan's – it is on those of another British officer who – ' he stopped suddenly and then went on, ' – who is probably gone to his account by this time.'

'And you are prepared to swear – '

'Great God, should I have worn his ring all these years if what you think were true? He drew it off his finger – 'twas the last thing he did – and put it into my hand. I will swear it – ' he glanced down in search of the dirk which he might not wear, and made a little gesture of desperation. 'I cannot; I have no weapon.'

'Let that pass; I will take your word,' said the young Englishman, speaking with difficulty. 'I can see that what you say is true, and I ask your pardon for my suspicions.' No one, indeed, could well have doubted that it was grief, not guilt, which had made the face of this Highland gentleman so drawn. 'But,' added Lord Aveling after a moment, 'I should be greatly your debtor if you could bring yourself to tell me a little more. All we heard was that while on patrol-duty on the western coast in the August of '46 my unfortunate brother was murdered by a Highlander, either a Cameron or a Macdonald, and was buried where he died. It was impossible, in the then unsettled state of the country, to have his body exhumed and brought to England. And now, I suppose, if this place be as wild as we have heard, his very grave is forgotten?'

'No, it is not forgotten,' answered Ewen, in a much quieter voice. 'I have been there twice – I was there last year. There is a stone I had put. ... He did not love the Highlands overmuch, yet 'tis a peaceful and a beautiful spot, Lord Aveling, and though the wind blows sometimes the sand is very white there, and when the moon is full. . . .' He broke off, and stood with his deep-set blue eyes steady and fixed, the young man staring at him a trifle awed, since he had heard of the second sight, and the speaker was a Highlander.

But Ardroy was seeing the past, not the future, and after a moment sat down again at the table and covered his face with his hands. His half-drained glass rolled over, and the claret stain widened on the coarse cloth. Keith Windham's brother stood looking down at him until, an instant or two later, there came a knock at the door, when he went to it, and dismissed the intruder, the postilion anxious for his lordship to start.

When he came back Ardroy had removed his hands and regained control of himself.

'Since we have met so strangely, you would perhaps desire me to tell you the whole story, my lord?'

And sitting there, sometimes gazing with a strange expression at the stain on the cloth, sometimes looking as if he saw nothing, Ewen told it to the young man in detail.

Chapter 13

THE RELUCTANT VILLAIN

1

LORD AVELING'S elderly postilion may well have wondered when, at last, the two gentlemen came out to take their places in the chaise, why they both looked so grave and pale; yet, since he had been fidgeting over the delay, to see them come at all was welcome. He whipped up the horses, and soon the travellers, not much regarding it, had had their last glimpse of lovely Etive, had crossed the tumbling Awe, and began to enter the Pass of Brander.

The emotions of the inn had left both Ewen and Lord Aveling rather silent, but at last the younger man said, indicating the view from his window:

'As you say, Mr Cameron, my poor brother did not like the Highlands. I, too, find them, with exceptions, uncongenial. This gloomy defile, for instance, and the great mountain beneath which we are travelling, are to me oppressive.'

'Others, and Highlanders to boot, have found Ben Cruachan oppressive, my lord,' returned Ewen with meaning. 'For were you not told at Dunstaffnage that the name of this fine mountain above us has been adopted by the Campbells as their war-cry?'

Lord Aveling looked at him. 'Your clan is no friend to the Campbells, I think.'

Ewen smiled a trifle bitterly. He wondered whether Lord Aveling had heard that enmity in his voice, or had learnt of it otherwise.

'Forgive me if I seem impertinent in asking of your affairs, Mr Cameron,' went on the young man, 'and believe me that they are of interest to me because of your connexion with my poor brother. I understand from what you have told me that you left the country after the battle of

Culloden; did you find the Highlands much changed upon your return?'

He was obviously inspired only with a friendly interest, and Ardroy, though never very prone to talk about his own concerns, found himself, to his surprise, engaged upon it almost naturally with this unknown young Englishman, his junior, he guessed, by ten years or so. Yet how could he help it? the boy had Keith Windham's voice.

'And so it has been possible for you to settle down quietly,' commented Lord Aveling. 'I am very pleased to hear it. Not all of your name have been so wise – but then your clan is fairly numerous, is it not? For instance, that Doctor Cameron who is such a thorn in the side of the Government . . . ah, you know him, perhaps?' For Ewen had not been able to suppress a slight movement.

'Doctor Cameron? I . . . met him in the Rising,' he answered carelessly.

'It seems,' went on the youth, 'that he is one of the Pre – the Prince's chief agents. However, he has evidently come to the end of his tether in that capacity – or so I have heard from . . . from Edinburgh this morning.'

'Indeed?' remarked Ewen a little uneasily.

'Yes; I was told that the Lord Justice-Clerk had just received information as to his whereabouts, and, having communicated it to General Churchill, had issued a warrant, which the General immediately sent to the commander of the military post at Inver – Inversnaid, I think the name was. Probably, therefore, Doctor Cameron is captured by now.'

'Inversnaid,' repeated Ewen, after a second or two in which his hand had furtively tightened itself on his knee; 'Inversnaid – that's on the upper end of Loch Lomond. There *is* a barracks near it.'

'On Loch Lomond, you say, sir? I fear my knowledge of the geography of Scotland is but small, yet I remember that Inversnaid, or something very much like it, was the name . . . The prospect of this long lake upon our right – Loch Awe, is it not? – is very fine, Mr Cameron!'

'Yes, very fine indeed,' agreed his companion perfunctorily.

'But – excuse me, Lord Aveling – did your correspondent say ... I mean, was Doctor Cameron reported to be near Loch Lomond?' A growing dismay was fettering his tongue, while his brain on the contrary, had started to go round like a wheel, revolving possibilities. Could Archie really be in that neighbourhood?

'Loch Lomond was not mentioned in my letter,' replied the young man. 'He was said to be in Glen Something-or-other, of which I don't recall the name. You have so many glens in your country,' he added with an apologetic smile.

What glen could it be? Those running up respectively from Loch Lomond or Loch Katrine? But Archie would never 'skulk' so near Inversnaid as that. If that warrant had really been despatched from Edinburgh (for the whole thing might only be a rumour) then all one could hope for was that the information on which it had been issued was incorrect. Ewen stole a glance at his fellow-traveller.

'I'll hazard, my lord,' said he, trying to speak carelessly, 'that the place was either Glenfalloch or Glengyle.'

Lord Aveling turned his head from contemplating the twilight beauties of Loch Awe; he looked faintly surprised. 'No, it was neither of those, I am sure,' he replied; and Ewen felt that he was upon the point of adding, 'Why, may I ask, are you so anxious to know?' But he did not.

'If I could but get a sight of that letter!' thought Ewen. 'If he only received it this morning it is probably still in his pocket, not in his baggage. I wish he would bring it forth!' Yes, the letter was probably there, concealed from his longing eyes only by one or two thicknesses of cloth. How could he induce Lord Aveling, who so little guessed of what vital interest the name was to him, to read through his letter again? For to warn Archie was now beginning to be Ewen's one desire ... if he could only learn where to find him.

But then he thought despairingly, 'Even if I knew that, and could set off this moment, how could I possibly get there in time?' For if, as Lord Aveling had seemed to imply, the warrant had already left Edinburgh for Inversnaid by the time his letter was despatched to Dunstaffnage, then, by this morning, when he received it there, so much farther from the capital than was Inversnaid, all was over. . . . Unless, indeed, by God's mercy, this unnamed glen had been searched and found empty, as it was rumoured had happened to not a few places in the last six months.

'You have no doubt destroyed your letter, my lord?' he suggested desperately after a while – desperately and, as he felt, clumsily.

He saw the colour leap into the young man's cheek – and no wonder! The question was a most unwarrantable impertinence. He would reply 'And what affair is it of yours?' and there would be nothing to do save beg his pardon.

But no; the youth said – and he actually smiled, 'No, Mr Cameron, I have not done that. Indeed, I fancy 'twill be long before that letter is torn up.' He turned his head away quickly and once more looked out of the chaise window, but Ewen had the impression that the smile was still upon his lips. He was somewhat puzzled; it could hardly be that the news of Doctor Cameron's possible arrest was so agreeable to the young traveller that he meant always to preserve the letter which announced it. There must be some other reason; perhaps the missive contained some private news which had pleased him. At any rate, it still existed, and, as it was in his possession, why would he not consult it? Was it, after all, packed away in his valise?

'I wonder what glen it could have been,' hazarded Ardroy with a reflective air. 'I thought I knew all the glens in that neighbourhood' (which was false, for he had never been there).

Lord Aveling's left hand – the nearest to his companion – made a quick undecided movement to his breast, and Ewen held his breath. He was going at last to bring out the letter and look! But no . . . for some unimaginable reason he was not! The hand fell again, its owner murmuring something about not remembering the name, and immediately beginning, rather pointedly, to talk about something else.

It was useless to go on harping on the matter, even though the letter was indubitably in the young man's pocket. Perhaps, in any case, he himself was allowing its contents to assume quite undue proportions in his mind. It was some rumour of the dispatch of a warrant which Lord Aveling's correspondent had passed on to him, some gossip which was circulating in Edinburgh, nothing more.

2

So, by the time they came with lighted lamps to Dalmally, and the little inn in the strath where they were to spend the night, Ewen, by way of revulsion, was almost ready to laugh at himself and his fears. As if Archie would lie hid, as Lord Aveling's correspondent reported, within reach of Inversnaid barracks! Again, if it had been true, then, having regard to the time which had elapsed, and the extraordinary swiftness with which news was wont to travel from mouth to mouth in the Highlands, the news of Doctor Cameron's capture in Perthshire would certainly be known here at Dalmally, almost on the borders. And a few careful questions put to the innkeeper soon after their arrival, out of Lord Aveling's hearing, showed Ardroy that it was not. He sat down to supper with that young man in a somewhat happier frame of mind.

The most esteemed bedroom of the inn had been put at the disposal of the guests. There happened to be two beds in it, and for persons of the same sex travelling together – or even not travelling – to share a room was so usual that the landlord did not even apologize for the necessity; he was only overheard to congratulate himself that he could offer the superior amenities of his best bedchamber to these two gentlemen.

But the gentlemen in question did not congratulate themselves when they saw it.

'Did you say that you once shared a room with my poor brother?' inquired Lord Aveling when their mails had been brought in and they were alone together in that uninviting apartment.

'Hardly a room,' answered Ewen. 'It was but a little hut, where one slept upon bracken.'

'I believe that I should prefer bracken to this bed,' observed his lordship, looking with distaste at the dingy sheets which he had uncovered. 'I shall not venture myself completely into it.

Yet, by Gad, I'm sleepy enough.' He yawned. 'I wager I shall sleep as well, perhaps better, than I have done of late at Dunstaffnage Castle, where one heard the sea-wind blowing so strong of nights.'

'Yes, and I dare venture you found Edinburgh none too quiet neither,' observed Ewen idly, surveying his equally dubious sheets, and resolving to follow his companion's example.

'Oh down at General Churchill's quarters 'twas peaceful enough,' returned Lord Aveling, stifling another yawn, 'for the Abbey stands – but there,' he added, beginning to take off his coat, 'you must know better than I what is the situation of Holyrood House.'

Ewen's pulse quickened. 'So it was General Churchill whom you were visiting in Edinburgh, my lord?'

'Yes,' replied the young man. 'I thought I had already mentioned it.' And then he began to redden; even in the meagre candlelight the colour could be seen mounting hotly to his face. 'He is an old acquaintance of my father's.'

Ewen remained motionless, one arm out of his coat; but he was not speculating as to why the young nobleman had so curiously flushed. The thought had shot through him like an arrow: if he has been visiting the Commander-in-Chief, then his news about the warrant out for Archie is no hearsay, it is cold and deadly truth . . . and probably the letter which he received this morning announcing the fact was from General Churchill himself.

Talking amiably between yawns, Lord Aveling proceeded to remove his wig and coat. Ewen watched him almost without realizing that he was watching, so overcome was he with the revelation of the identity of the youth's correspondent. And in the same half-tranced state he saw his fellow-traveller bend rather hurriedly over the coat, which he had flung on a chair, extract something from an inner pocket and thrust it under his pillow. The Commander-in-Chief's letter, no doubt, which he seemed so oddly to guard from sight.

Ewen came to life again, finished taking off his own coat, and removed his boots, in silence. Meanwhile Lord Aveling had fetched a case of pistols from his valise, and, taking out a couple of small, handsomely mounted weapons, placed them on the rickety chair beside his bed. 'We are not like to use these, I hope, Mr Cameron, but there they are, to serve whichever of us wakes first and finds a housebreaker in the room.

A moment or two afterwards, apologizing for what he termed his unmannerly drowsiness, he had blown out his candle, thrown himself upon his bed, pulled a long travelling cloak over himself, and was asleep almost at once. Ewen blew out the light, and sat down on the side of his bed, his back to his fellow-traveller, and stared out through the greyish square of the uncurtained window.

Had he but known that General Churchill himself was the boy's informant, he would certainly have forced him somehow to look at his letter again, if not in the chaise, then at supper, and to tell him the name of that glen. But it was not yet too late. The letter was still there – here, rather, in this room, and only a few feet away. He had only to wake Lord Aveling and say, 'Show me the line, the word, in your letter which concerns Doctor Cameron, for I'll take no denial!'

And then? Was the young Englishman going to accede quietly to that demand? Naturally not. There would be an unseemly, an unchivalrous struggle, ending, no doubt, in his overpowering the boy and reading the letter by force. Meanwhile, the house would probably be roused, and all chance of his slipping away undetected on the task of warning Archie gone.

There was, it could not be denied, another method . . . the only prudent one . . .

'No, that I *cannot* do!' said Ardroy to himself. He took his head in his hands for a moment, then got up, fetched his cloak and, lying down and covering himself up, tried to compose himself to sleep.

The attempt was foredoomed to failure, for he could think of only one thing: Archie, betrayed but ignorant of his betrayal, and the soldiers already on their way from Inversnaid to surprise and drag him off. And here he, his cousin and friend, who had always professed so much affection for him, and into whose hands the knowledge of this attempt had so surprisingly come, lay peaceably sleeping while the tragedy drew nearer and nearer, and would not, on account of a scruple, put out one of those hands to learn the final clue – he was going to allow Archibald Cameron, his dead Chief's brother, to go unwarned to capture because a gentleman did not clandestinely read another's letters.

Ewen lay there in torment. Through the window close to his bed he could see a wild white sky, where the thin clouds drove like wraiths before a phantom pursuer, though there was no sound of wind at all. It was so light a night that even in the room he could probably see to do *that* without the aid of a candle; so light that outside, if he succeeded in getting away unhindered with one of the horses, the same witchlike sky would enable him to find his way without too much difficulty along the road to Tyndrum and Perthshire. He saw himself riding, riding hard . . .

What nonsense! Was he not almost convinced that the information on which the warrant had been issued was false, and that Doctor Cameron would not lie in any place within reach of Inversnaid? . . . so why indulge this overmastering desire to see the name of the alleged place? And, said the same voice, you are sure also that any action would be too late now, for the warrant sent express to Loch Lomond some days ago must either have been carried out by this time or have failed of its purpose. In either case the dishonourable and repugnant act which you propose is futile. . . . And if the boy wakes while you are engaged upon it, what will you say to him?

He wondered if Keith Windham, in his place, would have hesitated – Yes, any gentleman would hesitate. It was ignominious, a mean thing to do. But not a crime. It was not for himself. Had one the right to cherish selfish scruples when so much was at stake for another man? No! . . . For Archie's sake, then!

He rose very softly from his bed and put on the clothes he had laid aside, but not his boots. Then, standing up, he took his bearing in the dim room, where Aveling's breathing showed how soundly he was asleep. The first step was to find out where the young man had put the letter. Ewen had seen him take something from his coat and slip it under his pillow:

probably this was a letter-case or something of the kind and contained the carefully guarded epistle.

Ewen could see now, if not very distinctly, the position of everything in the room, which was important, lest he should stumble over any object and make a noise. The key was in the locked door; he tiptoed over and removed it to his own pocket, since above all things the lad, if he woke, must not be allowed to rouse the inn. Being light on his feet, for all his stature, Ardroy accomplished this without a sound. The next step was to remove the pistols, lest the youth, thinking, not unnaturally, that he was being robbed, should try to use them.

Then, tingling with repugnance but quite resolved and unrelenting, Ewen stood over him – he could only see him as a dark mass – and began carefully to slide his hand under the paler mass which was the pillow. Every fibre in his body and brain revolted from what he was doing, but he went on with it; it was for Archie. His groping fingers encountered something at last, and with infinite precautions he slipped it out at the top of the pillow and tiptoed away to the window with his prize.

It *was* a small leather letter-case which he held. Ardroy hastily pulled out the contents, rather dismayed to find how little he could make of them in the dusk. There came out first some bank-notes, which he stuffed back as though his fingers had encountered a snake; then some papers which might have been bills, and lastly three letters, of which, peer at them as he might, he could not distinguish a word.

This was extremely daunting. Either he would be obliged to light the candle, which he particularly wished to avoid doing, or he must take all three letters down to the stable with him, and trust to find a lantern there to read them by. But that would indeed be theft, and unnecessary theft. He only wanted one line – one word – in one letter, General Churchill's.

Annoyed, he took up his candlestick. The problem was where to put it, so that the light might not wake the sleeper. On the floor, he decided, between the window and his own bed, whose bulk would shield the flame. He did so, and knelt down on one knee by it. What a disconcertingly sharp sound flint and steel made; he had to strike more than once, too, for the tinder would not catch. At last the candle sprang into flame, and, kneeling there behind his bed, holding his breath, Ardroy examined the letters.

The first he took up was some weeks old, and bore a London address, so he did not examine it further; the second, in a small fine writing, was dated from 'The Abbey, March 16th', and signed – Ewen turned hurriedly to the end – yes, signed 'Churchill'.

But not 'William' or 'James' or whatever the General's name was . . . no – *'Georgina'*.

Ewen stared at the signature, horror-struck. This was infinitely worse than bank-notes, worse, even, than a real snake would have been. Now he knew why its recipient was reluctant to bring forth, in the close proximity of the chaise, this letter so palpably in a lady's hand, and – as the present reader could not avoid seeing – thick-studded with maidenly endearments. That was why Lord Aveling had coloured so, had repudiated the idea of destroying the epistle. Obviously he was not of the stuff of the complacent *jeune homme à bonnes fortunes*. His shy delicacy in the matter made the present thief's task tenfold more odious. But having gone so far he could not draw back, and the writer, be she never so fond, was also General Churchill's daughter . . . or niece, perhaps? No, at the bottom of the first sheet – there were two separate ones, of a large size – was a reference to 'Papa', presumably the Commander-in-Chief.

But where in all this was the name for the sake of which he had embarked upon the repulsive business? Ewen could not see it anywhere, as, hot with embarrassment, he picked his way among expressions not meant for the eyes of any third person, which seemed, too, to show that Lord Aveling was a recently accepted suitor. But the shamed reader of these lovers' confidences did not want to have any knowledge of the sort thrust upon him. Not yet finding what he wanted he put down this letter and took up the third; no, that was from London, and signed 'Your affectionate Father, Stowe'. So with an inward sigh he went back to the love-letter, wishing with all his soul that the enamoured Miss Georgina Churchill did not write so fine a hand and so long an epistle.

And, just as he thought that he was coming to the place, he heard a creak from Aveling's bed.

'Great Heavens, what's wrong? What are you at there, Mr Cameron – are you ill?' And then a further movement and an ejaculation, 'Who the devil has taken my pistols from this chair?'

Ewen was still on one knee beyond his bed, feverishly scanning the letter held below its level. 'It was I who removed them. I was afraid,' he said with perfect truth, 'that you might wake, and, seeing a light, use them by error.' And he went on searching – ah, thank God, here he was coming to it at last!

I must tell you that Papa had a message last night from the Lord Justice-Clerk informing him that Doctor Cameron –'

The word 'warrant' swam for a second before his eyes, but he could not get no farther, for now he was to pay the price of his villainy. Young Aveling, who must have thrust his hand instinctively under his pillow, had by this time discovered his second, his greater loss, and with one movement had thrown off his covering and was on his feet, his voice shaking with rage. 'You have stolen my wallet! Give it back to me at once, you damned lying, treacherous thief!'

Ewen rose quickly to his own feet and threw the little case on to his bed, which was still between them. 'You will find your money all there, my lord.' Then, very swiftly, he picked up the candle, put it on the window-sill behind him, found the passage again and tried to go on with his reading of it. But he knew that he would have the young man upon him in a moment, and so he had.

'Money! It's not the money! You have my letters, my most private letters. . . .' And uttering a cry of rage he precipitated himself round the bottom of Ewen's bed.

But Ewen, despite his preoccupation, could be just as quick. The young Englishman found himself confronted by the barrel of one of his own pistols. 'You shall have this letter in one moment if you wait,' said its abductor coolly. 'But if you desire it intact do not try to take it from me.'

'*Wait!*' ejaculated the boy, half-choking. Alight with fury – for instinct no doubt told him which of the three letters the robber held – he did a surprising thing: disregarding entirely the levelled pistol, he dropped suddenly to his knees, and, seizing his enemy by the leg, tried to throw him off his balance – and nearly succeeded. For a second Ardroy staggered; then he recovered himself.

'You young fool!' he exclaimed angrily; clapped the pistol on the window-ledge behind him, stuffed Miss Georgina Churchill's letter into his pocket, stooped, seized the young man's arms, tore their grip apart, and brought him, struggling and panting, to his feet. 'You young fool, I want to give you your letter unharmed, and how can I, if you persist in attacking me?'

'Unharmed!' echoed the young man, with tears of rage in his eyes. He was helpless in that grip, and knew it now. 'You call it unharmed, when you have read it!'

'I regret the necessity even more than you,' retorted Ardroy. 'But you would not tell me what I needed to know. If you will go back to your bed, and give me your word of honour not to stir thence for a couple of moments, you shall have your letter again at the end of them.'

'My word of honour – to you!' flashed the captive. 'You false Highland thief, I should think you never heard the term in your life before! Give me back the letter which you have contaminated by reading – at once!'

Ewen did not relish his language, but what right had he to resent it? 'You shall have the letter back on the condition I have named,' he answered sternly. 'If you oblige me to hold you like this ... no, 'tis of no use, you cannot break away ... God knows when you'll get it back. And if you attempt to cry for help' (for he thought he saw a determination of the kind pass over the handsome, distorted features) 'I'll gag you! You may be sure I should never have embarked upon this odious business if I had not meant to carry it through!'

' "Odious"!' his captive caught up the word. 'You are a spy and a thief, and you pretend to dislike your trade!'

Ewen did not trouble to deny the charge. He felt that no stone which his victim could fling at him was too sharp. 'Will you give me your word?' he asked again, more gently. 'I do not wish to hurt you ... and I have not read your letter through. I was but searching in it for what I need.'

But that avowal only raised the young lover's fury afresh. 'Damn you for a scoundrelly pickpocket!' he said between his teeth, and began to struggle anew until he was mastered once more, and his arms pinned to his sides. And thus, very white, he asked in a voice like a dagger:

'Did you turn out my brother Keith's pockets before, or after, you murdered him?'

As a weapon of assault the query had more success than all his physical efforts. This stone was too sharp. Ewen caught his breath, and his grip loosened a little.

The matter had come to something of an *impasse*. Ewen was no nearer to his goal, for as long as he had to hold this young and struggling piece of indignation he could not finish reading the passage in the letter. He decided that he should have to take a still more brutal step. At any rate, nothing could make his victim think worse of him than he did already.

'If you do not go back and sit quietly upon your bed,' he said, with a rather ominous quietness himself, 'I shall hold you with one hand, and thrust one sheet of your letter in the candle-flame with the other!'

'You may do it – for I'll not take it back now!' flashed out the boy instantly.

'But if you give me your word to do as I say,' went on Ewen, as though he had not spoken, 'I will restore you a sheet of it now as earnest for the return of the rest, when I have finished reading the one sentence which concerns me – Now, which is it to be, Lord Aveling?'

In that extremely close proximity their eyes met. The young man saw no relenting in those blue ones fixed on his, hard as only blue eyes can be at need. And Ewen – Ewen did not like to think to what desperate measures he might have to resort if the card he had just played were in truth not high enough ...

But the trick was won. Despite his frenzied interjection, the young lover wanted his property too much to see it reduced to ashes before him. He choked back something like a sob. 'I'll never believe in fair words ... and a moving story again! ... Yes, I will do it. Give me the sheet of my letter.'

'You pledge your word not to molest or attempt to stop me, nor to give any kind of alarm?'

'Before I do, I suppose I may know whether you intend to cut my throat, as you – ' But, frantic as the youth was, Ewen's face became so grim that he did not finish.

'I'll not lay a finger on you further.'

'Then I pledge you my word – the word of an Englishman!' said the boy haughtily.

'And I keep mine – as a Highlander,' retorted Ewen. He loosed him at once, selected that sheet of Miss Churchill's letter which he did not require, and handed it to its owner in silence. The youth thrust it passionately inside his shirt, went back to his own bed, and, shivering with rage and exhaustion, sat down and hid his face in his hands

Ewen, his back half-turned, found the passage again.

'Papa had a message last night from the Lord Justice-Clerk informing him that Doctor Cameron was said to be at the house of Stewart of Glenbuckie, and a warrant was immediately dispatched to the post at Inversnaid.'

Glenbuckie ... Glenbuckie ... in what connexion had he heard of that place before? Glenbuckie was ... good God, was it possible that he did not really know with sufficient exactitude ... that he had committed this shameful violence for nothing?

Then the knowledge returned to him, bearing with it a tragic recollection from the early days of the Rising, when the notoriety given to Stewart of Glenbuckie's name by the mysterious death of its then bearer, in Buchanan of Arnprior's house, had resulted in one's learning the whereabouts of the glen from which he came. Yes, Glenbuckie was somewhere in the Balquhidder district – a glen running directly southward from the farther end of Loch Voil, he believed ... a long way and a difficult. And, his mind already calculating distances and route, Ewen read the passage again. There was a little more, for Miss Georgina Churchill had been at the pains to tell her lover that the person who had sent this information to the Lord

Justice-Clerk was someone who claimed to have recently met and spoken with Doctor Cameron. . . . Ewen sat down and pulled on his boots.

For the last few moments he had almost forgotten Aveling. Putting the pistol in his pocket again he went over to him. 'Here is the other sheet of the letter, my lord. You will not accept my apologies, I know, but I make them to you none the less, and sincerely – and also for borrowing the horse from Bonawe, which I propose to do as far as Tyndrum, where I hope you will find him when you arrive. If I can, I will leave your pistols there also. If not, I will pay for them.'

The young Englishman jumped up and snatched his letter. 'You'll pay for everything one day, by God – in Newgate, or wherever in this barbarous country of yours they bestow their Highland robbers! And I'll have you indicted for my brother's murder as well as for assaulting me in order to assist an attainted rebel! Since you are his confederate, you shall swing with Doctor Cameron at Tyburn!'

But Ewen was already unlocking the door of the room. His great dread was that the young man, strung up by rage and disillusionment to what in a woman would have been hysteria point, might forget his promise and proceed unwittingly to rouse the inn. He did not want to use the pistols in order to get clear of the premises, so he slipped as quickly as possible out of the room and locked the door on the outside, hearing, not without remorse, sounds from within which suggested the boy had flung himself upon the bed and was weeping aloud.

So ended, in dishonour and brutality, this encounter with his dead friend's brother, who had acted so generously towards him, and to whom he had felt so strongly attracted. A moment only that thought flashed bitingly through Ewen's brain; it was no time to indulge in regret or to think of consequences to himself – his immediate task was to warn Archie. To his crimes of treachery and violence he must, therefore, if he could, add that of horse-stealing.

And even as Ardroy cautiously lifted the latch of the stable door at Dalmally, away in the little rebuilt barracks near

Inversnaid, on Loch Lomond, Captain Craven of Beauclerk's regiment was reading the belated dispatch from the Commander-in-Chief at Edinburgh which he had been roused from his bed to receive.

'Too late to do anything tonight,' was his comment. Then his eyes fell upon the date which it bore. 'Gad, man,' he said to the wearied messenger, 'I should have received this warrant yesterday! The bird may be flown by tomorrow. What in God's name delayed you so?'

Chapter 14

IN TIME – AND TOO LATE

1

THE fitful sun of the March afternoon came flooding straight
through the open door of Mr Stewart of Glenbuckie's house
into the hall, which was also the living-room, and on to little
Peggy Stewart, the room's sole occupant. Peggy had earlier
begged from her mother, who had been baking today, a piece
of dough, and had fashioned out of it, after countless remodel-
lings, an object bearing some resemblance to the human form,
with two currants for eyes. And while she sat there, regarding
her handiwork with the fond yet critical gaze of the artist,
before taking it to the kitchen to be baked, there suddenly
appeared without warning, in the oblong pale of sunlight which
was the doorway, the figure of a large, very tall man. This stalwart apparition put out a hand to knock, and then, as if disconcerted at finding the door open, withdrew it.

Miss Peggy, who was no shyer than she need be, rose from
her little stool near the spinning-wheel and advanced into the
sunlight. And to a man who had ridden all night on a stolen
horse, and had since, tortured by the feeling that every delay was
the final and fatal one, stumbled and fought his way over the
steep and unfamiliar mountain paths on the western slopes of
Ben More and Stobinian, to such a man the appearance at
Stewart of Glenbuckie's door of a chubby little girl of six,
dressed in a miniature tight-waisted gown of blue which almost touched the floor, and clasping in one hand what he took
to be an inchoate kind of doll, was vaguely reassuring.

'Is this the house of Mr Duncan Stewart?' he asked.

Gazing up at this tall stranger with her limpid blue eyes the
child nodded.

'Is he within, my dear?'

Miss Peggy Stewart shook her curly head. 'My papa is from home.'

'And . . . have you a gentleman staying here?'

'He is not here either. Only Mother is here.'

Instantly Ewen's thoughts swung round to the worst. They had both been arrested, then, Stewart as well as Archie. The noticeable quiet of the house was due to its emptiness – only a woman and a child left there. He was too late, as he had expected all along. He put his head mutely against the support of the door, and so was found an instant later by Mrs Stewart, who, hearing voices, had come from the kitchen.

'Is aught amiss, sir? Are you ill?'

Ardroy raised his head and uncovered. But this lady did not sound or look like a woman whose husband had recently been torn from her. Hope stirred again. 'Madam, have the soldiers been here after . . . any person?'

Mrs Stewart's calm, fair face took on a look of surprise. 'No, sir, I am glad to say. But will you not enter?'

At this bidding Ewen walked, or rather stalked, over the threshold; he was stiff. 'Thank God for that!' he said fervently. 'But they may be here at any moment.' He bethought him, and closed the door behind him. 'There is a warrant out for . . . that person.'

Mrs Stewart lowered her voice. 'Then it is fortunate that he is not in the house.'

'He is away, with your husband?'

'No, sir. Mr Stewart is in Perth on affairs. I do not know where "Mr Chalmers" has gone this afternoon, but he will return before dark.'

'He must at all costs be prevented from doing that, madam,' said Ewen earnestly. 'If he comes back here, he will be running into a trap. I cannot understand why the warrant has not already been executed, but, since it has not, let us take advantage of the mercy of heaven – My own name, by the way, madam, is Cameron, and I am "Mr Chalmers's" near kinsman. He must be found and stopped before he reaches this house!'

'Certainly he should be,' agreed Mrs Stewart. 'Unfortunately – be quiet, my child – unfortunately, I do not know in which direction he has gone, whether down the glen or up it.'

' "Mr Chalmers" was going to Balquhidder,' observed Peggy with composure. 'He told me; he said tell Mother, but I forgot – Mother, please put my bread mannie in the oven!'

The two adults looked down anxiously at the source of this information.

'Are you sure, Peggy, that that is where "Mr Chalmers" has gone? – Yes, darling,' added her mother hastily, 'I will have your bread mannie put in at once if this gentleman will excuse me.' She gave Ewen a look which seemed to say, 'I am not usually so weak and indulgent, but it is politic in this case, for if she cries we shall get no more out of her.'

Yet, as it happened, indulgence got no more either, for there seemed no more for Peggy to tell when she was asked, and so Ewen stood on the threshold of Mrs Stewart's spotless kitchen and watched with troubled eyes the consignment of Peggy's masterpiece to the oven.

Then Mrs Stewart came out, saying over her shoulder to someone within, 'Janet, keep the child with you for a while. Mr Cameron, you'll take some refreshment before you start?'

But Ewen refused, hungry and spent though he was, for he would not spare the time. Mrs Stewart, however, returned swiftly to the kitchen, and was heard giving orders for bread and meat to be made ready for him to take with him.

'Now I'll give you directions,' she said, hurrying out again. 'Yet, Mr Cameron, I cannot think that this is true about a warrant, for had there been any soldiers on the march from Loch Lomond side the country people would most certainly have sent messengers on ahead to warn us. For I have heard my husband say that since the garrison at Inversnaid makes a practice of selling meal and tobacco to the Highlanders, and there is a canteen in one of the barrack rooms itself, many a piece of news leaks out to us that way. For this is all, as you know, what the English call a "disaffected" region, and "Mr Chalmers" has been with us for some time quite unmolested.'

'Yet in this case extraordinary precautions may have been taken against any tidings reaching you,' urged Ewen. 'And I have seen a letter from a member of General Churchill's household which stated that a warrant had been issued on the fifteenth – six days ago. It was in fact that letter which brought me here, for I did not know my cousin's whereabouts. But they certainly know it in Edinburgh. Someone has informed against him, Mrs Stewart.'

She was plainly shocked. 'Oh, sir, that's impossible! No one in these parts would do such a thing!'

But Ardroy shook his head. 'It may not have been a man from this district, but it has been done – and by someone who had speech with the Doctor recently. It remains now to circumvent the traitor. Supposing the child to have been mistaken, have you any trusty person whom you can send in the opposite direction, or in any other where you think "Mr Chalmers" likely to have gone?'

'Only the gardener; but I will send him at once up the glen. Yet if Peggy is right, 'tis you will meet the Doctor, though I know not how far you'll have to go, nor whether you had best – ' She stopped and drew her brows together. 'Nay, I believe he ever takes the track through the wood when he goes to Balquhidder, for the path down the open glen gives no shelter in case of danger. It will be best for you to go by the wood. You saw the burn, no doubt, as you came up to the house? Follow it a space down the glen till it goes into the wood, and go in with it. The track then runs by the water till it mounts higher than the burn; but you cannot miss it. And I must tell you,' she finished, 'that "Mr Chalmers" is wearing a black wig, which changes him very much; and commonly, unless he forgets, he makes to walk with a stoop to reduce his height. But you'll be knowing his appearance well, perhaps?'

'Very well indeed,' said Ewen, checking a sigh. 'God grant I meet him! I am to begin by following the burn, then?' He repeated her simple instructions and went towards the door. Every moment he expected it to be flung wide by a redcoat.

But he opened it, and there was nothing by the pale unclouded sun, almost balanced now on one of the crests opposite, the sharp sweet hill air, and a murmur of wind in the pines below the house. On the threshold Mrs Stewart tendered him the packet of bread and meat, and a small voice from a lesser altitude was also heard offering him, as sustentation, 'my bread mannie'. It was true that this gift, withdrawn from too brief a sojourn in the oven, was far from being bread, but Ewen gravely accepted the amorphous and sticky object and wrapped it in his handkerchief.

2

As Mrs Stewart had said, the track through the wood was quite easy to find and follow. Ewen hurried along it at a very fast pace, since the farther from Stewart's house he could encounter Archie the better. And yet, it *might* be a wild goose chase into which he had flung himself; it might be for the sake of a mere rumour that he, Ewen Cameron of Ardroy, had assaulted the future Earl of Stowe and stolen, or rather borrowed, a horse. The pistols he had certainly stolen, for he had not left them, as he had the horse, at the inn at Tyndrum, but had kept them with him, and might be glad of them yet. For though, contrary to all his expectations, he was in time to warn Archie (if only he could come upon him) he could not feel at ease about the warrant, even though its execution was so strangely delayed, or believe that machinery of the kind, once set in motion, would cease to revolve.

So he hastened on; the path, fairly wide here, having quitted the stream, was full of holes crammed with damp, dead leaves; through the bare oaks and ashes and the twisted pine boughs on his left he saw the sun disappear behind the heights opposite. As its rays were withdrawn the air grew at once colder, and an uneasy wind began to move overhead; it left the oaks indifferent, but the pines responded to its harper's touch. Ardroy had lived his life too much in the open air and in all weathers to be much mentally affected by wind, yet the sound tuned with his anxious thoughts almost without his being aware of it.

So far he had not met or even seen a single person, but now, as he heard steps approaching, his pulse quickened. He was wrong – it was not Archie, for there came into sight an elderly man bent under a load of sticks which he had evidently been gathering in the wood. No word issued from him as they passed each other, but he turned, sticks and all, and stared after the stranger. Meanwhile Ewen hastened on; he must, he thought, have come a considerable way by now, and for the first time he began to wonder what he should do if he got to Balquhidder itself without encountering his cousin, and to regret that he had not asked Mrs Stewart's advice about such a contingency.

It was while he was turning over this difficulty in his mind that he came round a bend in the woodland path and perceived, at the foot of a tree, a man with one knee on the ground, examining something at its foot. Was it? . . . it looked like . . . yes! He broke into a run, and was upon Doctor Cameron before the latter had time to do more than rise to his feet and utter an amazed:

'Ewen! *Ewen!* . . . It can't be! How, and why –'

And not till that moment did it occur to Ewen that all this had happened before, in different surroundings. 'I am come to warn you – once again, Archie!' he said, seizing him by the arms in his earnestness. 'You must come no farther – you must not return to Stewart's house. There's a warrant out against you from Edinburgh, and soldiers coming from Inversnaid. Your hiding-place has been betrayed.'

'Betrayed!' said Archibald Cameron in incredulous tones. 'Dear lad, you must be mistaken. There's but six or seven people know that I am in these parts, and I could answer for every one of them.'

Ewen was not shaken. It was like Archie not to believe in treachery. 'You may think that,' he replied, 'but it has been done. I have the fact on too good authority to doubt it. I have seen Mrs Stewart, and told her, and have come to intercept you. You must not go back there.'

Archie slid his arm into his. 'But first, my dear Ewen, I must learn whence you come and how? I know that you escaped from Fort William before the New Year but –'

'I'll tell you everything in proper time,' broke in his kinsman, 'but in the name of good sense let us find a more concealed place to talk in than this path! – What is occupying you by this tree, pray?' For at the mention of leaving the path Doctor Cameron's gaze had strayed back to the spot over which he had been stooping. Ewen could see nothing there but some bright-coloured toadstools.

'It is, I think, a rare fungus,' said Archie meditatively. 'I should like – well, why not?' He stooped and picked one, and then allowed Ewen to draw him away into the undergrowth, just there waist-high or more, and find a spot under an oak, where, if they chose to sit or crouch, they would be invisible from the track.

But for the moment they stood beneath the oak tree looking at each other, the elder man still holding the little orange toadstool between his fingers. Even though the black tie-wig, in place of the brown one he usually wore, or of his own fair, slightly greying hair, did change Archibald Cameron, even though Ewen's gaze, scanning his face closely, did seem to find there a hint of a fresh line or two about the kindly mouth, he looked much the same as when Ardroy had last set eyes on him in the dark little croft up at Slochd nan Eun. And, as he might have done then, he wanted most to know of Ewen's affairs.

But Ewen took him to task. 'Are you fey, Archie, that you waste time over questions of no moment, and won't believe what I tell you? Someone has betrayed you and sent information to Edinburgh which has been acted upon. To come by the knowledge of this and of your whereabouts I have made a lifelong enemy of a man I liked, committed an assault on him, stolen a horse, and, worse than all, read a private letter by stealth. You must at least pay some heed to me, and pay it at once!'

His concern was too acute to be ignored any longer. 'Forgive me, *laochain*,' said the elder man. 'What do you wish me to do?'

'Move your quarters instantly. It means capture to return to Duncan Stewart's.'

Archie was attentive enough now. 'I doubt if there is anyone else in the neighbourhood who is anxious for my presence.'

'But it would be infinitely better to leave the neighbourhood altogether,' urged his cousin.

Doctor Cameron considered. 'I might lie for a while in the braes of Balquhidder on the far side of the loch – 'tis solitary enough there. But if the soldiers are coming from Inversnaid it would be well to avoid that direction, and better to make at right angles through this wood and up the slopes of Beinn an-t-Shithein. ... Yet, Ewen, 'tis sore hearing and hard believing that anyone can have informed of me. From whom was this letter which you – '

The sound of a shot, followed by a scream, both quite near, killed the question on his lips, and drove the blood from Ewen's heart, if not from the speaker's own. In a moment more, as they both stood mute and tense, a patter of light running feet and the pound of heavier ones could be heard, and along the path which they had left came flying, with terror on her face, a little barefoot girl of about twelve, closely pursued by a soldier, musket in hand, who was shouting after her to stop.

Both men started indignantly to make their way out of the undergrowth towards the pair, but Ewen turned fiercely on his companion.

'Archie, are you quite mad?' he whispered. 'Stay there – and down with you!' He gave him a rough push, and himself crashed through the bushes and burst out on to the path just in front of the runners. The little girl, sobbing with fright, almost collided with him; he seized her, swung her behind him, and angrily faced the panting soldier. 'Put down that musket, you ruffian! This is not the Slave Coast!'

The man's face was almost the colour of his coat from his exertions, but, at least, there was no evil intent written there. 'I were only trying ... to stop the varmint!' he explained, very much out of breath. 'She's sent on ahead by some rebels in a farm ... we marched by a while since ... to carry a warning belike ... I've bin a-chasing of her up and down hills for the last half-hour. Orders it was ... I wouldn't lay a finger on a child ... got two of me own ... only fired to frighten her into stopping – Hold her, or she'll be off again!'

But there did not seem much likelihood of that. The little

girl was on her knees in a heap behind the Highlander, her hands over her ears. He stooped over her.

'You are not hurt, my child, are you?' he asked in the Gaelic. 'Then get you home again; you have done your work. You need not be frightened any more; the redcoat will not harm you.' And he took out a piece of money and closed her fingers over it.

'What are you saying to her – what are you giving her money for?' demanded the soldier suspiciously. 'I believe you'll be in league with the rebels yourself!'

'I should scarce tell her to go home if I were,' answered Ewen with an indifference which he was far from feeling. Good God, if next moment a picket should appear and search the bushes – or if Archie did not now remain motionless beneath them! 'I do not know what you mean,' he continued, 'about a warning, but between us we have stopped the child, and the sixpence I have given her will make her forget her fright the quicker – Off with you!' he repeated to the girl.

Ewen's words had no doubt conveyed to the child a sense that she had accomplished her mission, though the eyes under the elf-locks of rusty hair were still fixed on him, and her whole eager, thin little face asked a wordless question to which he dared not make a further reply. Then, without a sign, she sprang up and slipped into the undergrowth, apparently to avoid the proximity of the redcoat, emerged from it on the other side of him, and ran back the way she had come.

Her late pursuer turned and looked after her, while Ewen's finger closed round one of Lord Aveling's pistols in his pocket. What was the soldier going to do next? If he took a dozen steps off the path to his right he must see Archie crouched there; and if he did that he would have to be shot in cold blood. If he even stayed where he was much longer he would have to be accounted for somehow, since his mere presence would prevent the Jacobite from getting away unobserved. And get away he must, at once.

'Where's your main body?' asked Ardroy suddenly.

The soldier turned round again. 'D'ye think I'm quite a fool that you ask me that?' he retorted scornfully. 'If you're one of the disaffected yourself, as I suspect you are, from speaking Erse so glibly, you'll soon find that out.' And swinging suddenly round again, he went off at a trot on the way he had come.

'Why, the Duke of Argyll himself speaks Erse on occasions!' Ewen called after him mockingly. But there was no mockery in his heart, only the most sickening apprehension. He was right, only too right, about the warrant, and the child had been sent on ahead to carry a warning, just as Mrs Stewart had said would probably happen. Had Mrs Stewart herself sent her? No, the man said she had come from a farm.

Directly the redcoat was out of sight Ardroy hurled himself into his cousin's lair. Doctor Cameron was already on his feet.

'You heard, Archie? There's not a moment to lose! He'll be back with a party, very like, from the child running this way . . . though how she knew . . .'

'Yes, we must make for the side of Beinn an-t-Shithein,' said Archibald Cameron without comment. 'That is to say I must. You –'

'Do you suppose I am going to leave you? Lead, and I'll follow you.'

'There's no path,' observed the Doctor. 'Perhaps 'tis as well; we'll not be so easy to track.'

For ten minutes or so Ewen followed his cousin uphill through the wood, but they were not yet in sight of its upper edge when Doctor Cameron came to an abrupt stop and held up his hand.

'Listen! I thought I heard voices ahead.'

The wind, which had risen a good deal in the last half-hour, and now tossed the branches overhead, made it difficult to be sure of this. Ewen knelt and put his ear to the ground.

'I hear something, undoubtedly.' He got up and looked at Archie anxiously. 'If we should prove to be cut off from the hillside, is there any place in the wood where we could lie hid – a cave, or even a heap of boulders?'

'There is nothing that I know of – Ewen, where are you going?'

173

'Only a little farther on, to reconnoitre. Oh, I'll be careful, I promise you. Meanwhile stay you there!' And he was off before Archie could detain him.

It took him but five minutes or so of careful stalking to be certain that there were soldiers between them and the slopes which they were hoping to gain. There were also, without doubt, soldiers somewhere in the lower part of the wood near the stream. If they could neither leave the wood, nor hide in it, Archie must infallibly be taken.

Ewen slid round the beech-trunk against which he was pressed, meaning to retrace his steps immediately to the spot where he had left his kinsman, but for a moment he stood there motionless, with a horrible premonition at his heart. O God, it could not be that this was the end for Archie! A sort of blindness seemed to pass over his vision, and when it cleared he found his eyes fixed on something farther down the slope of the wood, a little to his left, something that he must have been looking at already without recognizing it for what it was – a small thatched roof.

It seemed like a miracle, an answer to prayer at the least. Ewen slipped back with all speed to the Doctor.

'Yes, we are cut off,' he whispered, 'and we cannot go back. But, Archie, there's some kind of little building farther down the wood. I saw but its roof, yet it may serve us better than nothing. Let us go and look at it.'

They hurried down the slope again. Here the dead leaves were dry, and rustled underfoot, but the need of haste overrode that of silent going. And in a few minutes they both stood looking at Ewen's discovery, a small log hut. It stood on a level piece of the wood, with a little clearing of some ten yards square in front of it, but on its other sides bushes and stout hollies pressed close up to it.

'I never before heard of any hut in this wood,' commented Archie in surprise, 'but there it is certainly! Perhaps the Good People have put it there for us.'

If they had, it could not have been recently, for, as Ewen saw with relief, the logs of which it was constructed were so weathered and mossed that it was not at first very distinglishable from its surroundings. But it was in good repair, and, on going round to the front, the fugitives saw that it actually had a solid, well-fitting door – which, indeed, they found difficult to push open, though it was not secured in any way. To Ewen it seemed of good augury that it opened inwards. Some logs, years old, lay about near the entrance.

'I don't know that we are wise to hide here,' murmured Ardroy, 'but there seems no choice.' And they went in.

Within it was dark, for the hut had no windows. Finding that there was no means of securing the door on the inside save a crazy latch, Ewen suggested bringing in some of the stray logs and piling them against the door; so he and Archie hurriedly staggered in with several, and proceeded to lay some against the bottom, and to rear others against it at an angle in order to wedge it.

'But we cannot stand a regular siege in here, Ewen,' objected the Doctor, looking round their dim shelter.

'No; but if the soldiers find the door immovably fixed they may think it is so fastened up that no one could have got into the hut, and we meanwhile lying as close as weasels within they'll likely go away again – that is, if they come at all. Please God, however, they'll pass the place without seeing it, as we nearly did. Or they may never search this quarter of the wood at all.'

'Yes, I think they'll have to break the door to matchwood before they get it open now,' opined Archie. 'My sorrow, but it's dark in here!'

Indeed, the only light now came from the hole in the thatch intended to let out the smoke, which hole also let in the rain, so that the ground beneath, in the middle of the hut, was more puddle than anything else. It seemed as if the place had been occupied by a woodcutter, for, in addition to the felled logs outside, there was a big but extremely rusty axe propped against the wall in one corner, by the side of the rough bench built into the latter; axe and bench were, with the exception of the blackened stones of the fireplace (some of which they had added to the logs against the door) the only objects there.

So, having now no occupation but waiting upon Fate, the

cousins sat down in the gloom upon this bench; and it was then that Ewen realized that he was nearly famished, and ate his provisions. Archie would not share with him.

'And now, tell me –' each said to the other; and indeed there was much to tell, though they dared not utter more than a few sentences at a time, and those in a low voice, and must then stop to listen with all their ears.

And Ewen learnt that Archie had come to these parts because Lochaber and the West were getting too hot to hold him, owing to the constant searches which were carried out for him; he was, he admitted, all but captured in Strontian when he went to Dungallon's house. That was when Ewen was in Fort William. But here, up till now, he had been unmolested, and who had given notice of his presence he could not imagine.

'And the assistance you hoped for,' asked Ewen, 'is it to come soon?'

He heard his kinsman sigh. 'I'm as much in the dark about it yet, Ewen ... as you and I are at this moment. I begin to wonder whether Frederick of Prussia –'

Ewen gave a stifled exclamation. '*Prussia!* It is Prussia then –'

'You did not know? Prussia, and perhaps Sweden, if certain conditions were fulfilled. But how have you not learnt that?'

'You forget; you did not tell me that night at Ardroy, and since then I have either been a close prisoner or skulking in the wilds. One night in Appin did not teach me much, especially as my cousin Ian was away ... And so troops are to land?'

'They were to. 'Twas inspiring news at first to me and to those I visited. But time has gone on, and on ...' Archie paused. 'I am totally without information now, Ewen. My communications with Lochdornie are cut off, though I believe he is still in Scotland. But I doubt if he knows any more than I do. I verily think that if May comes and brings nothing I shall return to the Prince. Talk of what is promised is windy fare to give to longing hearts when the fulfilment tarries thus.'

A little chill ran through his listener. He had never heard Archibald Cameron so plainly dispirited. For himself, he knew too little to proffer any encouragement; and his uncle's words about the sunset of the Cause recurred to him. But he had not subscribed to them, nor did he now; it was too natural to hope.

'Yes, many thousands of men were, I believe, promised,' resumed Doctor Cameron, 'when the ground should be prepared. But the preparing of it has not been easy when the weeks slipped away and I could hold out naught more definite than the hopes I had brought with me in September – Not that I blame the Prince one whit for that!' he added quickly. And they both fell, and this time quite naturally, into one of the prudent silences which had continually punctuated this conversation in the semi-darkness.

It was a longer silence than usual. Ewen's thoughts went circling away. Had Archie, with all his devotion, merely been beating the air all these months?

'I hope Mrs Stewart has not been molested,' said Archie's voice after a while. 'But I begin to believe the soldiers have abandoned the search, or, at least, that they are not going to search this part of the wood.'

Ewen nodded. 'I begin to think that it is so. I wonder how soon we might with safety leave this place, or whether we had best spend the night here.'

'I've no idea what time it may be,' said his cousin. He pulled out his watch and was peering at it when Ardroy gripped his other wrist. 'Did you hear anything?' he asked in the lowest of whispers.

His watch in his hand, Doctor Cameron sat as still as he. With its ticking there mingled a distant sound of snapping sticks, of something pushing through bushes just as they had done in their approach to the hut. The sounds came nearer, accompanied by voices. Ewen's grip grew tighter, and the Doctor put back his watch.

'Ay, it is a hut!' called out a man's voice. 'Come on, cully – damn these hollies! I warrant he's in here! Come on, I tell you, or he may bolt for it!'

'I'm coming as quick as I can,' shouted another voice. The cracklings and tramplings increased in volume. Ewen slipped his hand into his pocket, took out one of Lord Aveling's elegant pistols, and closed his cousin's fingers over it.

Chapter 15

''TWAS THERE THAT WE PARTED – '

1

ARCHIE shook his head with a little smile which said that resistance would be of no use; that their only hope lay in keeping perfectly quiet. But Ewen would not take the weapon back.

The men outside could be heard fumbling over the door for the means of opening it, which, naturally, they could not find.

'Curse it, there's no way to open this door!' Kicks and blows were bestowed upon it. 'Come out of it, rebel!'

'If ye're in there!' added the other voice with a snigger.

'There ain't no means of knowing that till we get the door open,' said the first voice.

'If there was a lock we could blow it open, but there ain't none.'

'Do you stay and watch the place, then, and I'll be off and fetch the captain; he ain't far off now.'

'And while you're doing that the rebel will burst out and murder me and be off! Maybe, too, there's more than this Doctor Cameron in there!'

'You're a good-plucked one, ain't you!' observed the first voice scornfully. 'You go for Captain Craven then; and I'll warrant no one comes out of this hut without getting something from this that'll stop his going far!' By the sound, he smacked the butt of his musket.

'Good! I'll not be long, then, I promise you.' The speaker could be heard to run off, and the man who remained, either to keep up his courage or to advertise his presence, began to whistle.

Ewen and his cousin looked into each other's eyes, fearing even to whisper, and each read the same answer to the same question. If they attempted to break out and run for it before the captain and the main body came up, it was beyond question that, since they could not suddenly throw open the door, but must first pull down their barricade, at the cost of time and noise, the man outside, forewarned by their move-ments, could shoot one or both as they dashed out. Moreover, wounded or unwounded, they would undoubtedly be in worse case in the open, the alarm once given by a shot, than if they remained perfectly silent, 'as close as weasels', in their hiding-place. There was always a chance that the officer, when he came, would pooh-pooh the idea of anyone's being inside the deserted-looking little structure and would not have the door broken open ... even, perhaps, a chance that he would not bring his men here at all.

But it was a hard thing to do, to sit there and wait to be sur-rounded.

It was too hard for Ewen. After four or five minutes he put his lips to Archie's ear. 'I am going to open the door and rush out on him,' he breathed. 'I have another pistol. He will pro-bably chase me, and then you can get away.' He had brought off that same manoeuvre so successfully once – why not again?

But Archie clutched his arm firmly. 'No, you shall not do it! And in any case ... I think it is too late!' For the musician outside had ceased in the middle of a bar, and next instant was to be heard shouting, 'This way, sir – in the clearing here!'

Then there was the tramp of a good many feet, coming at the double. Oh, what did it matter in that moment to Ewen if the Cause were once more sinking in a bog of false hopes! For the safety of the man beside him, whom he loved, he would have bartered any levies that ever were to sail from Prussia or Sweden. But the issue was not in his hands ...

From the orders which they could hear being given the hut was now surrounded. The door was then pushed at hard from without, but as before, when it had been attempted, it would not budge an inch.

'Did you hear any sound within while you kept watch, Hay-ter?' asked the officer's voice.

'No, sir, I can't say that I did.'

'Yet the door is evidently made fast from within. It is difficult to see how that can be unless someone is still inside. There is no window or other opening, is there, out of which a man could have got after fastening the door.'

'No, sir,' was shouted, apparently from the back of the hut.

'Forbye the hole there'll be in the thatch for letting out the reek, sir,' suggested another voice, and a Scottish voice at that.

'But a man would hardly get out that way,' answered the officer. 'No, there's nothing for it but to break in the door.'

Two or three musket butts were vigorously applied with this intention, but in another moment the officer's voice was heard ordering the men to stop, and in the silence which ensued could be heard saying, 'Aye, an excellent notion! Then we shall know for certain, and save time and trouble. One of you give him a back.'

The two motionless men on the bench inside looked dumbly at each other. What was going to happen now? A scrambling sound was heard against the log wall of the hut, and Archie pointed mutely upwards. They were sending a man to climb up and look in through the hole left for the smoke.

Ewen ground his teeth. They had neither of them thought of that simple possibility. The game was up, then; they could do nothing against such a survey. His cousin, however, possibly from previous experience in 'skulking', advised in dumb show one precaution: pulling Ewen's sleeve to attract his attention, he bowed his head until it rested on his folded arms, thrusting his hands at the same moment out of sight. For a moment Ewen thought that the object of this posture was to escape actual identification, not very probable anyhow in the semi-darkness; then he realized that its purpose was that the lighter hue of their faces and hands should not be discernible to the observer. For a second or two he dallied with an idea which promised him a grim satisfaction – that of firing upwards at the blur of a face which would shortly, he supposed, peer in that fatal aperture in the thatch. But to do that would merely be to advertise their presence. So he followed Archibald Cameron's example, and they sat there, rigid and huddled upon themselves, trusting that in the bad light they would, after all, be invisible. And if so, then, to judge from the officer's words, the latter would be convinced of the emptiness of the hut and would draw off the party without breaking in the door. O God, if it might be so, if it might be so!

The scrambling sound had reached the thatch now. Half of Ewen's mind was praying for Archie's life, the other wrestling with a perverse inclination to glance up. And, queerly mingled with that impulse, came a memory of his childish interpretation of the text, 'Thou, God, seest me', when he used to picture a gigantic Eye, looking down through his bedroom ceiling ... Eternities of waiting seemed to spread out, and then, abruptly, to collapse like a shut fan with the jubilant shout from above: 'He's here, Captain, and there's two of them! I can see them plain!'

By the sound, the speaker slid down with the words from his post, and, almost simultaneously too, came another blow on the door, and the ritual command, 'Open in the King's name!'

The cousins both lifted their heads now, and Archie, hopeful to the last, laid a finger on his lips. The order was repeated; then, as if uncontrollably, blows began to rain on the door.

'Come out and surrender yourselves!' called the officer's voice sternly, and another shouted, 'Use that log there, ye fools – 'tis heavier than the butts!' and yet another cried excitedly, 'What if we was to fire the thatch, sir?'

And at that, quite suddenly, the battle madness of the Highlands, the *mire chatha*, came upon Ewen Cameron, and he went berserk. This was to be a trapped beast, an otter at bay ... an otter, any beast shows fight then! Did the redcoats anticipate coming in unhindered to take them, or that they, Highlanders both, would tamely suffer themselves to be burnt out?

Thrusting the second pistol at Doctor Cameron with 'Take this too – I'll need both hands!' Ewen seized the great rusty axe from the corner and flung himself against the barricaded portal just as one of the up-ended logs which wedged it slipped and fell, dislodged by the blows under which the door was quivering, and set against it the living prop of his own shoulder.

'Ewen, Ewen,' besought his companion in great distress,

' 'tis useless – worse than useless! My time has come!' But Ardroy did not even seem to hear him, leaning with all the might of his strong body against the door, his right hand gripping the axe, his left arm outspread across the wood trying to get a hold on the logs of the wall beyond the hinges.

Suddenly a crackling sound above showed that the suggestion just made had been carried out, and the roof-thatch fired, probably by a brand flung upwards. The thatch however, was damp and burnt sullenly; yet in a moment or two some eddies of smoke, caught by the wind, drifted in through the aperture. Then the flame caught, perhaps a drier patch, and a sudden thick wave of smoke, acrid and stifling, drove downwards in the gloom as though looking for the fugitives. But already the door was beginning to splinter in several places. The assailants seemed to guess that it was buttressed now with the body of one of the besieged. 'Stand away from that door, you within there,' shouted the officer, 'or I fire!'

But, instead of a bullet, there came stabbing through one of the newly made little breaches in the door, like a snake, a tongue of steel, bayonet or sword. It caught Ewen just behind and below the shoulder pressed against the door; a trifle more to one side and it might have gone through the armpit into the lung. As it was, it slid along his shoulder blade. Involuntarily Ardroy sprang away from the door, as involuntarily dropping the axe and clapping his right hand to the seat of the hot, searing pain.

'Are you hurt?' exclaimed his cousin. 'O Ewen, for God's sake – '

'They are not going to take you as easily as they think!' said Ewen between his teeth; and with the blood running down his back under his shirt, he pounced on the fallen axe again. The door shivered all over, and by the time he had recovered his weapon he saw that it was giving, and that nothing could save it. He pushed Archie, still imploring him to desist, roughly away. 'Keep out of sight, for God's sake! ' he whispered hoarsely, and, gripping the axe with both hands, stood back a little the better to swing it, and also to avoid having the door collapse upon him.

In another moment it fell inwards with a bang and a noise of rending hinges, and there was revealed, as in a frame, the group of scarlet-clad figures with their eager faces, the glitter of weapons, the tree-trunks beyond. And to those soldiers who had rushed to the dark entrance Cameron of Ardroy also was visible, against the gloom and smoke within, towering with the axe ready, his eyes shining with a light more daunting even than the weapon he held. They hesitated and drew back.

The officer whipped out his sword and came forward.

'Put down that axe, you madman, and surrender Archibald Cameron to the law!'

'Archibald Cameron is not here!' shouted back Ewen. 'But you come in at your peril!'

None the less, whether he trusted in his own superior quickness with his slighter weapon, or thought that the rebel would not dare to use his, Captain Craven advanced. And neither of these hypotheses would have saved him ... though he was saved (luckily for Ewen). For the Highlander in his transport had forgotten the small proportions of the place in which he stood, and his own height and reach of arm. The smashing two-handed blow which he aimed at the Englishman never touched him; with a thud which shook the doorway the axe buried itself in the lintel above it; and as Ewen with a curse tried to wrench it out, the haft, old and rotten, came away in his hand, leaving the head imbedded above the doorway, and himself weaponless.

As he saw the axe sweeping down towards him the young officer had naturally sprung back, and now, before Ewen had time to recover himself, the sergeant rushed past his superior and seized Ardroy round the body, trying to drag him out. As they struggled with each other – all danger from the axe being now over – another man slipped in, got behind the pair, and raised his clubbed musket. Archie sprang at the invader and grabbed at his arm, and though he only half-caught it, his act did diminish the fierce impact of the blow, and probably saved Ewen from having his head split open. As it was, the musket butt felled him instantly; his knees gave, and with a stifled cry he toppled over in the sergeant's hold, his weight bringing the soldier down with him.

But the redcoat got up again at once, while Ewen, with blood upon his hair, lay face downwards across the fallen door, the useless axe shaft still clutched in one hand; and it was over his motionless body that Archibald Cameron was brought out of his last refuge.

2

'Inversnaid,' said Ewen to himself in a thick voice. 'Inversnaid on Loch Lomond – that is where I must go. Which is the way, if you please?'

He had asked the question, it seemed to him, of so many people whom he had passed, and not one had answered him. Sometimes, it was true, these people bore a strong resemblance to trees and bushes, but that was only their cunning, because they did not want to tell him the way to Inversnaid.

It was not very dark in the wood, however, for it was a clear, windy night, and the starlight easily penetrated the stripped boughs of it; only under the pines were there pools of shadow. It was now some time since Ewen had discovered that he was lying out in the open, under a tree, and no longer sitting in the little hut which he faintly remembered, where Archie and he had been together one day; some time since he had got with difficulty to his feet, had lurched to that very hut, and, holding on tight to the doorway, had looked in at its black emptiness, and wondered why the door lay on the ground. Yet it was while he stood propped there that the name of Inversnaid had come to him with an urgency which he could not interpret, and he had turned at once in what he felt was the direction of Loch Lomond. He was in no state to realize that it was much less the absence of a warrant against him than the impossibility of transporting him, in his then inert condition, over miles of the roughest country to Inversnaid which had saved him, in spite of the resistance which he had offered, from being taken there as a prisoner himself.

Ah, here was a tree or bush of some kind, covered with red

flowers – holding a lantern – very odd, that! No, two of them, both with lights. The first was a female bush – a rose tree, by the look; one must be polite to it. He tried to doff his hat, but he had none. 'Madam, will you tell me the shortest way to Inversnaid?'

The kind bush replied that she would take him there; and then she drew an arm through hers, while the other lantern-bearing tree did the same. And so, at last, he found someone to help him on his journey.

'He's clean crazed, James,' said Mrs Stewart, showing an anxious face above her red and green flowered shawl as she looked round the lurching figure which she was guiding at the man who was performing the same office on the other side. 'I don't know what we are going to do with him now that we have found him.'

'Pit him tae bed and gar him bide quiet,' responded the practical James, the gardener. 'Haud up, sir; ye maun lift yer feet a wheen higher, if ye please.'

'I remember now, the blade came off the axe,' said Ewen suddenly, his eyes fixed as though he were seeing something ahead. He had been silent for some time, though talkative at first. 'If it had not, I should have killed that officer, and some of the other redcoats too, perhaps.'

'Ay, I mak nae doot o' it,' agreed James Stoddart soothingly, and they went on again, while behind the three pattered the little barefoot girl whom the soldier had chased that afternoon. It was she who, having hung about in the wood instead of going home, had played Mercury, and had given Mrs Stewart, already horrified by the news of Doctor Cameron's capture, the further tidings that the other gentleman had been left lying as if he were dead, at the spot of the disaster.

'I doubt this is not the way to Loch Lomond,' said Ewen, stopping dead all at once. 'Madam, you are misleading me, and that is worse than not answering.' He looked down at Mrs Stewart rather threateningly.

'Come, Mr Cameron,' added Mrs Stewart gently.

'My name is Grant,' retorted Ewen with some irritation.

'Hector Grant, an officer in the French service.' And under his breath he promptly began to sing snatches of 'Malbrouck'.

But when he got to *'Ne sait quand reviendra'*, he broke off. 'Yes, he's gone, and God knows when he will return. . . . *"Madame à satourmonte,"* it says. Will you go up into your tower, madam, to look out for him? But there was a man who looked in – through the roof. That is not in the song.' He wrinkled his brows, and added, like a pettish child, 'When shall we be through this wood? I am so weary of it!'

Yet for the rest of the night he walked in it, always trying to find the way to Loch Lomond, long after Mrs Stewart and James Stoddart had somehow got him into the house, and into the bed which Archie Cameron had occupied but the night before. And not until she had him lying there, still babbling faintly of doors and axes and eyes in the roof and Inversnaid and Loch Treig, and also of a stolen horse and some letter or other, and once or twice of his brother-in-law Ewen Cameron, did Mrs Stewart, just outside the room, bring forth her pocket-handkerchief.

'The Doctor betrayed and taken, this gentleman that tried to save him clean broke in his wits – O James, what a weary day's work! And to think that but this morning I was baking, and the bread never came forth better! Had I the second sight, as I might have, being Highland – '

'If ye had it, mem,' broke in James Stoddard ' – not that I believe any has it; 'tis an idle and mischievous supersteetion – ye and the laird wad ne're have ta'en the Doctor intil the hoose, and y'd hae been spared a' this stramash.'

But Mrs Stewart was already drying her eyes. 'If it comes to that,' she retorted with spirit, 'a body might think it wiser never to have been born, and that would be a poor choice.'

'There's ae man will be wishing the nich he hadna been, I'm thinkin',' observed the gardener uncompromisingly, 'and that's Doctor Cameron.'

'Doctor Cameron will be wishing no such thing,' returned his mistress. 'He's a brave man, and used to running risks, though he'll be grieving indeed for the blow his taking is to the

Prince. Ah me, what will the laird say when he hears the news!'

'Humph,' said her downright companion, 'the Doctor will be grieving for mair than Prince Charlie. He kens weel they'll hang him, the English.'

'Nonsense, James,' retorted Mrs Stewart. 'The English have not sufficient cause nor evidence against him. He has done nothing they can lay their fingers on. But no doubt they'll put him in prison, and for long enough, I fear.'

'Nay, ye'll see, mem, he'll not bide lang in prison,' predicted James Stoddart, shaking his head with a certain gloomy satisfaction. 'A kind and bonny gentleman too, the Doctor,' he went on, 'but for a' he never said aught as he went aboot his business in these pairts, whatever it was, he kenned fine what wad happen him if the redcoats catched him. I saw it whiles in his ee.'

'You have too much imagination, James Stoddart,' said Mrs Stewart a trifle severely – and most unjustly. Turning from him she tiptoed back into the room for a moment. 'I think the poor gentleman is quieting down at last,' she reported, returning. 'I shall go to bed for a while. Do you sit with him and give him a drink if he asks for it – and for God's sake hold your tongue on the subject of the Doctor's being hanged!'

Chapter 16

THE DOOR IN ARLINGTON STREET

1

THE trees of St James's Park this May afternoon made a bright green canopy over the hooped and powdered beauties who sailed below, over the gentlemen in their wide-skirted coats and embroidered satin waistcoats, the lap-dogs, the sedan-chairs, the attendant black boys and footmen, and also, since spring leaves flutter equally above the light heart and the heavy, over a tall, quietly dressed young man in a brown tie-wig who was making his way, with the air of looking for some-one, among the loungers in the Birdcage Walk. Of the glances, which despite his plain attire, more than one fine lady bestowed upon him he was completely unconscious; he was too unhappy.

The weeks of Ewen's convalescence at Glenbuckie had been bad, but this was worse – to come to London directly one was physically fit for it, only to find that no scheme of real value was on foot to save Archibald Cameron from the fate which seemed to be awaiting him.

Taken from Inversnaid to Stirling, and from Stirling to Edinburgh Castle, Doctor Cameron had been brought thence with a strong escort to London, arriving in the capital on the sixteenth of April, the very anniversary of Culloden. He had been examined the next day before the Privy Council at Whitehall, but it was common knowledge that they had got from him neither admissions nor disclosures, and he had been taken back a close prisoner to the Tower. That was nearly a month ago.

At first, indeed, his bandaged head on the pillow which had been Archie's, Ewen had known little about past or present. Mrs Stewart, aided by Peggy (so Peggy herself was convinced), had nursed him devotedly, and the task had perhaps helped her to forget her own anxiety on her husband's account, for Duncan Stewart had been arrested as he was returning from Perth. Luckily, however, for Ewen, once Mr Stewart's person was secured his house had not been searched. But a considerable harvest of suspects had been reaped, as Ewen was to find when he came perfectly to himself, for his own cousin John Cameron of Fassefern, Lochiel's and Archie's brother, had been imprisoned, and Cameron of Glenevis as well, and there was glee in Whig circles, where it was recognized what a blow to a dying cause was Archibald Cameron's capture. Of Lochdornie there was no news, but a warrant had been issued against him.

Ewen himself, who had arrived in London but the day previously, had now come to St James's Park merely to search for a Scottish Jacobite gentleman of his acquaintance, one Mr Galbraith, who, on inheriting a small estate from an English relative, had settled in England and had a house in Westminster. Had he not been told that Mr Galbraith was walking here with a friend Ewen would not have chosen so gay a promenade.

None too soon for his wishes, he caught sight of the elderly Mr Galbraith at a distance, talking earnestly to a tall, thin gentleman with a stoop. Just before the Highlander reached them this gentleman took his leave, and Mr Galbraith came on alone, his head bent, his hands holding his cane behind his back, so deep in thought that he almost ran into Ewen.

'I beg your pardon, sir ... why, it is Mr Cameron of Ardroy!' He held out his hand. 'What are you doing in London? I am very glad to see you again, however, very glad!'

Ewen glanced round. No one was within earshot. 'I have come to try what I can do for my unfortunate kinsman in the Tower. You have studied the law, Galbraith; you can tell me of what worth is any evidence which can be brought against him at his trial.'

'At his trial!' repeated Mr Galbraith with an intonation which Ewen found strange. He took Ewen's arm, and piloted him to a more secluded spot where a hawthorn-tree invited to a seat on the bench below it. But they did not sit down.

'Doctor Cameron will not be so fortunate as to have a trial,' resumed Mr Galbraith. 'You have not heard that – but no, I have only just heard it myself this afternoon. I was even now discussing it with a friend from the Temple.'

'No trial!' stammered Ewen. 'But Mr Galbraith, in Great Britain an accused man must have a trial ... it is illegal ... it – '

'It is perfectly legal in this case,' said Mr Galbraith gravely. 'Have you forgotten that Doctor Cameron's attainder of 1746 has never been reversed? He will be brought up quite soon now it is thought, for sentence to be pronounced ... and the sentence will probably take its course.'

'You mean to say,' and Ewen found a difficulty in speaking, 'that he will be put to death on a charge seven years old for a course of action on account of which so many have since made their peace and been amnestied?'

'But *he* has never made his peace nor been amnestied. He was exempted from the Act of Indemnity, as you know, because he did not surrender himself in time. Surely if he is your kinsman you must always have known that, Ardroy?'

'I knew, naturally, that he was exempted from the Act. But to proceed to this extremity is iniquitous,' said Ewen hotly, ' – unworthy even of the Elector and his parasites! To deny a man a fair trial – '

Mr Galbraith put his hand on his arm. 'My dear Ardroy, remember where you are, and be careful of your language! Come home with me now, and we will talk the matter over quietly.'

In Mr Galbraith's comfortable, dark-panelled house in Westminster Ardroy talked little; he listened. No, said his compatriot, there had not been a great deal of interest shown when Doctor Cameron was brought to London in April, so many people being out of town with the Duke, horse-racing at Newmarket. Should popular feeling be sufficiently aroused it was possible that pressure might be brought to bear on the Government. As to why the authorities preferred to rely upon the old sentence of attainder rather than to try Doctor Cameron for treason, it was said very secretly – and here Mr Galbraith in his own library, dropped his voice and glanced round – it was said that the Government had sufficient evidence to hang him if he were brought to trial, but did not wish to use it because to do so would probably reveal the source through which it was acquired.

'I should not have thought their hands so clean that they need hold back for that!' commented Ewen scornfully.

His host shook his head. 'Mind you, Ardroy, this is but a theory, and whispered only in corners at that! The Government are said to have the evidence from an informer whose identity they do not wish known. Whoever he may be, he is either too highly placed or too useful to expose.'

Disgust and wrath fought together in this hearer. 'An informer! Pah! But, yes, there has been treachery; I know that well. If Doctor Cameron is sacrificed I think it will not be impossible to find him, protected or no! But that's for . . . later on. Now, Mr Galbraith, what do you think of the chances of a rescue from the Tower?'

'I think nothing of them,' said the Scot emphatically. 'A rescue is impossible; an escape only feasible by some such stratagem as Lady Nithsdale employed to save her husband after the 'Fifteen, and such a stratagem has a very small chance of succeeding the second time. No, the only hope is that, for whatever reason, the Government should see fit to commute the sentence which is, I fear, sure to be pronounced.'

2

It was late, after eleven o'clock, when Ewen left Mr Galbraith's house in Westminster and started to walk back to Half Moon Street, off Piccadilly, where he lodged over a vintner's. All the time he wished that he were walking eastwards, towards the Tower. But what would be the use? He could not gain admission if he were.

The hand of Care lay fast upon his shoulder, and to dull the pressure he turned his thoughts, as he walked, to the one bright spot in the last few weeks – Alison's visit to Glenbuckie. Unknown to him, Mrs Stewart had contrived to get word of his condition to Ardroy, and the convalescent woke one day to feel his wife's lips upon his brow. He had made much more noticeable progress towards recovery after that.

There were other patches of sunlight, too, in those heavy days; little Peggy Stewart had made one of them. More than once, in the early part of his illness, he had wakened to find beside him a small, sedate and very attentive watcher whose legs dangled from the chair in which she was installed, and who said, when he opened his eyes, 'I will tell Mamma that you are awake, sir,' and slipped importantly down from her sentry-post. Peggy also expressed regret that his hair had been cutted off; and this was the first intimation which Ewen received that his fevered head had been shorn, and that when he was restored to the outer world he would in consequence have to wear a wig – as, indeed, most men did.

Alison on her arrival, like Peggy, had lamented that operation, and when her husband, making a jest suggested that he might take the opportunity of wearing a black wig in order to change his appearance, Alison had cried out in horror. She did not desire his appearance changed ... and then, understanding the reason of his speech, was all for anything that would serve to disguise him, particularly when she found that he was set upon going to London directly the journey was possible for him, entirely abandoning his idea of engaging an advocate for himself at Edinburgh. To that course, in the end, she became at last partially reconciled, and longed to accompany him. But the great obstacle to this plan had been, not the children, since Aunt Margaret was back at Ardroy now, but the stark, bare obstacle which wrecks so many desires – want of money. Alison had brought her husband all that she could raise at the moment, but it would barely suffice for his own outfit, journey and maintenance in London.

Ewen could not throw off the shadow which dogged him. Why, why had he ever persuaded his cousin to shelter in the woodcutter's hut? Indeed, if the fairies had put it there, as Archie had suggested, it had been for no good purpose. He saw it again, accursed little place, as he walked up St James's Street in surroundings so widely different, glancing back at the Palace front as he crossed to the farther side. And it occurred to him how strange it was that he should be walking about London perfectly unmolested, when if the authorities here knew of his doings at Fort William and Glenbuckie, or if he were to meet Lord Aveling coming out of one of the clubs or coffee-houses which abounded in this region – as well he might, though not perhaps at so late an hour as this. . . . But he felt beyond troubling over his own fate.

As yet the Highlander hardly knew his way about London, and at the junction of Bennet Street with Arlington Street made a mistake, turned to the left instead of to the right, and, being deep in thought, went on without at once realizing that he was in a cul-de-sac. Then, brought up by the houses at the end, he stopped, wondering where he had got to. As he tried to take his bearings the door of a house on the opposite side, almost in the angle, opened a little way, and a gentleman muffled in a cloak slipped very quietly, almost stealthily, out. A man who must have been waiting for him outside stepped forward and took the burning torch out of its holder by the door to light him home – though Arlington Street itself was sufficiently well lit. The two crossed near Ewen, whom perhaps they did not notice, and made for the little street up which he had just come. Ewen turned quickly and looked after them. For the cloaked gentleman had spoken to his attendant in Gaelic, bidding him, somewhat sharply, hold the torch more steady.

The two were Highlanders then! Ewen stifled the half-impulse to follow and accost them which the sound of that beloved tongue had raised in him. After all they were no concern of his, and he certainly did not know the speaker, who was young and wore his reddish hair unpowdered, for his hat cocked at a rakish angle suffered the torchlight to gleam for an instant upon it.

Some Highlander, Jacobite or Whig – more probably the latter who knew intimately a man of position, to judge from the elegant new brick house from which he had emerged. Well, God knew he only wished that *he* had a friend with influence, living in this street, which looked as if it housed people of importance.

3

Next evening, a rainy one, Mr Galbraith took Ewen, as he had promised, to the 'White Cock' in the Strand to introduce him to some of its *habitués*. The Highlander was struck with the discreet and unassuming appearance of this Jacobite resort – which some said should be called *en toutes lettres* 'The White Cockade' – the narrow passage in which it was situated, the disarming and rather inconvenient short flight of steps which led into its interior. But if its accessories were discreet there did not seem to be much of that quality about its customers. Already Ardroy had been a little astonished at the openness with which Jacobite sentiments were displayed in London.

He had been there perhaps three-quarters of an hour or more when the door at the top of the steps admitted a man who removed his wet cloak to his arm and stood a moment looking round with a certain air of hesitation, as one perhaps, a trifle unsure of his reception.

Ardroy got up. It could not be! Yet, unlikely as it seemed, it *was* Hector! Ardroy hurried forward, and Hector's eyes fell upon him.

'Ewen! you here in London!' There was not only astonishment but unmistakable relief in Lieutenant Grant's tone. Ewen was even more surprised to see him, but not particularly relieved. What on earth had brought Hector to London again – or had he never rejoined his regiment last January?

'I'll tell you in a moment why I am in England,' said the young officer hurriedly. 'What incredible good fortune that you should be here! Come with me to my lodging – 'tis not far off.'

Puzzled, Ewen said that he must excuse himself to his friend Mr Galbraith, and going back he did so. By the time he got up the steps Hector himself was outside. His face in the light of the lamp over the doorway had a strange wretchedness, or so Ewen thought.

'Hector, is aught amiss with you?'

'*Amiss?*' queried his brother-in-law with a sort of laugh. 'I'm ruined unless. . . . But come to my lodging and you shall hear.' Seizing Ardroy by the arm he thereupon hurried him off

194

through the rain. No, he had not got into trouble over his outstayed leave, and he had only arrived in London that morning.

'And God be praised that I have met with you, Ewen – though I cannot think why you are here.'

'Surely you can guess that,' said Ardroy. 'Because of Archibald Cameron. I thought it must be the same with you.'

'So it is,' answered Hector, with what sounded like a groan. 'Here we are – beware the stair, 'tis very ill lit.' He guided his kinsman into an upstairs room, fumbled with tinder and steel, and lit a lamp so carelessly that the flame flared high and smoky without his noticing it. 'Archibald Cameron – ay, my God, Archibald Cameron!' he said, and turned away.

'Don't take it so much to heart, Eachainn,' said Ewen kindly, laying a hand on his shoulder. ' 'Tis not quite hopeless yet.'

'God! you don't know yet what it is I'm taking to heart!' exclaimed Hector with startling bitterness. 'Oh, I'm grieved to the soul over the Doctor ... but unless I can disprove the slander about his capture I am ruined, as I told you, and may as well blow my brains out!'

Ewen stared at him in astonishment. 'My dear Hector, what slander? Ruined! What in Heaven's name are you talking about?'

Hector seized his wrist. 'You have not heard it then? Nor have they, I suppose, at the 'White Cock' or they would have turned me out *sans jaçon*. I tell you I was in a sweat of fear when I went in; but thank God that I did go, since by it I found you, and there's no man in the world I'd sooner have at my back ... more by token since you know the circumstances.'

'But those are just what I don't know!' exclaimed Ardroy, more and more bewildered. 'See, Hector, calm yourself a little and tell me what you are talking about. Has it anything to do with Archie?'

'Everyhing in the world. They are saying over there in Lille, in the regiment – the Doctor's own regiment and mine – that 'twas an officer in French service who betrayed him, and some think that the officer is – ' He stopped, his mouth twitching, his eyes distracted, and made a sort of gesture of pointing to himself.

'Good God!' ejaculated Ewen in horror. '*You!* On what possible – '

'On what grounds? Because of the fatal letter which I lost that day on Loch Treig side, the letter which in any case was taken from me by treachery and violence. But they hint, so I am told, that it was written in order to convey information, and that I *gave* it to the spy! O my God, that men should whisper such a thing of me, and that I cannot kill them for it!'

But Ewen stood a moment half-stupefied. Too well he knew, at least from hearsay, of mutual accusations among Jacobites of divergent views. But in Hector's own regiment, among his fellow-officers. . . . Then he recovered himself.

'Hector,' he said with emphasis, 'that story is sheer nonsense! 'Twas a much more recent piece of information than any contained in your letter which led to Archie's capture.'

'How do you know?' asked the young man, swinging round with a tragic face. 'How do you know that?'

'Because I – but I'll tell you the whole story in a moment. First do you tell me – '

'Ewen,' interrupted his brother-in-law vehemently, 'if you'll only clear me I give you leave, with all my heart, to dirk me afterwards if you like.'

Ewen could not keep back a smile. 'The inducement is not overwhelming. But, Hector,' he added, 'I hope to God that you have not deserted – have not come over without leave?'

'No, no, Lord Ogilvie gave me leave. He thought that if I came over I might be able to find out who really was responsible for the Doctor's capture and thus clear myself. And it goes without saying that if there is any scheme on foot for Doctor Cameron's release or rescue you may count on me *de tout mon coeur.*'

'Alas, I fear that there is none at present,' said Ewen sadly. 'Yet, as regards his capture, though I cannot give you the name of the man responsible, I can prove that it was not you. But, Hector, who can have put about this slander? Who started it?'

Hector shook his head. 'I could not find out – how does one discover a thing like that? Nor has anyone dared to tax me with it directly; 'twas more hints, sneers, looks, avoidance of me.'

'You must,' said Ewen, considering, 'have been too free with your tongue over your unlucky loss of that letter last autumn.'

'Too free with my tongue! I never breathed a word about it to a soul over there, not even to Lord Ogilvie. I was far too much ashamed.'

'And did you not tell anyone when you were in Scotland?'

'Save you, no one.'

' 'Tis very strange. Well, tell me what chanced after our sudden parting that dark morning at Ardgour, and how you succeeded in getting over to France.'

Hector told him.

'*Dhé!*' exclaimed his brother-in-law at the end, 'so 'twas young Glenshian who helped you to papers! How the devil did he contrive to do it?'

'Faith, I don't know overwell. He gave me a letter to someone whom I never saw, with a feigned name at that. I was grateful enough to the future Chief, though there is something about the man which I find it hard to stomach.'

'Stay one moment,' said Ardroy slowly. 'You told young Glenshian of the loss of your necessary papers; perhaps you told him of the loss of the letter too?'

A flush fell over Hector's face and his jaw fell a trifle. He thumped the table. 'You're right; I did! But he, surely, could not have spread – '

'No, no, I do not suppose that for an instant! It was only that you said you had told nobody save me.'

'Nobody over the water nor in Scotland. I vow I had forgotten Finlay MacPhair in London. He was so anxious to know whether I had lost any compromising document. But that he could have put about such a libel is out of the question. I fear, however, that he may have mentioned my misfortune to some third person. ... But now for your proof, Ewen, which is to clear me! And tell me, too, how soon you got back from Ardgour, and all that has befallen you of late. You look, now that I see you closer ... have you been ill by any chance?'

Chapter 17

FORESEEN AND UNFORESEEN

1

IT had been arranged that Hector should come to Ewen's lodging early next morning, and that they should both go to wait upon Mr Galbraith. Ewen therefore remained in his room writing a letter to Alison, but when an hour and a quarter had elapsed he was walking about his room really anxious. What had the boy been doing?

And then he heard his landlady's voice explaining to someone that she thought Mr Cameron must by now have gone out.

'No, I have not,' said Ewen, appearing on the threshold of his bedroom. 'Is that you at last, Hector? What on earth has delayed you so?'

'I'll tell you in a moment,' said young Grant rather hoarsely. 'I have made what haste I could.' And indeed his brow was damp, and he sank down in a chair in the sitting-room as if exhausted. Ewen asked him if he were ill, for he was clearly under the sway of some emotion or other; and, when Hector shook his head, said, 'Then 'tis this business of the slander on you. Have you discovered something?'

'No, no, it is not that,' said Hector. And then he got it out with a jerk. 'Ewen, Doctor Cameron was this morning condemned to death, without trial.'

A club seemed to strike Ewen's head – like that musket butt in the wood. Yet this news was expected.

'How did you hear it?' he asked after a moment's silence.

'I . . . O Ewen, I would have given anything to get to you in time. I tried to send a messenger. In truth it should have been you, not I, but it was not my fault!'

A light broke on Ardroy. 'You mean that you actually heard him sentenced?'

Hector nodded, 'It was all chance and hurry. Had your lodging not been so far away – '

'You have seen Archie this morning! Where was he brought up for sentence, then?'

'At the Court of King's Bench in Westminster Hall.'

Ewen sat down at the table. 'Tell me about it. – No, I do not blame you, Hector; why should I? Yet I would have given much. . . .' He clenched his hand a second on the edge of the table. 'Tell me everything.'

So Hector told him. The story began with his going for an early walk along the riverside, and finding himself, when he got to Westminster, in the presence of a considerable crowd, waiting in the hopes of getting a glimpse of that Jacobite as he was brought by coach from the Tower to have sentence passed upon him. 'After the first astonishment I was for coming at once to fetch you. But it appeared that the Court was already assembled, and that the prisoner might arrive at any moment. Then I thought, "I will at least do my best to get a sight of the Doctor, to tell Ewen how he seems." I had no hope of entering Westminster Hall, since the press was so great; and moreover those who went in appeared to have tickets of admission. After a while, indeed, I found myself penned with one or two others into an angle of the building where I could see nothing. However, there was in this angle a small door, and when the man nearest it, in a fit of annoyance, began to beat upon it, it was suddenly opened by an official, who grumblingly consented to find places for four or five of the nearest – and this he did.'

'And so you heard – or saw?'

'I did both, though with difficulty, being at the back of the court. The proceedings were quite short. The Doctor was extremely composed, neither defiant nor a whit overwhelmed; he appeared, too, in good health. Nor did he attempt to deny that he was the person named in the Act of Attainder.'

'Did he make no defence – had he not an advocate?'

'No. The only defence which he made was to say that he could not have acted otherwise than he did, having to follow Lochiel, his brother and Chief, that in the troubles he had always set his face against reprisals or harsh treatment, of which he gave some instances, and that his own character would bear investigation in the same light. Then came that barbarous sentence for high treason, pronounced by one of the three judges present – the Lord Chief Justice, I think it was – and, Ewen, it was not imagination on my part that he laid particular emphasis on those words respecting the hanging, "but not till you are dead", glowering at the Doctor as he uttered them. Many people remarked it, and were talking about it afterwards. But Doctor Cameron was perfectly calm, and merely made a civil bow at the end; after that, however, he asked earnestly that the execution of the sentence, which had been fixed for this day fortnight, might be deferred a little in order to enable him to see his wife, to whom he had already had permission to write bidding her come to him from France. And he added that she and their seven children were all dependent upon him, and that it would be worse than death to him not to see her again. So the Court decided to instruct the Attorney-General that the sentence should not be carried out until a week later, on the seventh of June, in order to permit of this. Then the Doctor was removed, and everyone fought their way out again; and I came away feeling that if I really believed my rashness and carelessness last September were the cause of Archibald Cameron's standing there I would blow my brains out tonight!'

'Be reassured, Hector, they are not the cause!' said Ardroy in an emotional voice. But his face was very haggard. ' 'Tis I am' the person most immediately responsible, for it was I who found that accursed hut in the wood at Glenbuckie and persuaded him to lie hid in it. . . . Yes, I expected this news, but that makes it no easier to bear – Hector, he must be saved somehow, even if it should mean both our lives!'

'I am quite ready to give mine,' answered young Grant simply. 'It would be the best means, too, of clearing my honour; far the best.'

'Let us go to Westminster and see Mr Galbraith,' said his brother-in-law.

They walked for some distance in silence, and when they were nearing the top of St James's Street Ewen pulled at his companion's arm.

'Let us go this way,' he said abruptly, and they turned down Arlington Street. 'Just from curiosity, I have a desire to know who lives in a certain new house in the bottom corner there.'

Hector, usually so alert, seemed too dulled by his recent experience to exhibit either surprise or curiosity at this proceeding. They walked to the end of Arlington Street.

'Yes, that is the house,' observed Ewen after a moment's scrutiny. 'Now to find out who lives in it.'

'Why?' asked Hector. And, rousing himself to a rather perfunctory attempt at jocularity, he added, 'Remember that you are in company with Alison's brother, Ardroy, if it's the name of some fair lady whom you saw go into that house which you are seeking.'

' 'Twas a man whom I saw come out of it,' replied Ewen briefly, and, noticing a respectable-looking old gentleman in spectacles advancing down Arlington Street at that moment, he accosted him with a request to be told who lived at Number Seventeen.

'Dear me,' said the old gentleman, pushing his spectacles into place, and peering up at the tall speaker, 'you must, indeed, be a stranger to this part of the town, sir, not to know that Number Seventeen is the house of Mr Henry Pelham, the chief minister, brother to my Lord Newcastle.'

'I am a stranger,' admitted Ewen. 'Thank you, sir.' He lifted his hat again, and the old gentleman, returning the courtesy, trotted off.

'Mr Pelham the minister?' remarked Hector with reviving interest. 'And whom pray, did you see coming out of Mr Pelham's house?'

'That is just what it might be useful to discover,' replied Ewen musingly, 'now that one knows how important a personage lives there.'

'But I suppose that a good many people must come out of it,' objected the young officer. 'Why does the particular man whom you happened to see so greatly interest you?'

'Because he was a Highlander, and it was close upon midnight. And as a Highlander – though, naturally, a Whig – if one could interest him on a fellow-Highlander's behalf ... and he an intimate of Mr Pelham's –'

'How did you know that he was a Highlander, since I take it that he was not wearing the Highland dress?'

'Because I heard him rate his servant in Erse.'

'That's proof enough,' admitted Hector. 'Would you know him again if you saw him?'

'I think so. However, the chances are against my having the good fortune to do so.'

2

Darkness had fallen for some time when Ewen neared his lodging in Half Moon Street again; in fact it was nearly eleven o'clock. But when he was almost at the door he realized that to enter was out of the question. He must do something active, and the only form of activity open to him was to walk. So, not knowing or caring where he was going, he turned away again.

His brain was swimming with talk – talk with Hector, talk at Mr Galbraith's, talk at the 'White Cock', where the three of them had supped. There it had been confidently announced that public opinion would be so stirred over Doctor Cameron's hard case that the Government would be obliged to commute the sentence, for already its severity seemed like to be the one topic throughout London. It was reported that many Whigs of high standing were perturbed about it and the effect which it might have upon public opinion, coming so long after the Rising of '45, and having regard to the blameless private character of the condemned man.

For fully half an hour Ewen tramped round streets and squares until, hearing a church clock strike, he pulled himself out of the swarm of unhappy thoughts which went with him for all his fast walking, saw that it was between half past eleven and midnight, and for the first time began to consider where he might be.

He had really become so oblivious of his surroundings as he went that it was quite a surprise to find himself now in a deserted, narrow, and not particularly reputable-looking street. Surely a few minutes ago – yet on the other hand, for all the attention he had been paying, it might have been a quarter of an hour – he had been in a square of large, imposing mansions.

It was a light spring night, and he could see that beyond the end of this narrow street, there *were* much larger houses, mansions even. He was right. But he also saw something which kept him rooted there – two men, armed with weapons of some kind, stealing out of a passage about fifty yards away, and hastening to the end of the street where it debouched into the square. When they got there they drew back into the mouth of an entry and stood half-crouching, as if waiting.

Surprise and curiosity kept Ewen staring; then he realized that these men were probably lurking there with a purpose far from innocent. And even as he started back towards the entry this purpose was revealed, for the bulk of a sedan-chair, with its porters, came suddenly into view, crossing the end of the street, on its way, no doubt, to one of the great houses in the square; and instantly the two men darted towards it, flourishing their weapons, which had the appearance of bludgeons.

Ewen quickened his pace to a run, ran in fact with all his might to the succour of the sedan-chair, which very probably contained a lady. He was certainly needed by its occupant, of whichever sex, for the two chairmen, calling loudly for the watch, had taken ingloriously to their heels at the approach of danger. Before Ewen came up one of the footpads had already lifted the roof of the chair, opened the door, and was pulling forth no female in distress, but a protesting elderly gentleman in flowered brocade, stout and a trifle short. Yet he was a valiant elderly gentleman, for, the moment he succeeded in freeing his right arm, out flashed his sword. But the next instant his weapon was shivered by a cudgel blow, and he himself seized by the cravat.

That, however, was the exact instant also at which another sword, with a longer and a younger man behind it, came upon the assailants from the rear. Apparently they had not heard Ardroy's hurrying footfalls, nor his shouts to them to desist. Now one of them turned to face him; but his stand was very short. He dropped his cudgel with a howl and ran back down the narrow street. His fellow, of a more tenacious breed, still held on to the cravat of the unfortunate gentleman, trying to wrest out the diamond brooch which secured the lace at his throat. Ewen could have run his sword through the aggressor from side to side, but, being afraid of wounding the gentleman as well, took the course of crooking his left arm round the man's neck from behind, more than half-choking him. The assailant's hands loosed the cravat with remarkable celerity and tore instead at the garotting arm round his own throat. The rescuer then flung him away, and, as the footpad rolled in the gutter, turned in some concern to the victim of the attack, who by this time was hastily rearranging his assaulted cravat.

'My dear sir,' began the latter in a breathless voice, desisting and holding out both his hands, 'my dear sir, I can never thank you enough . . . most noble conduct . . . most noble! I am your debtor for life! No, thank you, I am shaken, but little the worse. If you will have the further goodness to lend me your arm to my house – 'tis but a few paces distant – and then I must insist on your entering that I may thank my preserver more fittingly. I sincerely trust,' he finished earnestly, 'that you are yourself unharmed?'

Ewen assured him that this was the case, and, sheathing the sword which in England there was no embargo upon his wearing, offered his arm. By this time the second footpad had also vanished.

'The outrageousness,' went on the rescued gentleman, 'the insolence, of such an attack within a few yards of my own door! Those rascally chairmen – I wonder were they in collusion? I vow I'll never take a hired chair again. . . . There come the watch – too late as usual! My dear sir, what would have befallen me without your most timely assistance heaven alone knows!'

They were by this time mounting the steps of a large house in the square. Almost before he knew it, Ewen was inside, having no great desire to enter, but realizing that it would be churlish to refuse.

'A most disgraceful attack has just been made upon me, Jenkins,' said the master of the house, to a resplendent functionary who then hurried forward. 'Had it not been for this gentleman's gallantry – If that is the watch come to ask for particulars,' as another knock was heard at the hall door, 'tell them to come again in the morning; I'll not see them now.'

'Yes, my lord,' said the resplendent menial respectfully. 'Your lordship was actually *attacked*!' His tone expressed the acme of horror. 'May I ask, has your lordship suffered any hurt?'

'None at all, none at all, thanks to this gentleman. All my lady's company is gone, I suppose? Has she retired? No? I am glad of it. Now, my dear sir,' he went on, laying his hand on Ewen's arm, 'allow me the pleasure of presenting you to my wife, who will wish to add her thanks to mine.' He steered his rescuer towards the great staircase, adding as he did so, 'By the way, I fancy I have not yet told you who I am – the Earl of Stowe, henceforward very much yours to command.'

Chapter 18

CROSSING SWORDS

IF a man ever wished himself well out of a situation in which, as it happened, his own prowess had landed him, it was Ewen Cameron of Ardroy. What fatality had induced him to succour and be brought home by the father of the very man whom he had treated so scurvily two months ago. Obviously the wisest course was to excuse himself and withdraw before he could meet that injured young gentleman.

But already Lord Stowe was motioning him to ascend the imposing staircase. Without great incivility he could not withdraw now, nor, it seemed to him, without great cowardice to boot. Ewen's was a stubborn courage as well as, on occasions, a hot-brained one; he never relished running away. He therefore went on up the wide shallow staircase, and was looked down upon with haughty disapproval by Aveling's ancestors.

Outside a door the Earl paused. 'May I know the name of my preserver?'

'I beg your pardon, my lord,' returned Ewen. 'I forgot that I had not made myself known to you. My name is Ewen Cameron of Ardroy, at your service.'

Now, what had Lord Stowe heard of Ewen Cameron of Ardroy? If anything at all, nothing of good, that was certain. The bearer of that name lifted his head with a touch of defiance, for its utterance had certainly brought about a change in his host's expression.

'A kinsman of the unfortunate Doctor Cameron's, perhaps?'

'Yes. He is my cousin – and my friend,' answered Ewen uncompromisingly.

'Ah,' observed Lord Stowe with a not unsympathetic intonation, 'a sad business, his! But come, Mr Cameron.' And, opening the heavy inlaid door, he ushered him into an enormous room of green and gold, where the disposition of the furniture spoke of a gathering now dispersed. But the most important person still remained. On a sofa, in an attitude of incomparable grace, languor and assurance, with a little book poised lazily between her long fingers, half-sat, half-reclined the most beautiful woman whom Ewen had ever seen. And then only, in the suddenness of these events and introductions, did he realize that he was in the presence of Keith Windham's mother as well as of Lord Aveling's.

As the door shut Lady Stowe half-turned her head, and said in silver tones, 'You are returned at last, my lord. Do I see that you bring a guest?'

'I do, my love,' replied her husband, 'And one to whom we owe a very great debt indeed.' And Ewen was led forward across the acres of carpet to that gilt sofa, and kissed the cool, fragrant hand extended to him, but faintly conscious of embarrassment at the praises of his courage which the Earl was pouring forth, and with all thoughts of an avenging Aveling dissipated. It was of Lady Stowe's elder son, his dead friend, whom he thought as he looked at that proud and lovely face. Not that there was any likeness. But surely this could not have been Keith Windham's mother; she seemed no older, at least by candlelight, than he when he died seven years ago!

Then Ewen found himself in a chair, with the Countess saying flattering things to him, rallying him gently, too, in those seductive tones.

'You are a Scot, sir, a kinsman of that unfortunate gentleman who is in all our minds just now, and yet you come to the rescue of an Englishman and a Whig!'

'It was an Englishman and a Whig, Lady Stowe, who once saved me from a far greater danger,' replied Ewen. He said it of set purpose, for he wished to discover if she knew what her elder son had been to him.

Apparently Lady Stowe did not, nor was she curious to learn to what he referred, for she merely said: 'Indeed; that is gratifying!' and, in fact, before the subject could be enlarged upon from either side, Lord Stowe was remarking to the guest by way of conversation suitable to his nationality, 'My son has recently been visiting Scotland for the first time.'

The menace of Aveling returned to Ewen's memory. By the tense it seemed as if that young gentleman had now returned from the North.

'You are from the Highlands, I suppose, Mr Cameron,' went on the Earl pleasantly. 'My son visited them also for a short while, going to Dunstaffnage Castle in Lorne. Do you happen to know it?'

Ewen intimated that he did, from the outside. And now a voice was crying out to him to end the difficult situation in which he stood by offering of his own will some explanation of the episode at Dalmally. For, with this mention of Lord Aveling in the Highlands, not to acknowledge that they had made each other's acquaintance there seemed so unnatural and secretive as to throw an even worse light upon his behaviour towards him. He pulled himself together for the plunge.

'I must tell you, my lord – ' he was beginning, when his voice was withered on his lips by an extraordinary grating, screeching sound which, without warning, rent the air of the great drawing-room. Startled as at some supernatural intervention, Ewen glanced hastily round in search of its source.

'Do not be alarmed, Mr Cameron,' came Lady Stowe's cool tones through the disturbance. ''Tis only that my macaw has waked up ... but I apologize for the noise he makes.'

And then the Highlander beheld, in a corner not very far away, a gilded cage, and therein a large bird of the most gorgeous plumage, with a formidable curved beak and a tail of fire and azure, who was pouring forth what sounded like a stream of imprecations.

'Good Gad, this is insupportable!' said Lord Stowe indignantly. And, slightly red in the face, he tugged at the nearest bell-pull. Meanwhile the infernal screeching continued unceasingly, except for one short moment when the macaw made a vicious grab at the Earl's lace-bordered handkerchief, with which he was exasperatedly flapping the bars of the cage in an endeavour to silence its inmate.

A footman appeared. 'Remove this bird at once!' shouted his master angrily. (He was obliged to shout.) The man hesitated.

'Montezuma will bite him, and he knows it,' observed Lady

Stowe, raising her voice but slightly. 'Send Sambo, John.'

The man bowed and withdrew with alacrity. 'This is worse than footpads!' declared the Earl, with his hands to his ears. 'I cannot sufficiently apologize, Mr Cameron!' – he had almost to bawl the words. 'Really, my lady, if I could wring your pet's neck without getting bitten, I would!'

'I know it, my love,' returned her ladyship, with her slow, charming smile. 'And so, I am sure, would poor Mr Cameron.'

Then black Sambo appeared in his scarlet turban and jutting white plume. Smiling broadly, he strutted off with the great gilt cage, whose occupant continued to scream, but made no onslaught upon those dusky fingers.

'I really cannot sufficiently apologize,' began the Earl once more to his half-deafened guest, 'for my wife's fancy – '

'What?' called a young, laughing voice from the door, 'has Montezuma been misbehaving again?' Someone had come in just as the exiled and vociferating fowl was borne out. 'But for that noise, I had thought you gone to bed by this time. You promised, my dear mother, that he – ' But here the speaker realized that there was a stranger in his family circle, pulled out a handkerchief, flicked some probably imaginary grains of powder off his gleaming coat, and advanced across the wilderness of the carpet to the three by the sofa, a veritable Prince Charming in peach-coloured satin and a deal of lace. And Ewen silently cursed the departed macaw with a mortification a thousand times deeper than the Earl's. But for that ridiculous contretemps he might either have made his confession, or escaped meeting his late victim, or both.

But there was no escape now. Lord Aveling, still smiling, got within a yard or two of the group when he saw who the stranger was. He stopped; the smile died, his face froze, and the hand with the filmy handkerchief fell, gripping the Mechlin.

Lord Stowe must have been blind had he not noticed the startling change on the countenance of his heir. But, if not blind, he was possibly short-sighted, for he did not by any means appear to read its full significance.

'You are surprised to see a guest here so late, Aveling, I

perceive,' he said mildly, 'but you will be still more surprised when you learn the reason for this gentleman's presence tonight.

'I was this evening,' went on Lord Stowe with empressement, 'the victim of a murderous attack – perhaps you have already heard of it from the servants.'

'An attack!' repeated Lord Aveling, at last turning his gaze upon his parent. 'On whose part – this gentleman's?'

'Good Gad, Aveling, what can you be thinking of?' exclaimed his father, shocked. 'This gentleman, Mr Cameron of Ardroy, had the great goodness to risk his own person for mine – Mr Cameron, this is my son, Lord Aveling.'

Ewen bowed, not very deeply.

'An introduction is not necessary, my lord,' observed Lord Aveling. 'We met not long ago in Scotland, Mr Cameron and I.' And with that he turned his back carelessly on the guest and went over to the sofa to speak to his mother.

Lord Stowe looked as if he could hardly believe his ears or eyes, partly at this announcement, partly at the sight of his son's uncivil behaviour. 'You met in Scotland!' he repeated after a moment, in tones of amazement.

'I was just on the point of making that fact known to your lordship,' said Ewen, 'when the bird interrupted me.' He was white with chagrin. 'Lord Aveling and I did, indeed, meet as he was returning from Dunstaffnage Castle.'

'Yes,' cut in the young man, turning round again, 'and owing to a difficulty over posthorses I had the privilege – as I see I must now consider it – of offering Mr Cameron a seat in my chaise as far as Dalmally.'

'My dear Aveling, why did you not tell us this before?' asked Lady Stowe.

'How could I guess that it would be of any interest to you to learn that I gave a lift to a stranger in the wilds of Scotland? Moreover, I can affirm, with my hand upon my heart, that Mr Cameron of Ardroy is the last person in the world whom I expected to find in this house.'

His manner, if controlled, was patently full of some ironical meaning which, though clear enough to Ardroy, was puzzling to his parents. The Countess said, with a smiling authority, 'Then it behoves you all the more, Francis, to hear how Mr Cameron beat off the footpads who assailed your father's chair this evening at the corner of the square.'

'English footpads?' queried the young man, and he looked meaningly for an instant at the rescuer.

'Why, what else?' asked his father. 'Two footpads armed with cudgels. I had the narrowest escape of being robbed, if not of being murdered.'

'I can quite believe that you had, sir,' observed Lord Aveling, looking at Ewen again.

But Ewen had by now resolved that he was not going to suffer these stabs any longer. He therefore took advantage of the check to Lord Stowe's imminent narrative, brought about by these (to him) unintelligible remarks of his son's, firmly to excuse himself on the score of the lateness of the hour.

'You must promise to visit us again, Mr Cameron,' said the Countess with the utmost graciousness, and Lord Stowe said the same, adding that if there were any way in which he could serve him he had but to name it. Ewen thought rather sardonically how surprised the Earl would be if he responded by a request that he should prevent his son from landing him in Newgate, but he merely murmured polite thanks as the Earl conducted him to the door of the drawing-room.

'I will escort Mr Cameron down the stairs, my lord,' said Lord Aveling easily, slipping in front of his father. 'You must remember that we are old acquaintances.'

He sounded perfectly civil and pleasant now, and after a barely perceptible hesitation the Earl relinquished the guest to his care, shook hands with great warmth, repeating his assurance of undying gratitude and a perpetual warm welcome at Stowe House. Then the door closed, and Ewen and Lord Aveling were alone together.

'Will you come into the library downstairs?' asked the young man, somewhat in the tone he might have used to a mason come about repairs, and with as little apparent doubt of the response.

'Yes,' answered Ardroy with equal coldness, 'I will,' and followed him down the great staircase.

In the marble-pillared hall a footman stepped forward. 'Take lights into the library,' commanded the young lord, and in another moment the lackey was preceding them with a couple of branched candlesticks into a room lined with books. He made as though to light the sconces too, but Lord Aveling checked him impatiently, and the man merely set the lights on the big, polished table in the centre and withdrew. The son of the house waited until his footsteps had died away on the marble outside.

'Now, Mr Cameron!' he said.

Ewen had always known that to come to London was to invite the Fates to present him with the reckoning for his behaviour at Dalmally. Well, if it had to be, it was preferable to have it presented by the victim himself rather than by some emissary of the justice which he had invoked.

'I suppose, my lord,' he now answered gravely, 'that you must say what you please to me. I admit that I have little right to resent it.'

The admission, unfortunately, appeared to inflame the young nobleman the more. 'You are vastly kind, Mr Cameron, upon my soul! You lay aside resentment, forsooth! I fear I cannot rise to that height, and let me tell you, therefore, that what I find almost more blackguardly than your infamous conduct at Dalmally is the *coup* you have brought off tonight, in – '

'The *coup* I have brought off!' exclaimed Ewen in bewilderment. 'My lord, what – '

Aveling swept on ' – in forcing an entrance to this house, and ingratiating yourself with my parents, having put my father under a fancied obligation by a trick so transparent that, if he were not the most good-natured man alive, he would have seen through it at once.'

At this totally unexpected interpretation of the sedan-chair incident a good deal of Ewen's coolness left him.

'You cannot really think that the attack on Lord Stowe was planned – that I was responsible for it!'

'How else am I to account for your being there so pat?' inquired the young man. 'You hired the ruffians and then came in as a deliverer. It has been done before now. And having succeeded in laying Lord Stowe under an obligation you know that I cannot well – ' He broke off, his rage getting the better of him. 'But the insolence, the inexpressible insolence of your daring to enter this house after what has happened!'

'Since I did *not* plan the attack, Lord Aveling,' said Ewen firmly, 'I had no notion whom I was rescuing. Nor did Lord Stowe tell me his name until he was on the point of taking me upstairs. It was too late to withdraw then.'

'As I am henceforward unable to believe a word that you say, sir,' retorted the young man, 'it is of small use your pretending ignorance of my father's identity.'

'Yet perhaps you are still able to recognize logic when you hear it,' rejoined Ewen with some sharpness, his own temper beginning to stir. 'Had I known that the gentleman in the sedan-chair was Lord Stowe – which, if I had planned the attack, I must have known – the merest prudence would have kept me from entering a house in which I was so like to meet you.'

'Yes,' said Aveling with a bitter little smile, 'you would have done better to part sooner from my father after this pretended rescue!'

'And yet,' said the Highlander, looking at him with a touch of wistfulness in his level gaze, 'as chance has brought us together again, is it too much to hope, my lord, that you will at least endeavour to accept my most sincere and humble apologies for what my great necessity forced me to do that evening?'

'Apologies?' said Viscount Aveling. 'No, by heaven, there are no apologies humble enough for what you did!'

'Then I am ready to give you satisfaction in the way usual between gentlemen,' said Ewen gravely.

The young man shook his powdered head. 'Between gentlemen, yes. But a gentleman does not accept satisfaction of that kind from a highwayman; he has him punished, as I swore I would you. But you doubtless think that by gaining the Earl's goodwill you have put that out of my power? Let me assure you, Mr Highwayman, that you have not; the law is still the law!'

'I doubt if the law can touch me for what I did,' answered Ewen.

'Not for theft, horse-stealing and assault? Then this must indeed be an uncivilized country! ... And behind those crimes remains always the question of how my brother really met his end.'

'That I have already told you, Lord Aveling.'

'Yes; and I was fool enough to believe you! I am wiser now; I know of what you are capable, Mr Ewen Cameron!'

Ewen turned away from the furious young man, who still maintained his position by the door. He was at a loss what to do next. There was no common ground on which they could meet, though once there had seemed so much; but he himself had shorn it away. One of the candles in the massive silver-branched candlesticks which had been deposited upon the table was guttering badly, and, in the strange way in which a portion of the mind will attend to trifles at moments of crisis, he took up the snuffers which lay there in readiness and mended the wick with scarcely the least consciousness of what he was doing.

His action had an unexpected result. Lord Aveling started a few paces forward, pointing at the hand which had performed this service. 'And you still have the effrontery to wear the ring which you took from poor Keith!'

Ewen laid down the snuffers. 'I have the effrontery, since you call it so, to wear the ring he gave me; and I shall wear it until my own dying day.'

The words, though they were very quietly uttered, rang like a challenge; and as a challenge the young man took them up.

'Will you?' he asked. 'I think not. Here in this house, above all, I have no liking to see my poor brother's property on your finger. You will kindly surrender it to his family.'

'Although I take you to be jesting, my lord,' began Ewen very coldly.

'Jesting!' flashed out Aveling. 'No, by God! You will give me back Keith Windham's signet ring, or – '

'Or?' questioned Ewen.

'Or I'll have it taken from you by the lackeys!'

'Then you will hardly be in a position to throw my theft of your property in my face!' retorted Ardroy.

'I had not stolen my pistols and my horse,' riposted Lord Aveling.

'Nor have I stolen my friend's ring. He gave it to me, and I give it up to nobody!'

'I dispute your statement!' cried the young man with passion. 'You took that ring, whether you are guilty of my brother's death or no. You are very capable of such an act; I know that now. Give it up to me, or I shall do what I say. My father has retired by now; do not imagine that he can protect you!'

'As to that, my lord, you must follow your own instincts,' said Ewen scornfully, 'but you'll not get my friend's dying gift from me by threats – no, nor by performances either,' he added, as he saw Lord Aveling move towards the embroidered Chinese bell-pull hanging by the mantelpiece. Ewen watched him. It needed a great effort of self-control on his part not to seize the young man and tear it out of his hand before he pulled it, as he could easily have done. And, in view of events in the bedroom at Dalmally, still only too fresh in his mind, this abstention evidently struck the angry Aveling as strange.

'I observe,' he said tauntingly, still holding the strip of silk, 'that you are not so ready to assault me now, Mr Cameron when you know that you would instantly have to pay for it!'

'It was in someone else's interests that I used violence on you then, my lord. I have no one else's to serve now,' said Ewen sadly.

Lord Aveling dropped the bell-pull. 'You mean Doctor Cameron. No, you did not benefit him much. You were too late, I imagine.'

'I was just too late.'

'And if you had not been,' remarked the young man, 'I should not, perhaps, have heard him sentenced this morning.'

Ewen gave a little exclamation, 'You were at the King's Bench this morning, my lord? You were there – you heard it all? But they cannot, they cannot, mean to carry out so cruel and iniquitous a sentence!'

Suddenly and oddly reflective, Lord Aveling gazed at him, the tassel of the abandoned bell-pull still moving slowly to and fro across the wall. 'I would have given wellnigh all I possess to be in your place, my lord,' went on Ardroy, his own dangerous and unpleasant situation clean forgotten, 'to see how he looked . . . though I have heard how well he bore himself. But if the judges knew what manner of man he was, how generous, how kind, how humane, they would not have condemned him on that seven years' old attainder.'

Francis Delahaye, Lord Aveling, was a very young man, and he had also been in an extreme of justifiable rage. But even that fury, now past its high-water mark, had not entirely swamped his native intelligence and sensitiveness, which were above the ordinary. He continued to look at Ewen without saying anything, as one in the grip of a perfectly new idea. Then, instead of putting his hand again to the bell-pull, he slowly walked away from its neighbourhood with his head bent, leaving the door unguarded and his threat unfulfilled.

But Ewen neither took advantage of these facts nor looked to see what his adversary was doing. The full wretchedness of the morning was back upon him; Archie had only three weeks to live.

It was at this moment, during the silence which had fallen, that steps which sounded too authoritative to be those of a servant could be heard approaching along the marble corridor outside. Lord Aveling, at any rate, could assign them to their owner, for he came back from whatever portion of the library he had wandered to, murmuring with a frown, 'My father!' On that the door opened, and the Earl came in. His expression was perturbed.

'I waited for your reappearance, Aveling,' he said to his son; 'then I was informed that Mr Cameron had not left the house and that you were both closeted in here. And your manner to him had been so strange that I decided to come in person to find out what was amiss.'

There was dignity about Lord Stowe now; he was no longer

a somewhat fussy little gentleman deafened by a macaw, but a nobleman of position. His son seemed undecided whether to speak or no. Ewen spoke.

'An explanation is certainly owing to you, my lord, and by me rather than by Lord Aveling. His manner to me a while ago was, I regret to say, quite justified by something which occurred between us in Scotland.'

'And which, if you please,' put in Aveling like lightning, 'I wish to remain between us, Mr Cameron.'

'That is very unfortunate,' observed Lord Stowe gravely, looking from one to the other. 'As you know, I am under a great obligation to Mr Cameron.'

'From his past experience of me, my lord, Lord Aveling doubts that,' observed Ewen quietly.

'Doubts it! Good Gad, Aveling, are you suggesting that I was drunk or dreaming this evening?'

'No, my lord,' said his son slowly. He was examining his ruffles with some absorption. 'Since I gave voice to my doubt, I have ... revised my opinion. I do not question your very real debt to Mr Cameron.'

'I should hope not,' said the Earl with some severity. 'And, as I said before, I am extremely anxious to repay it. If I can do this by composing the difference which has arisen between you –'

'No, you can't do that, my dear father,' said the young man with vivacity. 'Leave that out of the question now, if you will, and ask Mr Cameron in what way you can best repay that debt. I believe I could give a very good guess at what he will reply.'

Ewen gave a start and looked at the speaker, upon whose lips hung something like a smile. How did Lord Aveling know – or did he not know? Such intuition savoured almost of the supernatural.

'Well, Mr Cameron, what is it?' inquired the Earl. 'In what can I attempt to serve you? You have but to name the matter.'

But Ewen was so bewildered at this *volte-face* in his enemy, not to mention his uncanny perspicacity, that he remained momentarily tongue-tied.

'Mr Cameron's request is not, I believe, for himself at all,' said Lord Aveling softly. 'There is a person upon whose behalf he has done and risked a good deal. I think he wishes, if possible, to enlist you on the same side.'

'I take it,' said his father, 'that you are referring to the unfortunate gentleman, Mr Cameron's kinsman, who was today condemned to death. Am I right, Mr Cameron?'

Ewen bent his head. 'I ask too much, perhaps, my lord.' He lifted it again, and speech came to him, and he pleaded earnestly for commutation of the sentence, almost as though the decision had lain in Lord Stowe's hands. 'And surely, my lord,' he finished, 'clemency in this case must prove to the advantage, not to the disadvantage, of the Government.'

The Earl had listened with courtesy and attention. 'I will certainly think over what you have said, Mr Cameron,' he promised, 'and if I can convince myself, from what I hear elsewhere, that a recommendation to mercy is advisable, I will take steps in the proper quarters. Come and see me again tomorrow afternoon, if you will give yourself the trouble. – Aveling, you wish me, I gather, to leave you to settle your own difference with Mr Cameron?'

'If you please, my lord.' He smiled a little, and opened the door for his father to pass out.

'Why did you do that? How, in God's name, did you know?' cried Ewen directly it was shut again.

The dark mahogany panels behind him threw up Lord Aveling's slight, shimmering figure. 'It was not so difficult to read your mind, Mr Cameron. I wish I could think that among my friends I numbered one with . . . the same notions that you have. As to my own mind . . . well, perhaps Doctor Cameron made an impression on me this morning other than I had expected, so that, to tell truth, I half-wished that you *had* been in time with the information which you stole from me.'

Ewen sat down at the table and took his head between his fists. Once more Keith Windham's ring glittered in the candlelight.

'We heard a rumour in Edinburgh,' went on Aveling, 'that there was one man and one man only with Doctor Cameron when he was taken, and that he resisted desperately, and was left behind too badly hurt to be taken away by the soldiers. I begin to have a suspicion who that man was . . .'

Ewen was silent.

' – Although you said that you arrived too late . . . But I do not wish to press you to incriminate yourself.'

'Yes, you have enough against me without seeking any more,' answered Ardroy without raising his head.

'I think that I have wiped out that score,' said Aveling reflectively. 'Indeed, that I have overpaid it.' He was silent for a second or two, and then went on 'I can see that you are much fatigued, Mr Cameron. Will you take a glass of wine with me before you go?'

Chapter 19

'LOCHABER NO MORE'

1

'A GENTLEMAN to see you, sir,' said the voice, not of Ewen's landlady, Mrs Wilson, but of the impish boy from the vintner's shop below. And, coming nearer, he added confidentially, 'He ain't given no name, but he's mighty fine – a lord, belike!'

The impish boy's diagnosis was exactly correct; the young gentleman who entered *was* fine – though not so fine as last night – and he *was* a lord.

'I am not intruding, I hope, Mr Cameron, visiting you thus early?' inquired the young man in the voice which was so like his dead brother's. 'I wished to make sure that you would keep your promise of waiting upon my father this afternoon, for he is genuinely anxious to afford you any assistance in his power. Yet I feared that you might be kept away by the memory of my . . . my exceedingly inhospitable behaviour last night.'

All the frank and boyish charm which had formed the essence of Ewen's first impression of him was back – more than back.

'I assure you, my lord,' replied Ewen warmly, 'that any memories of that sort were drowned in the glass of wine we took together. I shall most gratefully wait upon Lord Stowe at any hour convenient to him. But will you not be seated? It is exceedingly good of you to have come upon this errand.'

Lord Aveling laid down his tasselled cane upon the table, and lifting the full skirts of his murrey-coloured coat out of the way, complied.

'I do not think that Lord Stowe can promise much, Mr Cameron,' he said, 'and it may be that any step will take time. But I believe that strong feeling is being aroused by the sentence, which is a hopeful sign. My father was himself present

220

when judgement was given, and was much impressed, as I was, by Doctor Cameron's bearing.'

'Everyone seems to have been at the Court of King's Bench but I,' said Ewen sadly.

'Yet surely,' objected the young man, 'it would have been very painful for you, Mr Cameron, to hear the details of that sentence, which sound so barbarous and cold-blooded when enumerated beforehand.'

'Yes, I have already been told that,' said Ewen. 'Yet I should have seen my kinsman had I been present, even though I could not have had speech with him – that, I knew, would be too much to expect in the case of a State prisoner. It is I, alas,' he added with a sudden impulse towards confidence, 'who am, in a measure at least, responsible for his capture.'

'My dear Mr Cameron,' exclaimed young Aveling with vivacity, 'considering how you . . . moved heaven and earth to warn him, and that you, if I guess rightly, were the man struck down defending him, how can you say that?'

'Because it was I who suggested our taking refuge in the fatal hut in which he was captured,' answered Ewen with a sigh.

Lord Aveling was looking grave. 'You have touched, Mr Cameron, on the other reason which brought me here. It seems to me that you are going openly about London without a thought of your own safety. But you must be a marked man if any note were made, at the time of Doctor Cameron's capture, of your personal appearance – of your uncommon height, for instance. Have you taken any precautions against recognition?'

'What precautions could I take?' asked Ewen simply. 'I can only hope that no such note was made. After all, *I* am of no importance to the Government, and, as it happened, I did not even touch a single soldier. My weapon broke – or rather, came to pieces.'

'I should call that fortunate,' observed his visitor with the same gravity.

'I suppose it was, since I must have been overpowered in the end; there were too many of them . . . I think I *am* singularly fortunate,' he added with the same simplicity. 'Last night, for instance, Lord Aveling . . . I am still at a loss to know why you changed your mind, and did not carry out your threat, and showed besides so much generosity to me.'

The blood showed easily on Aveling's almost girl-like complexion. He rose and resumed his cane, saying meanwhile, 'If you do not guess why you turned my purpose – but no, why should you? 'twould be out of keeping – I'll tell you some day.' And here he hesitated, half-turned, turned back again, then, fingering with deep interest the tassels of his cane, said in a lower tone: 'You have a secret of mine, Mr Cameron. I hope I can rely upon you . . . to preserve it as such?'

'A secret of yours, my lord?' exclaimed Ewen in surprise. Then a flush spread over his face also, and he became more embarrassed than his visitor. 'You mean – that letter! Lord Aveling, if I were to spend the rest of my life apologizing – '

'I do not desire you to do that, sir,' interrupted the young lover. 'We have closed that chapter. Nevertheless – ' He stopped.

'Then at least believe me,' put in Ewen earnestly, 'that anything I may have had the misfortune to read is as though I had never seen it!'

The young man ceased stabbing the chair. 'I thank you, Mr Cameron. and I have no hesitation in relying upon that assurance. Nevertheless, since you are shortly to wait upon my father, it is as well that you should know that, though the lady has consented to my unworthy suit, my parents, that is to say, my mother. . . .' Again he stopped.

'My mother,' went on Lord Aveling after a second or two, 'has, I know, other views for me. I doubt if she suspects this attachment; but of my father's I am not so sure; yet he may very well give his consent to the match. And as for me – ' here he threw back his head and looked at Ewen, 'as for me, my heart is immutably fixed, though at present I find it more politic to say nothing as yet of pledges which I am firmly resolved never to relinquish until they are exchanged for more solemn vows at the altar!'

Ewen bowed, touched at this lofty declaration, which promised well for the happiness of Miss Georgina Churchill. 'There is no conceivable reason, my lord, why any member of your family should suppose me aware of this attachment.'

'No, that is true,' said his visitor; 'and you must forgive me for troubling you at such a time with my affairs. And now, if you will excuse me, I will take my leave. Do not fail to wait upon my father, Mr Cameron; and if you should get into trouble with the authorities over your doings in that glen whose name I still cannot remember,' he added with a half-shy, half-mocking smile, 'send for your humble servant!' And he bowed himself out of the door.

When Ewen had recovered from the surprise of this visit he went out in search of Hector, who was sufficiently amazed at the tale of his brother-in-law's doings on the previous night. 'But the fact remains,' was his summing up, 'that you have made an exceedingly useful friend in the Earl of Stowe, not to speak of the young lord.'

'And your own investigations as to the source of that slander, Hector, how are they going?'

Hector frowned. 'Not at all. And 'tis a ticklish matter to investigate – to ask men, for instance, if they have suspicions of you.'

'That I can well believe. Promise me that you will do nothing rash. Don't, for God's sake, get involved in a dispute just now, Hector! You must forgive me for lecturing you, but you know that you have a hot temper!'

'Yes,' agreed Hector Grant with surprising meekness, 'I know that I have. And you know it too, Ewen – none better. I will be careful.'

2

The Earl of Stowe received the Highlander in his own study that afternoon. He announced that, after reflection, he had come to the conclusion that the Government would certainly do well to spare the life of so amiable and humane a gentleman as Doctor Cameron appeared to be, and that he should use his utmost endeavours to persuade them to do so. He could not, naturally, say what success would attend his efforts, and he warned his visitor not to be too sanguine.

'You, I understand, Mr Cameron, were not able to be present in the King's Bench when he was sentenced. My son made a suggestion to me with regard to that, after seeing you this morning. I fancy, from what he said, that you would be gratified if I could procure you an order to visit Doctor Cameron in the Tower?'

'Gratified!' exclaimed Ewen, in a tone which left no doubt of the fact. 'My lord, you would be repaying my trifle of assistance last night a hundred times over! Does your lordship mean that?'

'Certainly I do,' replied his lordship, 'and I think that it is a matter within my power, since I know Lord Cornwallis somewhat well. Today is Friday; I will try to procure you an order for the next Monday. But if it is granted you would, I fear, have to submit to a search on entering the Tower, for I understand that they are keeping Doctor Cameron very strictly.'

Ewen intimated that the process would not deter him, and, thanking the Earl almost with tears in his eyes, prepared to withdraw.

3

So smart a coach drawing up on Tower Hill this fine May morning soon drew a little crowd of idlers, mostly small boys, some shouting their conviction that it contained the Lord Mayor, against others who upheld that the Prince of Wales would emerge from it. But the two gentlemen who presently stepped out did not fulfil either expectation.

'I have brought you to this spot, Mr Cameron,' said the younger of the two in a lowered voice, 'that you may see for yourself how vain are any dreams of a rescue from that!'

'It is a bitter kindness, Lord Aveling, but it is a kindness, and I thank you.'

The young man motioned to him to enter the coach again, and they drove down to the entrance under the Lion Tower, where he would leave him.

It was indeed a kind thought of the young lord's, not only

to bring him, on his father's behalf, the permit from Lord Cornwallis to visit Doctor Cameron, but also to carry him to the Tower in his own coach. Yet as Ardroy, showing the precious paper with the Constable's signature, followed his conductor over the moat and under the archway of the Middle Tower, he felt how powerless after all were the very real friendship of the Earl of Stowe and his son, and all their prestige. Archibald Cameron was in a place whence it would take more than aristocratic influence to free him.

At the third, the Byward Tower, his guide halted and informed him that he must be searched here, and led him to a room for that purpose. The officials were extremely civil and considerate, but they did their work thoroughly, taking from him every object about him and in his pocket, save his handkerchief; his sword as a matter of course, his money, a little notebook of accounts and a pencil, even his watch.

And then he heard, to his surprise, that Doctor Cameron was confined in the Deputy-Lieutenant's own quarters. Soon he found himself in a house within the fortress – in reality the lodgings of the Lieutenant of the Tower, who occupied the rank next the Constable's in this hierarchy. On one side this house looked out to the river, and on the other to the Parade, Tower Green and the Chapel of St Peter, and Ewen was told that several of the Jacobite lords had been imprisoned here.

Then he was suddenly in the presence of the Deputy-Lieutenant himself, General Charles Rainsford. The soldier was as considerate as the rest, and even more courteous. His affability chilled Ewen to the core. Had the authorities seemed hostile or anxious ... but no, they knew that once they were on their guard no one escaped or was rescued from the Tower of London.

'You will find Doctor Cameron well, I think, sir,' volunteered the Deputy-Lieutenant. 'My orders are so strict that I cannot allow him out of doors, even attended by a warder, to take the air, but as he has two rooms assigned to him he walks a good deal in the larger, and by that means keeps his health.'

'Does he know that I am to visit him?'

'He does, and has expressed the greatest pleasure at it.'

'Mrs Cameron is not yet arrived in London, I think?'

'No, but the Doctor expects her shortly.'

And on that the visitor was entrusted to a warder, and went with him up the shallow oaken stairs. They stopped before a door guarded by a private of the regiment of Guards, and when it was opened Ewen found himself in a long, narrowish room, almost a gallery, at whose farther end a figure which had evidently been pacing up and down its length had turned expectantly. They each hurried to the other, and, for the first time in their lives, embraced.

Ewen could never remember what were the first words which passed between them, but after a while he knew that Archie and he were standing together in the embrasure of one of the windows, and that Archie was holding him by the arms and saying, in a voice of great contentment, 'Ever since I heard that you were coming I have been asking myself how in the name of fortune you contrived to get permission!'

'It was fortune herself contrived it,' answered his cousin, laughing a trifle unsteadily. 'I will tell you of it presently. But first,' and he looked at him searchingly, 'are you well, Archie? They told me you were, but are you?'

'Ay, I am wonderfully well,' said the Doctor cheerfully; 'and more, I am happy, which you don't ask me. I have done my duty, as well as I can, to my Prince; I am to have my Jean's company for more than a week; none of the Privy Council nor any of the Government is a whit the wiser for aught I have told them. And for the resolution which God has given me to die without enlightening them – and, I hope, with becoming firmness – I thank Him every day upon my knees. You cannot think how well content I am, Ewen, now that there is no hope left to torment me.'

Ewen could not look at him then. Yet it was obviously true; one had only to hear the ring of quiet sincerity in Archibald Cameron's voice to know that this attitude was no pose. That was the wonder, almost the terror of it.

'But there is hope, there is hope!' said Ewen, more to himself than to Archie. 'Meanwhile, is there not anything you want?'

'Yes, one thing I do stand in need of, and have displayed a good deal of impatience, I fear, because it is denied me, and that is paper and pen. You have not such a thing as a bit of old pencil about you, '*ille*?'

'I haven't a thing about me save my pocket-handkerchief,' answered Ewen regretfully. 'And why have they denied you writing materials? Oh, if I had but known, I might have smuggled in the pencil I had when I came, and some paper, perhaps, in my hat.'

'As to that, I must be patient,' said Archie with a little smile. 'And, indeed, I am no hand at composition; yet there are some matters that I desire to set down. Perhaps I'll contrive it still.' Then Archie put his hand on his arm and drew him into a smaller room, not ill-furnished, looking in the opposite direction, and they sat down on the window-seat.

'Yes,' said the Doctor, 'I fare very differently here from poor Alexander. I have been thinking much of late of him and his sufferings – God rest him!'

It was long since Ewen had heard any reference to that third of the Lochiel brothers who, by turning Roman Catholic and Jesuit, had cut himself off from his family, but who had been the first to die for the White Rose, a martyr to the horrible conditions on board the ship which brought him as a prisoner to London. 'Yes,' went on Archie, 'this is a Paradise compared to the place where Alexander was confined.'

'And your head, Ewen?' asked his cousin after a moment's silence. 'How long was it before you recovered from the effects of that blow?'

'It was you, then, who bound up my head? I thought it must have been. Oh, Archie, and by that the soldiers must have known for certain who you were! You should not have done it!'

'Tut – the redcoats knew that already! And I could not accomplish much in the way of surgery, my dear Ewen; I had not the necessaries. As you may guess, I have not had a patient since – you'll be my last. So take off that wig, in which you seem to me so unfamiliar, and let me see the spot where the musket-butt caught you.'

'There's naught to see, I am sure, and not much to feel,' said Ewen, complying. 'My head is uncommon hard, as I proved once before. I was laid by for some weeks, that was all,' he went on, as the cool, skilful fingers felt about among his close-cropped hair. 'Just when I naturally was a-fire to get to London after you. But now, when I am here, there seems nothing that one can do. And, Archie, 'tis I have brought you to this place!'

Doctor Cameron had ended his examination and now faced him with, 'My dear Ewen, I can, indeed, feel small trace of the blow. Yet it is clear that it must have severely shaken your wits, if you can utter such a piece of nonsense as that!'

' 'Tis no nonsense,' protested Ewen sadly. 'Was it not I who discovered that thrice-unlucky hut and persuaded you to go into it?'

'Nay, you'll be telling me next that 'twas you sent the information to Edinburgh –'

'God! when I can find the man who did – ' began Ewen, in a blaze at once.

'Ah, my dear Ewen,' said his kinsman soothingly, 'leave him alone! To find him will not undo his work, whoever he is. I had better have spent the time thinking of my own shortcomings. I can forgive him; he may have thought he was doing a service. It will cost me more of a struggle to forgive the man who slandered me over the Loch Arkaig gold ... but I think I shall succeed even in that before the seventh of June.'

'Who was that man?' demanded Ewen instantly, and all the more fiercely because he winced to hear that date on Archie's lips.

The Doctor shook his head with a smile. 'Is it like I should tell you when you ask in that manner? 'Tis a man whom you have never met, I think, so let it pass.'

'Is he known to me by name, however?'

'How can I tell,' replied Doctor Cameron shrewdly, 'unless I pronounce his name and see? But come, there are so many I should be glad to have tidings of. How is Mrs Alison, and the boys? And have you any news, since we parted, of your fellow-prisoner in Fort William?'

'Poor Hector's over here in London, and in great distress,' began Ewen without reflecting, 'for there's an ill rumour abroad, in Lille at least, accusing him – ' And there he stopped, biting his lip. He ought not to have brought up that subject in Archie's hearing, blundering fool that he was!

'Accusing him of what, lad?'

So Ewen had to tell him. He hurried over the tale as much as he could, and, seeing how shocked and grieved Archie appeared, laid stress on the fact that, if ever Hector was really brought to book, he himself was in a position to disprove his connexion with the capture of the Jacobite.

'But I would give much to know who set the story about,' he ended, 'for there are only two persons whom he told of the loss of that letter, myself and the man who helped him to return to his regiment in January, young Finlay MacPhair of Glenshian.'

But the end of that sentence left Ardroy's lips very slowly, in fact the last words were scarcely uttered at all. He was staring at his companion. Over Archie's face, at the mention of Finlay MacPhair, there had flitted something too indefinable to merit a name. But in another moment Ewen had reached out and caught him by the wrist. 'Deny it if you dare!' he said threateningly. 'I have named *your* slanderer too!'

The Doctor was plainly rather chagrined as he faced him. 'I am sorry that I have not better control of my features – Now, for God's sake, Ewen – ' for Ardroy, releasing his wrist, had got to his feet. 'Ewen, I implore you not to take advantage of a secret which you have surprised out of me!'

But Ardroy was in one of his slow white rages. 'The man who was associated with you when you risked your life for that accursed money in '49 was viper enough to traduce you over it! He, then, who poisoned his cousin Lochdornie's mind against you! And I warrant his dirty lie did not stop short with Lochdornie – did it now, Archie?'

Doctor Cameron, distressed, did not answer that. 'Oh, my

229

dear Ewen, if I could persuade you to leave this question alone. What does it matter now?'

'Your good name matters to me as much as my own,' said Ewen, towering and relentless.

'But 'tis all past history now, Ewen, and the slander will die with my death. ... Ewen, Ewen, promise me that you'll not go stirring up old scores with that young man! I cannot say I love him, but he is powerless to harm me any more now, and, as I say, I hope to forgive him without reservation. My dear lad, you will only cause me more distress than the lie itself, if I am to spend the short time which remains to me thinking of you quarrelling on my behalf with young Glenshian!'

Ewen had begun to stride up and down the little room, fighting with his resentment. 'Very good then,' he said after a moment, coming and sitting down again, 'I will not give you that distress; it is a promise. Moreover – perhaps this will reassure you a little,' he added with a wrathful snatch of a laugh, 'the man is not in London now, I believe.'

'Then let's cease to waste time over him,' said Doctor Cameron with evident relief. 'And you have not told me yet, as you promised, how you procured this order to see me.'

Trying to put away the thought of Glenshian, Ewen told him. 'Had I not good fortune – though indeed, at first, when I found myself in Stowe House, I thought it was the worst kind of ill-luck which had befallen me. The Earl and his son were both at the King's Bench that day, too, which prejudiced them, it is clear, in your favour. – By the way,' he added with some hesitation, 'was it a surprise to you that you had no trial?'

'No,' replied his cousin. 'I always suspected that the Government would make use of the old sentence of attainder if ever they caught me.'

'Yes, perhaps it was inevitable,' murmured Ewen, but he was thinking – though he did not mean to speak – of the unknown informer protected by the Government, whose identity, according to Jacobite belief, a trial would have revealed.

'Yes, I was not long before their lordships in the King's Bench,' went on Archie. 'The Privy Council examination at Whitehall a month before was a more lengthy affair, but, I fear, very unsatisfactory to those honourable gentlemen. My memory was grown so extraordinarily bad,' he added, with a twinkle in his eye.

'All the world knows that you told them nothing of the slightest importance,' said Ewen admiringly. 'Was that how you contrived to outwit them?'

'If you can call it outwitting. I think no man on earth could possibly have forgotten so many things as I made out to have done.' The remembrance seemed to entertain him.

'You know, Archie,' said Ewen earnestly, ' – or more probably you do not know – that popular feeling is very strongly stirred about you, and that remonstrances are preparing on all sides. And when Mrs Cameron comes, if she has any intention of petitioning – '

'I expect she will desire to – poor Jean! Can I commend her to you a little, '*ille*?'

'You do not need to. I was about to ask you where she is likely to lodge? Near the Tower, no doubt?'

'I will tell her to leave her direction at the Tower gates, that you can learn it if necessary; and give me yours, that I may tell her of it. She may be lonely, poor soul; I doubt she will be allowed to stay here with me all day. And afterwards . . .'

It was Ewen who looked out at Tower Green this time, but more fixedly than Archie had done. 'Afterwards,' he said in a moment, 'if there is to be no "afterwards" you mean, I will take Mrs Cameron – ' He stopped, wrenched his fingers together for a second, and said with great difficulty, 'I cannot speak of that "afterwards", Archie – I don't know how you can. . . . Oh, if one could but push time back, and be again as we used to be eight years ago! The sunshine out there makes me think of that fine spring in Lochaber, before Lochiel and you had staked everything on the sword that was drawn in summer at Glenfinnan.'

Doctor Cameron laid his hand on his. 'But I am not unhappy, Eoghain,' he said gently. 'Eight years ago I had done nothing for my Prince. I do not know that I would change.'

Hector Grant was having his supper when Ewen walked in upon him that evening.

'At last,' said Ardroy, throwing his hat upon a chair. 'This is the second time that I have tried to find you today.'

'And I have been seeking you,' retorted Hector. 'Where were you?'

'I have been in the Tower,' answered Ewen, and went and stood with his back turned and an elbow on the mantelpiece, and for a while said no more. After a moment Hector rose and put a hand on his shoulder, also without a word.

'I see no hope of rescue, even by guile. I see no way in which any man's life can be given for his,' said Ewen after a long pause. 'Nothing but a reprieve can save him. But I do not think that he is hoping for one.'

'I am,' said the sanguine Hector. 'The Government must soon be aware how widespread is the feeling in favour of it.'

There was another silence.

'Go on with your supper,' said Ewen. 'I have a piece of news for you meanwhile. From something which I learnt from Archie I think it may well have been young Glenshian who put about that slander on you concerning his capture.'

Hector showed no disposition to continue his forsaken meal. '*Dieu du ciel*, what makes you think that?'

'Because he was the man who vilified Archie himself over the matter of the Loch Arkaig treasure – Archie did not tell me that it was he; I surprised it out of him. Yet, by the same token, Finlay MacPhair is quite capable of having traduced you.'

Hector frowned. 'Yes; and now that I come to think of it, he repeated that story about Doctor Cameron to me last January.'

'Archie has made me promise that I'll not make it an occasion of quarrel with Glenshian,' said Ewen, looking not at all like a man who had given so pacific an undertaking. 'Otherwise I would challenge him directly he returns to town, and make him withdraw his slander publicly.'

'But I have not promised to abstain from making *my* injury a cause of quarrel,' quoth Hector in tones of anticipation. 'When Mr MacPhair of Glenshian is returned, will you come with me, Ewen, and we will ask him a question or two?'

But Ewen, instead of replying, suddenly sat down at Hector's supper-table and covered his face with his hands.

Chapter 20

FINLAY MACPHAIR IS BOTH UNLUCKY AND FORTUNATE

1

WHEREVER Ewen went during the next few days the hard case of Doctor Cameron seemed to be the all-absorbing topic of conversation, and that among persons of no Jacobite leanings at all. Mrs Wilson, when she encountered her lodger, could talk of nothing else, and reported the general feeling of her compeers to be much roused.

Had, therefore, a name been mentioned, it would probably have been with tears of sensibility that Mrs Wilson conducted to Ewen's little parlour, one day at the end of the week, a lady, very quietly dressed, who said, on hearing Mr Cameron was out, that she would await his return. Mrs Wilson would have liked to indulge in visions of some romance or intrigue, but that the lady, who was somewhat heavily veiled, seemed neither lovely nor very young. Ardroy, when he came in a little later and was informed of her presence, was at no loss to guess who it was, and when he entered his room and found her sitting by the window with her cheek on her hand, he took up the other listless hand and kissed it in silence.

The lady drew a long breath and clutched the strong, warm fingers tightly; then she rose and threw back her veil. Under the bonnet her face appeared, lacking the pretty colouring which was its only real claim to beauty, but trying to smile – the brave face of Jean Cameron.

'Oh, Ardroy ...!' She bit her lip to fight down emotion. 'Oh, Ardroy, I have just come from him. He ... he looks well, does he not?' And Ewen nodded. 'He says that he has not been so well for years. You know he suffered from ague all the winter, two years ago, but now.... And they seem so kind and

234

well-disposed . . . in that place.' She seemed to shrink from naming the Tower.

'I think that there is a great deal of hope, madam,' said Ewen gently, in his grave, soft voice. 'And now that you have come, there is even more than there was, for if you have any purpose of petitioning, all popular feeling will be with you.'

'Yes, I thought. . . . I have been drawing up an appeal. . . .' She sought in her reticule. 'Perhaps you would look at what I have roughly written – 'tis here at the end.' And into his hand she put a little paper-covered book. Opening it where it naturally opened, Ewen saw that it was a record of household accounts, and that on a page opposite the daily entries made at Lille, sometimes in English, sometimes in French, for 'bread', or 'coffee', *'pain de sucre'*, or 'stuffe for Margret's gowne', figured alien and tremendous terms, 'Majesty' and 'life' and 'pardon'.

'I thought that when I had made a fair copy I would present the petition to the Elector at Kensington Palace on Sunday.'

'Yes,' said Ewen. 'But you will need an escort. May I have the great honour?'

Mrs Cameron gave a little exclamation of pleasure, soon checked. 'Archie tells me that you have got into serious trouble with the Government on his account. You should not show yourself in so public a place, and with me.'

'No one would dream of looking for me at Kensington Palace. Moreover, I have someone to answer for me now,' said Ewen, smiling down at her. And he told her about Lord Stowe.

2

When, that afternoon, Ewen had taken Jean Cameron back to her lodging in Tower Street he went to the 'White Cock', where he had arranged to meet Hector Grant. But that young man was to be seen walking to and fro in the Strand itself, outside the passage, evidently waiting for him.

'Don't go in there, Ewen,' he said eagerly, 'till I have at least told you my news. Young Glenshian is back in town – if he ever left it!'

'Are you sure?'

'I have seen his gillie. I met him by chance about an hour ago. He said that his master had been ill, though I could not make out from him whether he had really been away from London or no. At any rate, the man, who recognized me, admitted that Glenshian was able to receive visitors. So now I can perhaps find out the part which Finlay MacPhair has played in this slander upon me, for I am no nearer the truth than when I arrived here. Will you come with me? I think you have a score to settle too.'

'I promised not to settle it,' answered Ardroy. 'And you, Hector, do not yet know that you have one.'

'Oh, I'll be prudent,' promised the young soldier. 'But I must at least put the question to him, and what time better than the present, if you are at liberty?'

Ewen said that he was, and would accompany him, though he was not himself anxious to meet Archie's traducer. But it seemed unwise to let Hector go alone, and his presence might conceivably keep the bit a shade tighter in that young gentleman's mouth.

At the house in Beaufort Buildings Hector was prepared to find his way unannounced to the upper floor, but the woman this time said that she would take the two gentlemen up, since Mr MacPhair's servant was out, and she thought his master as well. Indeed, she seemed sure of the latter's absence, for she threw open the door with barely a knock, advanced into the room, and was consequently brought up short.

'I beg your pardon, sir,' she said in half-abashed tones. 'I quite thought you was out. Two gentlemen from Scotland to see you.'

And there was visible, in a room less disorderly than Hector remembered, Mr Finlay MacPhair sitting by a small fire fully dressed, with a large flowered shawl about his shoulders, and a book in his hand.

He turned his red head quickly. 'I thought I had given orders – ' he began with a frown – and then seemed by an effort to accept the inevitable. 'Visitors from Scotland are always welcome,' said he, and rose, holding the shawl together. 'Why, 'tis rather a visitor from France! Is it not Mr Hector Grant?'

Hector bowed. 'And my brother-in-law, Mr Cameron of Ardroy. Ewen, let me present you to Mr MacPhair of Glenshian.'

'The gentleman, I think, who went to prison in order to shield Doctor Cameron last autumn?' said Glenshian, and held out his hand. 'I am honoured to make your acquaintance, sir – very greatly honoured. Be seated, if you please, gentlemen, and forgive my being happed up in this fashion. I am still somewhat of a sick man after a recent illness.'

Mr MacPhair was easy and fluent, and apparently more concerned with apologies for his shawl than observant, which was perhaps as well, for the man whose acquaintance he professed to be so proud to make was gazing at him in what would have been a disconcerting manner had young Glenshian been fully aware of it.

Hector took a chair and said that he was sorry to hear of Mr MacPhair's indisposition. Ewen also seated himself, more slowly, but he said nothing. The cloaked gentleman who had come so secretly out of Mr Pelham's house that May night was here before him, and he was no Whig, but Finlay MacPhair, the son and heir of a great Chief whose clansmen had fought for the Cause. What had he been doing in Arlington Street?

'Yes,' said young Glenshian, going to a cupboard, 'I had the ill-luck to take a cold at the Carnival ball in Paris (for I was over there, on the King's affairs, in the spring). I doubt I shall not be my own man again for a while. – Now, gentlemen, before you tell me why I am thus honoured by your company, you'll pledge me, I hope, in this excellent Bordeaux – But where the devil has Seumas put the glasses?'

His guests, however, both refused the offer of the Bordeaux with so much decision and unanimity that Finlay, raising his eyebrows, left the cupboard and came and sat down.

'Not even to drink the King's health?' he observed. 'Well, gentlemen, if you will not drink, let us get to business – unless this is a mere visit of ceremony?'

'No, 'tis not a visit of ceremony, Mr MacPhair,' answered Ewen gravely. 'Mr Grant has a question to ask of you, which you will oblige him by answering; and I, too, find that I have one which I should like to put when you have answered his.'

'This sounds, I declare, like an examination before the Privy Council,' remarked young Glenshian, his lip drawing up a little. 'Pray proceed then, sirs, each in your turn! You'll allow me, I hope, the liberty of not replying if I so wish?'

'Nay, Mr MacPhair, do not imagine that we come as inquisitors,' said Hector with unwonted suavity. 'It will be of your courtesy only that you reply.'

'Ask, then!' said Finlay, fixing his piercing light eyes upon him.

Even Hector hesitated for a second, choosing his words. 'Mr MacPhair, while eternally grateful to you for your assistance in procuring my return to France last January, I should nevertheless be glad of your assurance that you did not, by pure inadvertence, let it be somewhat freely known that I had lost, along with my other papers in the Highlands, the compromising cipher letter of which I told you?'

There was no outburst from Glenshian, but all and more of his native arrogance in his reply. 'Certainly I did not,' he said contemptuously. 'Why should I speak of your private affairs, Mr Grant? They are nothing to me!'

Hector bit his lip. 'I thank you for the assurance, Mr MacPhair. Yet that letter was hardly a private affair, and ... the knowledge of the loss of it has undoubtedly gone about, and has much damaged my reputation.'

'Well, I am very sorry to hear that, Mr Grant,' responded his host, pulling the shawl about him and crossing his legs. 'But you must forgive me if I say that to lose a paper of that nature could hardly be expected to enhance it!'

Hector remained surprisingly controlled, and answered, though with rather pinched lips, 'Yet the strange thing is, that I told no one save Mr Cameron and yourself that I *had* lost it!'

Fionnlagh Ruadh turned his dangerous gaze on Mr Cameron. 'I suppose he has satisfied you that he is not the culprit?' he asked, again in that half-humorous tone. To this Hector vouchsafed no reply, and apparently Glenshian did not expect one, for he went on, 'But surely, Mr Grant, if a letter such as you told me of were sent, upon capture, to the English Government, as is natural, you could scarcely expect them to be so tender of your reputation as not to let it be known upon whom it was captured?'

'Ay, but was it sent to the Government?' demanded Hector.

Glenshian's haughty head went back. 'And pray how do you expect *me* to know that?'

Ewen leant forward. It *was* the same man; after this prolonged scrutiny he felt sure of it. 'That is indeed an idle question, Hector,' he observed. 'And Mr MacPhair has assured you that he had no hand in spreading the knowledge of your misfortune, which assurance no doubt you accept. I think the moment has come for me to ask my question, if he will be good enough to answer it.'

'I hope yours is less offensive than the last!' rapped out Glenshian.

'I am afraid it is not very pleasant,' admitted Ardroy, 'and I must crave your indulgence for putting it. . . . I should wish to learn how it is, Mr MacPhair, that you know Mr Pelham so well as to leave his house in Arlington Street between eleven and twelve at night?'

Oddly enough, it was Hector, not young Glenshian, who appeared the most affected by this shot. 'What!' he exclaimed, 'do you mean to say that Mr MacPhair was the man you saw that night?'

But Mr MacPhair himself was frowning at his questioner in an angry and puzzled astonishment which seemed genuine enough. 'Mr Pelham, sir?' he said sharply ' – whom do you mean? You cannot, I imagine, refer to Mr Pelham the minister of state?'

'Yes,' said Ewen unperturbed, 'I do – Mr Henry Pelham, my Lord Newcastle's brother. And as you leave his house so late at night, I conclude that you must know him very well.'

Now young Glenshian pushed back his chair, his eyes glittering. 'You are crazy as well as infernally insulting, Mr Cameron of Ardroy! I do not know Mr Pelham even by sight.'

'Then why were you coming out of his house that night?' pursued Ardroy. 'You were speaking Erse to your servant, who was carrying a link. I happened to be passing, and by its light I saw enough of your face and hair to recognize you. Perhaps you had quite legitimate business with Mr Pelham, but it would be less disquieting if we knew what it was.'

The young Chief had jumped to his feet, the shawl sliding to the ground; his expression was sufficiently menacing. Hector, all attention, had sprung up too, and was now at Ewen's side.

'Do you imagine,' said Glenshian between his teeth, 'that we are in Lochaber, Mr Cameron, and that you can safely come the bully over me, the two of you? I thought the late Lochiel had tried to civilize his clan; it seems he had not much success! I tell you that I do not know Mr Pelham, and have never been inside his house – and God damn you to hell,' he added in an access of fury, 'how dare you put such a question to me?'

'Because,' answered Ewen unmoved, 'I desire to find out who *was* the man that came out of Mr Pelham's house on the night of the fifteenth of May, a red-haired, Erse-speaking man as like you, Mr MacPhair, as one pea is like another.'

'I'd like to know,' broke in Finlay bitterly, 'why, if you see a red-headed Highlander coming out of an English minister's door, you must jump to the conclusion not only that he is a Jacobite playing fast and loose with his principles, but that it is the future chief of Glenshian, a man who has lain near two years in the Tower for Jacobitism? *Dhé*, if it were not so amazing in its impudence – '

'You mean that I am to consider myself mistaken?'

'I do indeed, Mr Cameron; and before you leave this room you'll apologize for your assumption in any words I choose to dictate! Faith, I am not sure that an apology, even the humblest is adequate!'

'I am quite ready to apologize, Mr MacPhair,' he said, 'if you'll prove to me that I was wrong. On my soul, I am only too anxious that you should. Or if you will convince me that your clandestine business with the Elector's chief minister was such as an honourable man of our party might fairly have.'

'And who made you a judge over me?' cried Finlay the Red, and his left hand went to his side, gripping at nothing, for he was not wearing his sword. Then he flung out the other in a fiery gesture. 'I'll have that apology, by Heaven! You'll be only too ready to offer it when you hear my secret!'

'If you tell me that your errand to Mr Pelham's house – ' began Ewen.

'God's name!' broke out the angry MacPhair, 'am I to shout it at you that I never went there! *He* went, I don't doubt, and you saw him coming out. I suppose therefore that I should not have been so hot with you just now. You'll pardon me for that when you hear ... and perhaps you'll pardon me if I sit down again. I am still weakly.' Indeed he was palish, and there was moisture on his brow. 'Be seated again, gentlemen, and I will tell you both why Mr Cameron thought he saw me coming out of the minister's house one night – a night, too, when, if he had inquired, he would have found that I was not in London.'

The visitors somewhat doubtfully reseated themselves, Hector frowning tensely on their host, but content to leave the weight of the business for the moment on Ardroy's shoulders, where Mr MacPhair himself seemed to have put it.

'The explanation,' said Glenshian, coughing a little, and picking up his shawl, 'is – that I have, to my sorrow, a double.'

'A double!' exclaimed Ewen, raising his eyebrows. 'Do you mean a man who resembles you?'

'Ay, a man who so resembles me that even my close acquaintance have been deceived. He dogs my path, Mr Cameron, and I get the credit of his ill-deeds. He can even imitate my hand of write.'

'But who – who is he?'

Young Glenshian shrugged his shoulders. 'Some by-blow of my father's, I must believe. And that, no doubt (since I never heard of the Chief's recognizing him nor doing aught for him), has led him to take this method of revenge, by bringing discredit, when he can, upon my good name. 'Tis not, as you may guess, a pleasant secret for a man of honour to unveil, and I must be glad that I am dealing with gentlemen.'

'You hardly called us that a while ago,' retorted Ewen, knitting his brows. *Had* he been mistaken that night, in the quick, passing glare of the torch? If he had been, then he was wronging young Glenshian even more deeply than young Glenshian had wronged Archie.

Hector's voice, silent for some time, broke in. 'Is it not possible, Mr MacPhair,' it said, 'that this discreditable double of yours counts for something in *my* affair?'

'And how could that be?' asked Finlay with a shade of contempt. 'I hold no communication with him; he has not access to my papers.'

'Your *papers*!' said Hector like lightning. 'If he had had access – you mean that he might know something of my loss? – By Heaven, Mr MacPhair, I believe you *have* communicated the circumstances of it to someone!'

For a second a very strange look had slid over Glenshian's features. He drew himself up under the shawl. 'Allow me to say, Mr Grant, that I am heartily tired of this inquisition about the damned letter over which you make such a pother. My friends would tell you that I am incapable of setting about anything resembling a slander.'

Ewen could not let it pass. 'If you search your memory, Mr MacPhair,' he said meaningly, 'I am afraid that you will find that is not true. I have it on the best authority that it was you who put about the slander concerning Doctor Cameron and the Loch Arkaig treasure.'

'Slander?' queried Finlay with an undisguised sneer. 'My dear Mr Cameron, the fact that the unfortunate gentleman is shortly to suffer for his loyalty, which we must all deplore, does not make my statement a slander! And, upon my soul, your presumption in coming here to take me to task, first for one supposed action, then for another, is ... by the God above us, if we were alone in the Highlands, or somewhere quiet ...' He did not finish, but gritted his teeth.

'I am not going to quarrel with you over it,' said Ewen very sternly, ' – at least, not now. Perhaps some day we may argue as to the ethics of your conduct – in the Highlands or elsewhere. For the moment I'll say no more than that the action of traducing an innocent and scrupulously honourable man of your own party is worthy of this unnamed shadow of yours in whom you invite me to believe.'

'But surely, Ewen,' broke in Hector, suddenly pushing back his chair, 'you are not taken in by that cock-and-bull story of a double! Why, a child – ' He stopped, and involuntarily glanced behind him, as a mild crash announced that his abrupt movement had overturned some small article of furniture, and, on seeing that this was a little table with some books upon it, he got up with a muttered apology to set it on its legs again. 'Such a tale might deceive a child,' he went on meanwhile, picking up the fallen books and some papers which had accompanied them to the floor, 'but not a grown – ' He gave a great gasp, and was silent.

Ewen looked round once more to see the reason for the sudden cessation of his brother-in-law's remarks. Hector was standing rigid, staring at a paper which he held, as if he could not believe his senses. And Glenshian, Glenshian the invalid, was flinging himself like a wild beast out of his chair. 'Give me that!' he shouted. 'My private papers . . . how dare you – '

Ewen got quickly between them. 'What is it – what is it, Hector?'

Hector looked at him with a livid, dazed face. 'My stolen letter's *here*, in his own possession! . . . it fell out from these books . . . *he had it all the time!* Stand aside, Ewen, and let me get at him! No, he's not worth steel, I'll wring the treacherous neck of him!'

'Will you?' rang out Glenshian's voice, breathless yet mocking, behind Ardroy. 'You'll lose a little blood first, I fancy!' He had snatched up his sword from somewhere and was awaiting them, a flush on his pale face and his lips drawn back over his teeth – a real wolf at bay. 'I suppose you'll need to come on both at once to give each other courage!'

Ewen gripped at Hector's shoulder, but fury had lent that young man the agility of an eel. He slipped past Ardroy and his sword came out with a swish. 'Keep the door, you, lest we be interrupted!' he cried, pushed aside the chair, and next moment was thrusting frantically at the man backed against the wall.

Himself shocked and revolted, Ewen rushed to the door and locked it, but ran back at once crying, 'Hector, stop! this is madness!' To have Hector either wounded by or wounding young Glenshian here, in a brawl in a London house, would be disastrous; moreover, by the vigour of his assault, it looked as if more than wounding was in Mr Grant's mind, and that would be more disastrous still. Ardroy's protest went entirely disregarded. Glaring at each other, the two combatants thrust and parried without pause, steel clicking upon steel with a celerity rarely heard in a school of arms. But Glenshian was already panting, and the sweat was running in little rivers down his face. '*Stop,* in God's name!' cried Ewen again; 'the man's ill, remember, Hector!'

For all response the young officer unexpectedly cut over his opponent's blade, and all but got him in the chest; and Ewen in despair tugged out his own sword with the intention of beating up both blades. But that was not easy to do without exposing one of the duellists to a thrust from the other; and if – another method – he seized Hector, the nearer, by the shoulder and dragged him away, Glenshian would almost certainly rush at his adversary and run him through during the operation. So Ewen dropped his own sword and snatched up the heavy shawl which had fallen from the convalescent's shoulders; then, waiting his opportunity, flung it unfolded over its owner's head, seized his brother-in-law by the collar and swung him away staggering, and rushing in, at no small risk to himself, upon the entangled young man against the wall, who, almost screaming with rage, was just freeing himself, he seized him round the body, pinning his arms to his sides so that his still-held sword was useless.

Behind him Hector, cursing *him* now, was evidently preparing to come on again, and Ewen was by no means sure that he might not find his excited point in his own back. But from Finlay MacPhair there was a most unlooked-for end of resistance. His objurgations ceased, his head fell back and his knees gave; the sword in his hand went clattering to the uncarpeted floor. He would have followed it had not Ewen held him up. Hector, breathing hard, came to a standstill.

'Where have you wounded him?' demanded Ewen.

'I haven't touched the filthy carrion,' answered Hector, in

expressibly sulky. 'You prevented me, curse you! Why the devil – '

'Then it is merely exhaustion,' said Ewen. 'Here, help me lift him to the bed, or that chair; he's swooning.'

'Shamming, more like,' said Hector disgustedly. 'Put him on the floor; I'd say throw him out of the window but that. . . . Oh, very well.'

He came to lend a hand, for big and powerful as Ewen was, the now completely unconscious Glenshian was neither small nor light. They carried him with little ceremony to the bed in the corner and dumped him on it. Ewen leant over him for a moment, shrugged his shoulders and left him there, merely observing, 'He said he had not recovered of his illness.'

'Luckily for him,' was Hector's comment.

The two stood looking at each other in the middle of the room.

'I cannot believe it!' said Hector, out of breath and still a trifle livid. 'But here's the letter.' He pulled it out of his pocket. 'I knew my own writing in an instant. But what would he want with it – and how did it get into his hands?'

'We do not know yet what he wanted with it,' answered Ewen gropingly. 'As to the way in which it came to his hands – he may have got it from Mr Pelham.'

'You don't believe that tale of a double, of course?'

'Not now.' Ewen put his hand over his eyes. 'Oh, Hector, as you say, 'tis incredible! It's like a dark, dark passage . . . one cannot see where it leads. A MacPhair of Glenshian!'

'I am going to see if there are more papers of the sort,' said Hector, beginning to rummage feverishly among the books which he had tumbled to the floor. Ewen came to his assistance. But the little pile of volumes – most of them French, and indecent – had evidently not been used as a hiding-place. A few bills had been pushed underneath or between them, and with the bills, by some extraordinary inadvertence, Hector's stolen letter.

'Look at your letter again,' suggested Ardroy, 'and see if it bears traces of what hands it has been in.'

Hector studied it anew. 'Yes, the names have been deciphered, sometimes with queries. And on the back, see, are some words in pencil. "You will please to return this when you have finished with it." But they are not signed.'

'The question is,' said Ewen reflectively, 'whether Mr Pelham handed over the letter to Glenshian. for whatever purpose, or whether Glenshian sent it to him in the first instance.'

'Yes, that is the question. And how, in the latter case, did it first come into Glenshian's hands?'

Dark and slippery paths indeed, such as Archie had hinted at last autumn! Ewen looked round the room. There was a writing desk in one corner. Should they break it open? The key, no doubt, was on that limp, unstirring figure on the bed, but Ewen, at least, could not bring himself to search for it there. Hector was apparently less troubled with scruples of repugnance. He went and stooped over it, and came back not with the keys, but with a pocket-book, and pulled the contents out on to the table.

'More bills,' said he. 'A paper of accounts . . . an assignation, or what looks like it . . . a letter in cipher, addressed to Mr Alexander Jeanson (who is he? 'tis probably an alias) and – hallo, here's a letter from Lille!'

He caught it up, ran his eyes over it, uttered a sound as if he had been stabbed to the heart, and handed it to Ewen.

Ewen read: 'Lille, 15 February 1753. I shall punctually attend to the recommendation which you sent me by the young gentleman from Troy, and should it come to pass that my name-sake is taken, I'll contrive that the loss which that gentleman has sustained shall serve as a cloak to cover Pickle, to whom commend me. C.S.'

'I don't understand,' said Ewen, puzzled. 'Who signs "C.S." – is it a pretended letter from the Prince? Who is "Pickle", and who is "the young gentleman from Troy"?'

'Myself,' answered Hector in a suffocated voice. 'Is not my name a Trojan one? And "C.S." – I know his writing; he has but reversed his initials, and see the reference to "my namesake's" capture – is that fox Samuel Cameron, of my regiment, to whom, to oblige Glenshian there, I took a letter in January. . . . Was there ever such infamy – double infamy!' He glared at

246

the bed. 'And he made me his catspaw – made me myself the instrument of what may yet be my ruin. I think I'll –'

But Ewen, as white as a sheet, was gripping his arms with vice-like strength.

'Hector, let's go, let's go! A terrible thought has just come to me, and if I stay I, too, shall be tempted to run my sword through him! God preserve us both from murdering a senseless man! Come, come quickly!'

'But what ails you – what is it, your thought?'

Ewen shuddered, and began to drag at him. 'Come!' He glanced at the bed in a kind of horror. 'I saw him move; he is coming to himself.'

He unlocked the door, still in the same nervous haste, and only just in time to avert suspicion, for steps were hurrying up the stair. A thin, pale young man, who seemed a servant, stopped at the top on seeing the two gentlemen in the doorway.

Hector kept his head. 'We were just about to seek assistance for your master, Seumas,' he said in Gaelic. 'He has had some kind of fainting fit, and we have laid him on his bed.'

The gillie uttered an inarticulate cry and rushed past them. Exclamations of grief and of endearment, in the same tongue, floated out through the open door.

'That was his gillie,' whispered young Grant when they were outside. 'Did you recognize him as the man who held the torch that night?'

'Instantly,' answered Ardroy, who had a strange look, as of a man sleep-walking. 'But it needed not that. That was not the first time his master had come out of that door! . . . Oh, Hector, Hector, now I know, I think, on whose account it was that Archie had no trial. For whether Finlay MacPhair himself, or the unknown man who sent the information to Edinburgh from Glenbuckie, be the "Pickle" whom Samuel Cameron – of Archie's own clan and regiment – has slandered you to shield, there's not a doubt that the centre of the black business is Finlay – a MacPhair and a Chief's son! God help us all! is there no faith or loyalty left . . . save in the Tower?'

Chapter 21

'STONE-DEAD HATH NO FELLOW'

1

'AVELING,' said the Earl of Stowe with determination, one morning eight days later, 'I have decided to go about this matter today to one of the Secretaries of State, Jardyne for choice.'

'But, my lord,' protested his son in astonishment, 'you cannot – you are quite unfit to leave the house.'

'My dear child,' said Lord Stowe, 'consider the situation! Here we are at the second of June, and in five days, unless a miracle be performed for him, that unfortunate gentleman suffers at Tyburn. For all my promises to Mr Cameron, I have accomplished nothing on his kinsman's behalf. Nor can I see any sign of the petitions delivered to His Majesty and the two princesses at the beginning of this week having had any effect whatsoever. I must make yet another effort, for when a man's life is at stake, what is a gouty toe? Call Rogers, let him dress me, and I will be carried down to my coach, and go to see Mr Jardyne.'

Lord Aveling looked at his father with real admiration. Then he rang the bell for Rogers, and to that horrified elderly valet Lord Stowe conveyed his self-sacrificing intention.

The heroic, no doubt, must pay for their admirable deeds; nevertheless, the consciousness of their heroism is probably sustaining during the latter process. Besides, this particular piece of heroism had not been in vain. When, about an hour and a half later, Lord Aveling heard the rumble of his father's returning coach, he hurried down to find the courageous nobleman being assisted from it, and hardly suppressing his cries of anguish.

'No, no – not like that! Jenkins, don't be so damned clumsy! Yes, that's better. My God, what an infernal invention is gout!

248

Is that you, Aveling? I am going straight to bed; come and see me in a quarter of an hour.'

But when he entered the bedchamber Lord Aveling found his parent disposed in an easy chair as before.

'No, I was sure I could not endure the pressure of the bed-clothes. The foot is better thus. Oh – h – h, damn it, don't speak, there's a good fellow!'

The young man went and looked out of the window at the swaying green in the square garden. More and more did he respect his progenitor. Yet it must be worse to hang ... and rest ... in beautiful summer weather too.

' 'Tis easier now, for the moment,' said the sufferer's voice, 'Come and sit down by me, Francis – only, for God's sake, nowhere near my foot! At any rate, I have got something out of this inferno. ... Jardyne put the case in a nutshell. "Why", asked he, "do you come to me? Go to the Duke of Argyll. If he will but intercede for Doctor Cameron's life, he will not be refused. He is our first man in Scotland, and it is not our interest to deny him a favour when he thinks proper to ask for it!" So you see, Aveling, that if only the Duke can be got to make intercession for Doctor Cameron the thing is done! Now, why did no one ever think of applying to him before, for there is no doubt that Jardyne is right?'

And father and son looked at each other.

'It must be done at once,' said Lord Stowe. 'The Duke, I think, is in town.'

'But who is to do it?'

'Why, the person best qualified – the poor gentleman's wife.'

Aveling nodded. 'But what if it be true, as my mother seems to have heard, that Mrs Cameron has been shut up in the Tower with her husband? What then?'

'Shut up in the Tower!' exclaimed the Earl. 'Oh, surely not!' He turned his head. 'What is it, Rogers?'

'I understand, my lord, from the footman, that Mr Cameron is below, inquiring for my Lord Aveling.'

'Mr Cameron? I'll see him at once,' quoth Aveling, getting up. 'This is very opportune; I can tell him this hopeful news of yours, my lord.'

'Yes; and tell him to urge the poor lady to appeal to the Duke without wasting an hour ... don't for Heaven's sake come near this foot, boy! ... Tell him that I will give her an introduction to His Grace. Egad, I'll be writing now to the Duke to ask for an audience for her, while you interview Mr Cameron.'

Downstairs, in the library, Ewen Cameron was standing, staring at the marble caryatides of the hearth so fixedly that he hardly seemed to hear the door open. Aveling went up to him and laid a hand on his shoulder.

'I have some hopeful news for you, my dear Mr Cameron.'

Ewen turned. Aveling thought him looking very pale and harassed. 'I have need of it, my lord.'

'In spite of his gout, my father has just been to see one of the Secretaries of State – no, no,' he added quickly, for such a light had dawned upon the Highlander's face that out of consideration he hastened to quench it – ' 'tis no *promise* of anything, but an excellent piece of advice. Mr Secretary Jardyne says that if his Grace of Argyll would intercede for Doctor Cameron's life the Government would undoubtedly grant his request. Neither my father nor I can imagine why we never thought of that course earlier.'

A strange hot wave of colour passed over Ardroy's face, leaving it more haggard looking than before.

'Then I suppose it must be done,' he said in a sombre voice. 'Do you know why I am here, Lord Aveling? I came to ask what his lordship thought of the prospects of an application to the Duke of Argyll!'

'Why,' cried the younger man, 'this is indeed extraordinary, that you, also, should have thought of making application in that quarter!'

'Not I! I doubt if I should ever have thought of it,' responded Ewen, frowning. 'The notion is Mrs Cameron's.'

'Excellent!' cried Lord Aveling, 'because she is the one person to carry it out, as my father and I were just agreeing. If she will go, he will give her – '

'She cannot go,' broke in Ardroy. 'That is the difficulty. She is herself a prisoner in the Tower now, at her own request in order that she may be with her husband for . . . for the few days that remain. The only way, it seems, in which this request could be complied with was to make her as close a prisoner as he is. It was done the night before last. This morning I received a distracted letter from her; evidently this thought of appealing to the Duke to use his influence had come to her there – too late for her to carry it out.' He paused; his hands clenched and unclenched themselves. 'So . . . she has asked me to be her deputy.'

'Well, after all,' said Aveling reflectively, 'you are a near kinsman of her husband's, are you not, which would lend you quite sufficient standing. My father will give you an introduction to the Duke; indeed, I believe he is now writing to him on Mrs Cameron's behalf.'

'Yes, I suppose I must do it,' said Ewen between his teeth. He was gazing at an impassive caryatid again.

'You will not carry so much less weight than poor Mrs Cameron,' observed Aveling consolingly. 'Of course – to put it brutally – there is much appeal in a woman's tears, but on the other hand you will be able to plead more logically, more – '

'Plead!' exclaimed Ewen, facing round with flashing eyes. 'Ay, that's it, *plead* – beg mercy from a Campbell!'

Aveling stared at him, startled at his look and tone. 'What is the obstacle? Ah, I remember, your clans are not friendly. But if Doctor Cameron can countenance – '

'He knows nothing about it,' said Ewen sharply.

'And his wife, not being a Cameron born, does not understand your natural repugnance.'

'She does,' answered Ewen starkly, 'for she *is* a Cameron born. She knows what it means to me, but she implores me . . . and could I, in any case, hold back if I thought there were the faintest chance of success? And now you tell me that one of the Secretaries of State actually counsels it. God pity me, that I must go through with it, then, and kneel to MacCailein Mor for Archibald Cameron's sake! I'd not do it for my own!'

The blank-eyed busts which topped the bookshelves in Lord Stowe's sleepy, decorous library must have listened in amazement to this unchaining of Highland clan feeling, even Lord

Aveling was taken aback by the bitter transformation it had worked in a man already wrought upon by grief and protracted anxiety.

'Let *me* go, then, Cameron!' he cried. 'God knows I am sorry enough for your cousin, and I have no objection to appealing to the Duke of Argyll. I would do my very utmost, I promise you. . . . Or, perhaps, you could find some other substitute?'

'You are goodness itself,' said Ewen in a softened tone. 'No, I am the man, since Jean Cameron cannot go. It may be,' he added in a rather strangled voice, 'that, just because I am a Cameron and an enemy, MacCailein Mor may be moved to do a magnanimous act. . . . O God, he *must* do it, for all other hopes are breaking . . . and there is so little time left!'

2

It was with that despairing cry in his ears that Aveling had hastened upstairs to his father's room and held council with him. As a result of this conclave Lord Stowe wrote a fresh letter to the Duke of Argyll, saying that he was anxious to wait upon his Grace with a friend whom he was desirous of presenting to him (he did not mention the friend's name, lest by chance the audience should be refused), but that as he was himself confined to his room with gout he would send his son in his stead, if the Duke would allow. The same afternoon the Duke replied very civilly by messenger that he would receive Lord Aveling and his friend at eleven o'clock on Monday morning. The Sabbath, he explained, he kept strictly as a day set apart from all worldly matters.

So two days were lost; but, as Aveling assured that friend, the Duke's influence was so great that he could no doubt have Doctor Cameron reprieved on the very steps of the scaffold.

Nor did Ardroy have to go to the Duke of Argyll with his hat in his hand and a latter of recommendation, like a lackey seeking a place, since he went under the auspices of the Earl of Stowe, and accompanied by that nobleman's heir.

'I shall present you,' said Aveling to him as they went, 'and then take my leave at the first opportunity.'

'As you will,' replied Ewen; and then, forcing a smile, 'You are always consideration itself, my dear lord.'

That was almost all that passed between them till they came to Argyll House. And waiting in the portico, into which there drifted a faint perfume of late lilacs from the Duke's garden, Ewen thought, 'When next I stand here, the die will have been cast, one way or the other.' His heart began to beat violently, and when the door was flung open he was so pale that his companion looked at him with some uneasiness.

But as he stepped over MacCailein Mor's threshold Ardroy regained at least his outward composure. The two were ushered into a large and lofty room, sparsely but massively furnished, at the end of which hung a great blue velvet curtain suggesting another room beyond. Over the hearth voyaged the lymphad, the proud galley of Lorne, a sinister device to many a clan of the West. Ewen averted his eyes from it. How long, he wondered, would he on whose ancestral banners it had fluttered keep the suppliant waiting? . . .

But the Duke was punctual to the moment. A large clock by the wall with a heavy pendulum of gilt and crystal struck the hour, and the velvet curtain parted in the middle, held back by an announcing lackey.

'His Grace the Duke of Argyll!'

And he who was sometimes called the King of Scotland came through – a man of seventy, upright, dignified, and rather cold, plainly but richly dressed, with a heavy full-bottomed wig framing a delicate featured face of much intelligence – a man who had long wielded great authority, though he had only succeeded his brother the second Duke a decade ago. For more than forty years Archibald Campbell, once Lord Islay, had been the mainstay of the English Government in the North; and all this was written, without ostentation, in his air.

'My Lord Aveling, I think?' said Argyll pleasantly, and the young man bowed. 'I'm sorry to hear that the Earl of Stowe is indisposed; it gives me, however, the chance of making your acquaintance.'

He came forward with a little smile and held out his hand.

'Pray present me also to this gentleman, whose name I have not the honour of knowing.'

And all at once young Lord Aveling, used as he was to all the demands of society, knew nervousness – though not for himself. Something of it was apparent in his voice as he replied, 'This, your Grace, is Mr Ewen Cameron of Ardroy, a near kinsman of the gentleman now under sentence in the Tower.'

What age had left of the Duke's eyebrows lifted. A line appeared on either side of his mouth. 'And what does Mr Ewen Cameron' – there was the faintest stress on the patronymic – 'want of me?'

And his gaze, not hostile, not piercing, but unmistakably the gaze of command, rested on Aveling's tall companion.

'Your Grace,' began Ewen; but it seemed to him that his voice was frozen in his throat. It was not awe which enchained it, but realization of this man's power for life or death, and of his personality. He was MacCailein Mor, the Chief of the hated, swarming and triumphant race of Campbell . . . and he seemed to be feigning ignorance of why he, the Cameron, was there to wait upon him, so that he might have the reason, which he could well have guessed, put by the petitioner into words.

'Your Grace, I am come on behalf of Mrs Cameron, and by her express desire, she now having made herself close prisoner with her husband, and being therefore unable to wait upon you herself.'

'You come as the emissary of a lady, sir?' inquired the Duke smoothly. 'Your errand must have my best attention then. But we stand all this while. Pray be seated, gentlemen.' He waved them towards chairs.

'If your Grace will excuse me,' put in Lord Aveling, 'I will withdraw. I came but to present Mr Cameron in my father's stead.'

'Both of you deputies, in fact,' said Argyll, looking from one to the other, and again he smiled the little smile which did not reach his eyes. 'I am sorry to lose your company, my lord, but I know that you young men (if you'll forgive me for calling you one) have better things to occupy you than talking affairs with an old one.' He shook hands again with every appearance of cordiality, a footman appeared, and Aveling was gone.

The Duke turned with equal courtesy to the visitor who remained.

'And now Mr Cameron – Cameron of Ardroy, is it not. . . . Ardroy near Loch Arkaig, if I am not mistaken? Pray be seated, and let me know in what I can serve you on Mrs Cameron's behalf?'

'If your Grace will permit me, I had rather stand,' said Ewen somewhat hoarsely. 'I am come, as I am sure you can guess, as a suppliant.'

'Is that so?' remarked the Duke, looking long and steadily at him. His face betrayed nothing. 'You will forgive me, perhaps, if I myself sit, for I am old and weary.' And he seated himself slowly in a high-backed chair. 'You come, you say, as a suppliant, and I am to see in you the representative of Mrs Cameron?'

'If you please, my Lord Duke – of a woman who turns to you, in her mortal distress, as her last hope.'

'I think,' said the Duke of Argyll in a soft voice, 'that with a Highland gentleman such as yourself I prefer to be MacCailein Mor.'

Ewen swallowed hard. It had come to him that he could only get through his mission if he forgot that fact.

'Because for one thing,' went on Argyll, 'if you are a kinsman of Doctor Cameron's you are equally a kinsman of his brother, the late Lochiel, and of the boy who is Lochiel now.'

'Yes, I am a kinsman of all three,' said Ewen in a low voice. Archibald Campbell was trying, was he, to fancy that in some sort he had the Chief of the Cameron before him, about to beg for mercy? 'A kinsman by marriage. And do not think, MacCailein Mor,' – he gave him the title since he wished it, and had every right to it – 'do not think that Doctor Cameron himself knows of his wife's appeal to you!'

'No? But let us be clear, Mr Cameron, on what score she . . . you . . . which am I to say? – is appealing to me. You have not yet informed me.'

Ewen's lip gave a little curl as he drew himself up. The Campbell knew perfectly well the nature of that appeal. He himself did not look much like a suppliant, but he did his best to keep his tone that of a petitioner. 'Mrs Cameron desires to throw herself at your Grace's feet, as at those of the foremost man in Scotland, to beg, to implore you to use your great influence to have the sentence on her husband commuted.'

'Commuted,' said Argyll after a moment. 'Commuted to what?'

'To imprisonment, to transportation – to anything save an undeserved death.'

The Duke leant forward, his fine hands, half-hidden by their ruffles, grasping the lion-headed arms of his chair. 'Undeserved, do you say, Mr Cameron? A man comes from abroad, with every circumstance of secrecy, not once or twice only, but constantly, during a period of seven years, to work against the established government in the North, to foment disaffection by any means in his power, to promise foreign intervention in aid of it – all this in a country just settling down after a most disastrous upheaval, in which he, too, bore a prominent part . . . and you call his death undeserved!'

'Having regard to Doctor Cameron's private character,' replied Ardroy firmly, 'I do. Your Grace must know – what on all sides is acknowledged to be the case – how blameless a reputation he bears and how humane, and how strenuously, before the troubles, he upheld all Lochiel's efforts for the betterment of the clan. Doctor Cameron's is not the case of an ordinary plotter, my lord.'

'In what manner can any plotter be extraordinary, Mr Cameron, save perchance in the amount of harm he does?' asked the Duke. 'In that certainly Doctor Cameron has been singular. Since the year 1747 his comings and goings, or his supposed comings and goings, have kept Lochaber and the West in a continual ferment. In his private character he may be all that you urge and more, yet he has proved the veritable stormy petrel of the Highlands, and the sentence on him is so well deserved that if I were to crawl on all fours to the English Government they would not remit it.'

'You underrate your power, MacCailein Mor,' said Ewen in

a low voice. O God, did he mean that, or was he merely holding out for more fervid, more grovelling entreaties? 'You underrate your power,' he repeated. 'And you would show more than your power, your ... generosity ... by intervening on behalf of a man whose ancestors and your – '

'No doubt,' broke in Argyll before the sentence was completed. 'But that would be somewhat of a selfish luxury. I have to consider my country, not my own reputation for magnanimity.'

Ewen seized upon this passionately. 'My lord, my lord, you *would* be considering your country! The best interests of this Government are surely not served by the carrying out of this extraordinarily harsh sentence, which your Grace must be aware is agitating all London!'

'When I spoke of my country, Mr Cameron,' said the Duke with emphasis, 'I meant my native land, Scotland, whose welfare and good settlement I had at heart before you were born. Now you desire that I should induce the English Government to commute Doctor Cameron's sentence in order that he may have the opportunity of going back to injure her again.' And as Ewen tried to protest he went on more strongly: 'No, Mr Cameron, if I advise His Majesty's ministers to commute the sentence to one of perpetual imprisonment, that is only to make of Doctor Cameron a constant centre of intrigue and trouble, ending after some years in his escape. If transportation is substituted for imprisonment, then he may escape and return to Scotland more easily still. No, I cannot now go back upon the work and convictions of a lifetime, and deliberately plant again in my country's breast the thorn which by good fortune has just been plucked from it.'

'You said a while ago,' murmured Ewen with stiff, cold lips, the great room grown a little misty and unreal about him, 'you said that the Government would not grant you this boon though you crawled to them – and yet one of its first officials has stated that such a request would not be denied for a moment if you made it. Now you say that it goes against your conscience to make it. Which is it, my Lord Duke?'

Argyll got up from his chair.

'You are a very bold young man, Mr Cameron of Ardroy! Are you trying to bring me to book?' The look which flickered over his pale, dignified features was nearer amusement than irritation. 'I do not think that Mrs Cameron would have taken that line. Believe me, it is not a wise one!'

'I will take any line that . . . that pleases your Grace!' declared Ewen, desperate. 'Do you wish me, who, though I am not of Lochiel, have a strain of the blood and am a cadet of the clan, do you wish me to kneel to you? I will, here and now, if you will ask for Archibald Cameron's life!'

'There is no need for you to assume that uncomfortable position, Mr Cameron,' replied the Duke dryly. 'Spiritually you are already upon your knees. . . . It is a harsh saying, no doubt, but a very true one, when matters of this kind are in question (and it was an Englishman who uttered it) – "Stone-dead hath no fellow". I am grieved that I must endorse it in the case of Doctor Cameron, for I consider that the Government is more than justified in carrying out this long overdue sentence.'

Ewen put his hand up to his throat. Otherwise he did not move. Those were the accents of finality; to entreat further was only to batter oneself against a rock, to lower Archie himself in the eyes of the Campbell.

'It is not,' went on Argyll, walking slowly to and fro with his hands behind his back, 'it is not as though Doctor Cameron had shown the slightest sign of real repentance for his ill-doings, the slightest intention of future amendment. His answers before the Privy Council in April were inspired by the most obstinate intention of concealing every fact he knew under cover of having "forgotten" it, and when last month, immediately after sentence had been passed upon him, he, in a conversation with Mr Sharpe, the Solicitor to the Treasury, seemed to lament his unhappy position, and to say that if His Majesty extended his clemency to him he would strive to lead his fellow-clansmen into less treasonable paths, there was not one word of the only course which could conceivably merit such clemency – the making of disclosures.'

Through the silence the slow swing of the pendulum of the great gilt clock behind Ewen seemed to emphasize how fast the sands were slipping in the glass of Archibald Cameron's life. Ardroy clenched one hand round the wrist of the other.

' "Disclosures",' he said at last; and there was nothing in his voice to show what he thought of the word or the thing. 'You mean, my Lord Duke, that if Doctor Cameron were to become a second Murray of Broughton, that if he would tell all he knows – '

The Duke held up his hand quickly. 'Pray, Mr Cameron, do not associate *me* with any suggestion so affronting to a Highlander! I merely mention that Mr Sharpe, as I remember, seemed much disappointed – for the Government are well aware that there is some new scheme afoot. You must draw what conclusion you can from that. For myself, I think the bargain would scarce be worth the Government's while. ... Yet, out of a perhaps misplaced humanity, I will go so far as to point out that that door, which was once open, may, for aught I know, be open still.'

Open still – open still; the crystal pendulum swung on – but that was not what it was saying.

'Your Grace is very good. ...' Ewen heard his own voice, and wondered at its cold steadiness, since his heart felt neither cold nor steady. 'But that is not a door at which a Cameron of Lochiel could ever knock. I will detain you no longer, Mac-Cailein Mor.'

Chapter 22

CONSTANT AS STEEL

THERE was no hope for Archibald Cameron now, except the faint possibility of that eleventh hour reprieve to which a few still pinned their faith. Lord Stowe, grave and disappointed, advised him not to trust to a miracle. It was remarkable that Aveling, young and generous-hearted though he was, gave the same advice, and would not take the easier path of trying to buoy up his friend's spirits with an anticipation which he did not share. But Lady Stowe, with whom Ewen had an interview, not of his seeking, on the Tuesday, proclaimed her conviction that the execution would not take place, and hinted at the influence which she herself had brought to bear on certain members of the Government. Hector Grant was in a frenzy, dashing hither and thither, sure that something could still be done, and talking wildly of a rescue at Tyburn itself, of kidnapping Lord Newcastle or Henry Pelham and holding them to ransom, and other schemes equally impossible.

But by noon on Wednesday Ewen had abandoned all dreams, sober and extravagant alike. His faint hope of seeing Archie once more was dead too; even the Earl of Stowe's influence could not procure him another interview. And in the afternoon he shut himself up in his lodging, and would see no one, not even Hector. He could talk about tomorrow's tragedy no longer, and, like a wounded animal which seeks solitude, only asked to be left alone.

He had sat for he knew not how long that afternoon immured in the close little parlour, with the window fast shut since the moment when he had overheard two men in the street below arranging to go to Tyburn on the morrow, and one of them, who was a trifle drunk, offering the other some only too vivid reminiscences of the execution of the Scottish Jacobites in 1746. Ewen had sprung up, and, calling upon his Maker, had

slammed down the window with such violence that he had
nearly shattered it. Then, after walking to and fro for a while
like a man demented, he had flung himself down on the settle,
and was still sitting there, his head in his hands, when a timid
tap at the door announced Mrs Wilson.

'I'd not disturb you, sir,' she whispered sympathetically,
'but that there's a messenger below from the Tower in a
hackney coach, and he brings this.' She held out a letter.

Ewen lifted his head from his hands.

'From the Tower?' he repeated, looking at her stupidly.
Surely she did not mean that?

But, opening the letter, he saw the heading; saw, too, that it
came from the Deputy-Lieutenant.

'Dear Sir,' it ran –

Doctor Cameron having very earnestly desired to see you once more,
and I myself having come to the conclusion that it were better Mrs
Cameron did not pass the night here, but left before the gates were
shut, and that some friend should be present to take her away, I have
obtained leave from the Constable for you to visit the prisoner and
also to perform this office; and have therefore sent the bearer in a
hackney-coach to bring you back with all speed, as the gates must
infallibly be closed at six o'clock this evening.

> Your obedient humble servant,
> CHARLES RAINSFORD.

Ewen drew a long breath. 'I will come at once,' he said.

Nearly all the way, jolting in the coach with the warder, or
whatever he was, Ardroy was turning over and over a once
entertained but long abandoned idea of changing clothes with
Archie. The same obstacle brought him up again – his own
unusual stature, though Archie was of a good height himself.
Yet this unexpected summons did so clearly seem as though
Fate were holding out a last opportunity of rescue – but what
opportunity? Ewen's former visit had shown him how impreg-
nable were the Tower walls, how closely guarded the gates.
Tonight every soul there would be doubly alert. And if Archie
were by now in irons there was no hope of any kind ... there
was little enough in any case.

To his surprise, when he came to the Byward Tower, they did

not offer to search him, and he was told, also, that Doctor Cameron had been moved from the Lieutenant's house and was there, in the Byward Tower itself. Ewen asked the reason.

'It was thought safer, sir. My Lords Kilmarnock and Balmerino were lodged here in '46, though my Lord Kilmarnock, too, was at first in the Lieutenant's house.'

'And Mrs Cameron, is she in this tower with her husband?'

'No, sir; she remains in the Lieutenant's house until she leaves, before the gates are shut.'

He could see Archie alone, then, and he could not but be glad of that.

It had indeed a very different setting, this last meeting, and one which better fitted the circumstances than the former. Unlike the pleasant apartments with their glimpses of the outer world, this place was heavily charged with an atmosphere of finality, for the roof curved cage-like above the large, circular, stone-vaulted room with its narrow windows. In the middle was a table with a couple of chairs; and at this table Archie was sitting with a book open before him; but his eyes were on the door. He was not in irons.

They clasped hands in silence as the door swung to and clashed home. Only then did Ewen see that they were not alone, for some distance away a wooden-faced warder sat stiffly on a chair against the wall.

'Cannot that man leave us for a little?' murmured Ewen.

'No,' said his cousin. 'I must have a shadow now until – until there's no more need of watching me. This good fellow must even sleep here tonight. But we can speak French or Erse; he'll not understand either.'

Ewen was bitterly disappointed. If there were a witness present they had not the faintest chance of changing clothes. He said as much in his native tongue.

'My dear Ewen,' replied Archibald Cameron smiling, 'Nature, when she gave you that frame, never intended you for such a rôle – and in any case it is quite impracticable. Come, sit down and let us talk. You see there is another chair.'

It seemed of a tragic incongruity to sit quietly talking at a table, but Ewen obeyed. Talk he could not, at first. But Archie began to speak with perfect calm of his last arrangements, such as they were; he had given his wife, he said, what he had been able to set down from time to time of his wishes and sentiments, by means of a bit of blunt pencil which he had contrived to get hold of after all.

'Four or five scraps of paper they are,' he concluded. 'I could not come by more, but I have signed my name to every one of them, that they may be known for authentic.'

Only once did he betray emotion; it was in speaking of his young children in exile, and their future, so desperately uncertain when he was gone.

'I have no money to leave them,' he said sadly. 'Had that gold from Loch Arkaig really stayed in my hands they would not be penniless now, poor bairns! But I have been very much pleased,' he went on, 'with a letter which my wife showed me from my eldest boy – you remember John, Ewen; he always had a great admiration for you. I have for some time observed in him a sense of loyalty and honour much beyond what might have been expected from a boy of his years, and in this letter of which I speak he expresses not only his conviction of my inviolable fidelity to the Cause, but a desire that I should rather sacrifice my life than save it upon dishonourable terms. I have great hopes of his future, even though the principles of uprightness and loyalty be not over-popular nowadays.'

'Did the Privy Council,' Ewen asked somewhat hesitatingly, 'ever hold out a promise of mercy if you would make disclosures?'

Archie nodded. 'Yes. And I believe that hopes of my doing so must have been cherished for some time after my examination, since Mr Sharpe, the Solicitor to the Treasury, certainly had them as late as the seventeenth of May, when I was sentenced. Tell me, Ewen,' he added, looking at him hard, ' – for Jean has confessed to me the step which she worked upon you to take – had his Grace of Argyll the same hopes?'

'You know of that?' exclaimed Ewen, half-apprehensive, half-relieved. 'You know – and you forgive me for going to him?'

'My dear lad, there's no question of forgiveness. I ought to thank you from the bottom of my heart for undertaking what I know must have been a very repugnant task. Moreover, as I am neither a saint nor a hermit, but an ordinary man like the next, I'll not deny that a span of forty-six years sometimes seems a little short to me.'

Ewen turned very pale. 'Archie ... you make me feel like your executioner! You might have had your life, perhaps – but I – in effect I refused it for you! I. ... But it's not too late.' He half-rose from his chair.

Archie caught at his arm. 'Ah, *loachain*, I guess why you refused it for me. I'd have liked to have had the refusing of it to MacCailein Mor myself, on the terms which I can divine that he offered.'

'To do him justice, he offered nothing. At the end indeed he spoke of ... of a possible door. You can guess what it was. He would have naught to do with it himself. Yet – ' Ewen turned his head away. 'Oh, Archie, if it were possible to accept! ... It was not so hard then to turn one's back on the chance; I did it without weighing the matter. I knew you would not consent. But it is much harder now.'

Archibald Cameron smiled and gave his head a little shake. 'You will be glad by this time tomorrow. What welcome do you think Murray of Broughton's former friends give him nowadays? And would you set the door of Ardroy wide for me, Ewen, were I to save my skin as he did? You know you would not! – But enough of this talk. There has been no choice in the matter. I *could* not bring myself to betray either my companions or my Prince's plans.'

'Yet you yourself have been betrayed!' came instinctively to Ewen's lips.

Archie's face clouded a little. 'I am glad to think that I do not know the informer, whether the thing was done of his own free will or at another's instigation. It is easier to forgive, thus.'

This time it was Ewen who was determined that Archie should read nothing upon his face, and he set it immovably. Of what use to burden his spirit, so soon to be gone, with the hatred and suspicion which lay so heavy on his own since the encounter with young Glenshian?

Moreover – luckily perhaps – Archie here pulled out his watch. 'Good Mr Falconar, the Scots nonjuring clergyman who has been visiting me, and will attend me to Tyburn tomorrow, is to bring me the Sacrament at five o'clock. I would have wished to take it tomorrow morning before I set out, but then Jean could not have received it with me, nor you, if you wish to do so?'

'Will it be here?'

'Yes.' The Doctor pointed to where a little table, covered with a white cloth, stood against the wall, with two or three footstools ranged before it. 'And Jean herself will be brought hither. But I have said farewell to her already. . . . Ewen, be patient with her – though, indeed, she has the bravest heart of any woman living.'

'You do not need to urge that,' said Ardroy.

'I know that I do not. It is you who are to take her away from the Tower, too, God bless you!'

'Shall I . . . take her back to Lille?'

'It is not necessary; that is arranged for.' Archie got up suddenly; Ewen had a glimpse of his face, and knew that he was thinking of the fatherless children to whom she would return.

He sat there, rapidly and quite unconsciously fluttering over the leaves of the book lying on the table, and then said in a voice which he could scarcely command, 'Archie, is there nothing else that I can do for you?'

Doctor Cameron came and sat down again. 'There is something. But perhaps it is too hard to ask.'

'If it be anything which concerns me alone it is not too hard.'

'Then . . . I would ask you to be there tomorrow.'

Ewen recoiled. 'I . . . I did not dream that you would ask *that*!'

'You would rather stay away?'

'*Archie* – what do you think I am made of?'

Archibald Cameron looked at him rather wistfully. 'I thought – but it was, I see, a selfish thought – that I should like to see one face of a friend there, at the last. I have heard that a Tyburn crowd, accustomed to thieves and murderers, is ... not a pleasant one; and I have been warned that there will be very many people there.'

'They will not be hostile, Archie; that I can stake my soul on. You do not know the sympathetic and indignant feeling there is abroad. But, if you wish it, I will be there; nay, if it is your wish, I will make it mine too. ... Yet even you will not ask me to remain until the end of all?' he added imploringly.

'No,' said his cousin gravely but serenely, 'not until that. Yet I think the end, thank God, will matter very little to me. In spite of the terms of the sentence and of Lord Chief Justice Lee, I have a good hope that I will not be cut down until I am quite dead. ... Ewen, Ewen, think it's yourself that's going to the gallows (as you nearly did once) and not I! You would not play the child over your own fate, I know that well!' For Ewen had his head on his arms, and his nails were digging into the table. He did not answer.

'I could wish it were not Tyburn,' Archibald Cameron went on, as if to himself. 'My lords Kilmarnock and Balmerino were luckier to suffer on Tower Hill, and by the axe. Yet I must not complain, being but a commoner; indeed, I should think of the great Marquis of Montrose, who was hanged likewise – and from a very lofty ladder too. And I thank my God I was always easier ashamed than frightened. ... Ewen, Mr Falconar will be here in a few minutes. Do you wish to make some preparation before you take communion with me?'

Ewen mechanically knelt down by the table where he had been sitting, put his hands before his face and tried to say a prayer. But he could not even say 'Lord, I am not worthy'; his heart was nothing but a burning stone.

Nevertheless he still knelt there, rising only when he heard the bolts withdrawn, and there came in, first a very tall, thin man in lay dress, who walked with a limp, and then, on the arm of Rainsford himself, Mrs Cameron. The Deputy-Lieutenant considerately dismissed the warder and himself took the man's place, and, almost before Ewen, dazed with pain, had realized it, the service was beginning. Archibald Cameron, his hand in his wife's, knelt at some distance from the improvised altar; Ewen a little way behind them. And, save that it was not dark, but a June evening, the bare masonry of the place might almost have suggested an Eucharist in the catacombs; but Ewen did not think of that. He seemed to be able to think of nothing, though he did perceive that Mr Falconar, who appeared to be greatly moved, was using the proscribed Scottish Liturgy of 1637.

When the moment of communion approached, the two in front of him rose, and Archie glanced round at him, but Ewen shook his head, and so Doctor Cameron led his wife to one of the footstools and knelt beside her. But when Ewen saw them kneeling there without him, the ties of human affection drew him more strongly, so, he got up after all, and knelt humbly on the floor by Archie's side; and drinking of the cup after him whose viaticum it truly was, felt for the moment wonderfully comforted, and that the Giver of that feast, first instituted as it was in circumstances of betrayal and imminent death, had pardoned the hard and rebellious heart in him. Then he went back to the table where he had sat with Archie, and knelt down again there with his head against the edge, for a long time.

At last he looked up. The service was over; Mr Falconar was gone. Archie, with his back to him, had his wife in his arms. Ewen thought that if he also went, the two might have a moment or two together – save for the presence of the Deputy-Lieutenant, who, considerate as ever, was looking out of one of the little windows. But he could not go without a last word. He got to his feet, approached a little way, and said his cousin's name.

Doctor Cameron put his wife into a chair and turned; and Ewen held out his hand.

'I shall not see you again to have speech with,' he said in Gaelic. His very hands felt numb in Archie's clasp. 'I wish I could die with you,' he whispered passionately.

Archie held his hands tightly. 'Dear lad, what then would Alison do, wanting you, and your boys, and your tenants? You have work here; mine is over.'

'Gentlemen,' came Rainsford's voice from behind, 'there remains but eleven minutes ere the gates are closed.'

Time, the inexorable, had dwindled to this! Ewen caught his

breath. 'Good-bye,' he said after a second of struggle. 'Good-bye, faithful and true! Greet Lochiel for me. I will keep the promise I have made you. Look for me there – give me a sign.' He embraced Archie and went out quickly, for the door was ajar, with the armed sentries close outside. Only Mrs Cameron and General Rainsford remained behind.

But outside, beyond the sentries, was still Mr Falconar, with his handkerchief to his eyes. As for Ewen, he leant against the wall to wait for Mrs Cameron and folded his arms tightly across his breast, as if by that constraint he could bridle a heart which felt as though it were breaking. Perhaps he shut his eyes; at any rate, he was roused by a touch on his arm. It was Mr Falconar, still painfully agitated.

'Sir, I shall spend this night praying less, I think, for *him* than for strength to carry me through this terrible business tomorrow without faltering.'

'You mean the attending Doctor Cameron to the scaffold,' asked Ewen in a voice which sounded completely indifferent.

'Yes,' said the clergyman. 'I declare to you, sir, that I do not know how I am to come through it. Doctor Cameron's composure shames me, who am supposed to uphold it. My great fear is lest any unworthy weakness of mine should shake his calm in his last moments – though that hardly seems possible.'

Ewen was sorry for him. 'You cannot withdraw now, I suppose, for he must have a minister with him.'

'It is usual, I understand; but *he* does not need one, sir. He has not left it until the eleventh hour, like some, to make his peace with God. I must carry out as much of my office as he requires, but he does not need me to pray for him on the scaffold, priest though I be. I shall ask his prayers. I would ask yours, too, sir, that I do not by any weakness add to his burden tomorrow.'

Ewen looked at him with a compassion which was shot through by a strange spasm of envy. This man, who dreaded it so, would see Archie once more at close quarters, be able to address him, hear his voice, go with him to the very brink . . .

Then through the half-open door came the Deputy-Lieutenant with Mrs Cameron again on his arm. She looked half-fainting, yet she walked quite steadily. Mr Falconar being now nearest the door, General Rainsford put her into his charge, and called hastily for the warder to take up his post again within. In a kind of dream Ewen watched the clergyman and the all but widow go down the stairs. His heart ached for her, little and brave and forlorn, her dress slipping slowly from one worn stone step to the next.

He had started to follow her, and had descended a step or two, when he was aware of a voice calling hurriedly but softly to him from above. He went back again, wondering.

It was the Deputy-Lieutenant who had called after him, and now met him at the top of the stairway. 'Doctor Cameron has remembered something which he had intended to give his wife; but it was you whom he wished called back, if possible.' He pulled out his watch. 'Four minutes, no longer, Mr Cameron!'

So he *was* to have speech with Archie once more. And, the warder being still outside, and the Deputy-Lieutenant not seeming to purpose coming in again, for that brief fraction of time they would be alone. Had Archie made a pretext to that end?

He was standing in the middle of the room with something in his hand. 'I forgot to give these to Jean, as I intended, for my eldest son.' And he held out to Ewen two shabby shoe-buckles of steel. 'Bid Jean tell him from me,' he said earnestly, 'that I send him these, and not my silver ones; and that if I had gold ones I would not send him the gold, but these, which I wore when skulking. For steel being hard and of small value is an emblem of constancy and disinterestedness; and so I would have him always to be constant and disinterested in the service of his King and country, and never to be either bribed or frightened from his duty. – Will you tell her that, Ewen?'

No, he had not been sent for under a pretext. Ewen took the buckles. 'She shall have them; and I will faithfully repeat your message.' Then he was mute; it seemed as if Archie were gone already, as if the immeasurable gulf already severed them. Archibald Cameron saw the dumb misery on his face and put his hand on his arm.

'Don't look like that, my dearest Ewen! I thank God I am ready to be offered, and you need have no apprehension for me tomorrow. It is poor Falconar I shall be sorry for.'

'Indeed,' said Ewen, finding his voice again, 'he seems most painfully apprehensive; he was speaking to me just now. I was about to ask him whether he could not procure another clergyman to take his place, but so few in London are nonjurors, and I suppose you would – '

He never finished. The colour came surging over his drawn face, as a wild arrow of an idea sped winging into his brain. 'Archie,' he said breathlessly in Gaelic, 'if a layman might ... if it could be contrived ... could not ... could not *I* take his place tomorrow?'

In the Doctor's face also the colour came and went for a moment. 'My dear Ewen ... if it is like to prove a trial to Falconar, how would you – '

'I'd rather stand with you in the cart than see you stand there from a distance, and be unable to get at you,' said Ewen with great earnestness. 'I should be near you – I could speak to you. And I would not break down, I swear to you! Archie, would you be willing?'

'Willing!' exclaimed Archie in the same low voice. 'I would give one of the few hours left me for your company! But it asks too much of you, Eoghain.'

'Not so much as to stand in the crowd and watch you like a stranger,' reiterated Ewen. 'And – my God, the four minutes must be nearly gone! – 'tis as if Providence had planned it, for Mr Falconar is little under my height, and lame of a leg as I am at times. If I wore his dark clothes – 'tis a pity he goes in lay dress, but that cannot be helped – and perhaps his wig, who would look at my face? And the clergyman always drives by himself to Tyburn, does he not?'

'I believe so,' said Doctor Cameron, considering, 'and in a closed carriage. You would not be seen on the way, since you would not travel publicly and slowly, as I shall.'

'I only wish I could, with you! But, Mr Falconar apart, would you not rather have some clergyman?' And, as Archie shook his head, Ardroy asked hastily, knowing that his time

270

must be almost up, 'Is there anything which I must do ... *there*? – To be sure I can ask Mr Falconar that.'

'I suppose it is usual to read a prayer. I should like the commendatory prayer from the Prayer Book ... and I'd a thousand times rather you read that for me than poor Mr Falconar.'

'Mr Cameron,' said Rainsford, impatiently appearing at the door, 'you must come instantly, if you please. You have but just time to join Mrs Cameron in the coach.'

'I have your leave, then, if I can contrive it?' whispered Ewen.

Archibald Cameron bent his head. 'Good-bye,' he said in English. 'Remember my message.'

And this time Ewen hurried from the room with but the briefest farewell glance, so afraid was he of being detained and prevented from carrying through his scheme.

By running down the stairs he reached the carriage just before it started. Mr Falconar, hat in hand, was at the door of it, Mrs Cameron invisible within.

'Give me your direction, sir,' said Ardroy hastily to the clergyman. 'I must see you when I have escorted Mrs Cameron home: 'tis of the utmost importance.'

Mr Falconar gave it. 'I shall await you this evening,' he said, and Ewen scrambled into the already moving coach.

But now, as they drove out under the archway of the Lion Tower, he must put aside his own plan, his own grief, and think of one who was losing even more than he. Jean Cameron was sitting upright in the corner, her hands clasped, looking straight in front of her, and alarming him not a little by her rigidity. Suddenly she said, without looking at him:

'He is not afraid.'

'No, madam,' answered Ewen, 'no man was ever less afraid.'

'*The pure in heart shall see God,*' she murmured to herself. And a moment afterwards, somewhat to Ardroy's relief, she broke into wild weeping.

Chapter 23

'THE SALLY-PORT TO ETERNITY'

THURSDAY, the seventh of June, 1753, dawned sunny and
clear-skied, yet not without the promise of a cloud or two later
on, whose shadow might be grateful if one had been standing
for some hours in the heat. For many of the spectators would
begin their pilgrimage to Tyburn very early in the day, in order
to secure good places, since, though the great triangular gallows could be seen from almost any distance, the scaffold beside it, for what came after the gallows, was disappointingly
low. Moreover, it was a thousand pities not to hear a last
speech or confession, if such were made, and that was impossible unless one were fairly near the cart in which the victim
stood before being turned off. So hundreds set off between six
and seven o'clock, and hundreds, even thousands, more came
streaming without intermission along the Oxford road all
morning; and the later they came the more they grumbled at
the inferior positions which they were necessarily obliged to
take up; yet they grumbled with a certain holiday good nature.
For though disgraceful scenes did take place at Tyburn, some
at least of those who in this eighteenth century came to see a
fellow-creature half-hanged and then disembowelled were quite
well-to-do citizens who were conscious of nothing callous or
unnatural in their conduct. An execution, being public, was a
spectacle, and a free spectacle to boot; moreover, today's was
a special occasion, not a mere hanging for coining, or murder,
or a six-shilling theft.

And Ewen Cameron, as he sat in Mr Falconar's clothes in
the shut carriage, which, with some difficulty at the last, had
brought him to Tyburn a little before noon, was appalled at
the density and magnitude of the crowd, and almost more at
the noise proceeding from it.

Mr Falconar had only agreed to the substitution with much

misgiving. He was afraid that he was turning his back upon his duty or that the fraud might be discovered by one of the Tower officials, if the coach appointed to take him to Tyburn had to follow in its slow course the sledge on which the condemned Jacobite would be drawn. But while Ewen was closeted with the clergyman there had come a message from the Deputy-Sheriff of Middlesex, in charge of the execution, to say that, owing to the crowds which were anticipated on the morrow, the carriage was to fetch Mr Falconar from his house at a later hour, and to go to Tyburn by a less frequented route. So Ewen did not follow Archibald Cameron in his sorry and yet perhaps triumphal procession through the streets of London.

But he was come now, by a less protracted pilgrimage, to the same heart-quelling goal; and he was come there first. He had not alighted nor ever looked out. There was a sheriff's man on the box beside the driver who would tell him, he said, at what moment his services would be required.

'Till then I should advise your reverence to stay quietly in the carriage,' he was remarking now. 'There's nothing to be gained by standing about, unless you'd wish to get used to the sight of the gallows, and seeing as you ain't in parson's dress, some mightn't know you was the parson.'

'I will stay in the coach,' said Ewen.

'You haven't never attended a criminal here before, sir, I should suppose?'

'No.' That was true, too, of the man whom he was impersonating.

The good-natured underling went away from the step, but came back a moment later. 'No sight of 'em,' he reported. 'The prisoner's long in coming, but that we expected, the streets being so thick with people. But we hear he's had a very quiet journey, no abuse and nothing thrown, indeed some folk in tears.'

'Thank God for that,' said Ewen; and the sheriff's officer removed himself.

Faces surged past the windows, faces young and old, stupid, excited, curious or grave. Some looked in; once a drunken man tried the handle of the door; and the babel of sound went on, like an evil sea. Ewen sat back in the corner and wondered, as he had wondered nearly all night, whether he had undertaken more than he had strength for. He tried to pray, for himself as well as Archie, and could not. He seemed himself to be standing on the edge of some vast battlement, about to be pushed off into naked, empty, yawning space that went down and down for ever, blackness upon blackness. In this nothingness there was no God, no force of any kind, not even an evil force ... certainly there was no God, or he could not allow what was going to take place here, when a life like Archibald Cameron's would be flung into that void, and those other lives twined with his wantonly maimed. Of what use to be brave, loyal, kind and faithful – of what use to be pure in heart, when there was no God to grant the promised vision, no God to see?

A louder hum, swelling to a roar, and penetrating the shut windows as if they had been paper, warned him that the prisoner's cortége was at last in sight. And as it seemed to be the only way of summoning up that composure which he would soon so desperately need, Ewen tried, as his cousin had yesterday suggested to him, to imagine that it was he who was facing this tearing of soul from body. The attempt did steady him, and by the time – it was a good deal longer than he expected – that the sheriff's man appeared at the window again he was tolerably sure of himself. And he had the comfort of knowing that Archie – unless he had undergone a great change since yesterday – was not a prey to this numbing horror.

'The Doctor's just gone up into the cart, sir, so now, if you please ...'

And with that Ewen stepped out from the coach into the brilliant sunshine and the clamour of thousands of voices and the sight of the gaunt erection almost above his head and of the cart with a drooping-necked horse standing beneath it. In the cart, with his arms tied to his sides above the elbows, stood Archie ... and another figure. It was then about half past twelve.

'You go up them steps, sir, at the back of the cart,' said the sheriff's man, pointing. 'Way there, if you please, for the clergy-

274

man!' he shouted in a stentorian voice. 'Make way there, good people!'

There was already a lane, but half-closed up. It opened a little as an excited murmur of 'Here's the parson!' surged along it.

Ewen made his way to the steps. They were awkward to mount; and when he reached the last two there was Archie, in what would have been the most natural way in the world had his arms been free, trying to extend a hand to him.

'So you are come!' he said, and the warmth of greeting in his voice and the smile he gave him was payment enough to Ewen for what he still had to go through.

Doctor Cameron was newly attired for his death, smarter than Ardroy had often seen him, in a new wig, a light-coloured coat, scarlet waistcoat and breeches, and white silk stockings. Ewen looked at him with a mute question in his eyes.

'I am very well,' said his cousin serenely, 'save that I am a little fatigued with my journey. But, blessed be God, I am now come to the end of it. This is a kind of new birthday to me, and there are many more witnesses than there were at my first.'

Still rather dizzily, Ewen looked round at the sight which he was never to forget – the sea of lifted faces, indistinguishable from their mere number, the thousands of heads all turned in the same direction, the countless eyes all fixed upon this one spot. Near the cart in which he now stood with Archie were two or three mounted officials, one of whom was having trouble with his spirited horse; not far away was the low wheelless sledge on which the Doctor had made his journey, the hangman sitting in front of him with a naked knife; each of its four horses had a plume upon its head. And on a small scaffold nearer still, its thin flame orange and wavering in the sunny breeze, burnt a little fire. Ewen knew its purpose. By it was a long block, an axe, and a great knife. Archibald Cameron's glance rested on them at the same moment with an unconcern which was the more astonishing in that it contained not the slightest traces of bravado.

At this juncture the gentleman on the restive horse tried to attract Ewen's attention in order to say something to him, but the noise of the multitude made it impossible for his words to be heard, though he beckoned in an authoritative manner for silence; he then tried to bring his horse nearer, but it would not obey. The rider thereupon dismounted and came to the side of the cart.

'I wished but to ask you, sir,' he began courteously, looking up at Ewen, ' – the Reverend Mr Falconar, is it not? – how long you are like to be over your office?'

But it was Archibald Cameron who answered – to save *him* embarrassment, Ewen was sure. 'I require but very little time, sir; for it is but disagreeable being here, and I am as impatient to be gone as you are.'

'Believe me, I am not at all impatient, Doctor Cameron,' replied the gentleman, with much consideration in his tone. 'I will see to it that you have as much time allowed you as you have a mind to.'

'You are Mr Rayner, the under-sheriff?' queried Archie. 'I was not sure. Then, Mr Rayner, as I do not intend to address the populace, for speaking was never my talent, may I have the favour of a few words with you?'

'Assuredly, sir,' replied Mr Rayner. 'And, for the better convenience of both of us, I will come up to you.'

And in a few seconds he had joined them in the straw-strewn cart. At this the clamour of the nearer portion of the crowd considerably increased, and it was plain from their cries that they imagined a reprieve had come at this last moment, and were not displeased at its arrival.

But Mr Rayner had no such document in his pocket. Ewen heard the brief conversation which ensued as a man hears talk in a foreign tongue; though every word of it was audible to him it seemed remote and quite unreal.

'Although I do not intend to speak to the people, Mr Rayner,' said Archibald Cameron very composedly, 'I have written a paper, as best I could by means of a bit of old pencil, and have given it to my wife with directions that you should have a copy of it, since it contains the sentiments which, had I made a speech from this place, I should have expressed as my dying convictions.'

'If Mrs Cameron will deliver the paper to me,' replied Mr

Rayner, 'I will take order that it is printed and published, as is customary in the case of a dying speech.'

The Doctor inclined his head. 'I thank you, sir,' he said with much gentleness, 'for your civility and concern towards a man so unhappy as I,' he paused a moment ' – as I appear to be. But, believe me, this day which has brought me to the end of life is a joyful one. I should wish it known that I die in the religion of the Episcopal Church of Scotland, which I have always professed, though not always practised. I know that I am a sinner, but I have no doubt of God's mercy and forgiveness, even as I forgive all my enemies, especially those who have brought about my death.'

'You have the sympathy of a great many persons, sir,' said Mr Rayner in a low voice. And after a second or two's pause he added. 'There is nothing further that you wish to say – no last request to make?'

'Yes, there is one,' answered the dying Jacobite; and Ewen saw him glance, but with no trace of flinching, at the little scaffold. 'It is that you would defer, as long as the law will admit, the execution of the latter part of the sentence. I think you know what I mean,' he added.

'I know so well,' replied the under-sheriff gravely, 'that I give you my solemn word of honour that it shall be deferred for at least half an hour. That much I can do for you, and I will.'

And, with a bow, he went down from the cart. His last words had lifted a great and sickening apprehension from Ewen's heart ... and, who knows, from Archibald Cameron's also.

'I think there's nothing now to wait for,' said Archie, and he suddenly looked rather weary, though he showed no other sign of the strain upon nerves which, however heroically commanded, were only human, 'And oh, my dearest Ewen,' – he dropped his voice until it was almost inaudible – 'take my last and best thanks for coming and facing this with me – and for me!'

'But I have done nothing,' said Ewen in a dead voice.

'Nothing? You have come to the threshold with me. What can any friend do more? – And now I must go through.'

'But ... you wished me to read a prayer with you, did you not? I think I can do it, and it would perhaps ... seem more fitting.' In his heart, still a thrall to that dark horror of nothingness, Ewen thought what a mockery the act would be. And yet ... would it?

'If you can,' said Archie gently. 'We'll say it together. You have a Prayer Book?'

Ewen took Mr Falconar's out of his pocket. And while the quiet horse in the shafts shook his bridle once or twice as if impatient, and the flame on the scaffold, replenished, shot up higher, Ewen read with very fair steadiness, and Archie repeated after him, the commendatory prayer for a sick person on the point of departure. Around the cart many bared their heads and were silent, though in the distance the noise of innumerable voices still continued, as unceasing as the oceans.

'O Almighty God, with whom do live the spirits of just men made perfect, after they are delivered from their earthly prison. We humbly commend the soul of this thy servant, our dear brother, into thy hands, as into the hands of a faithful Creator and merciful Saviour ...'

And, as Ewen went on, the poignancy, even the irony of that prayer, read as it was over a man in full health and in the prime of life, was softened by the perfect courage and readiness of him who joined in it. The black void was neither black nor void any longer; and for a moment this parting under Tyburn's beams almost seemed like some mere transient farewell, some valediction on the brink of an earthly sea, some handclasp ere crossing one of their own Highland lochs when, as so often, the mist was hanging low on the farther shore ...

He finished. 'Amen,' said Archibald Cameron in a low voice. He looked up for a moment into the June blue, where the swallows were wheeling. ' "Lord, into Thy hands I commend my spirit." – Ewen, you had best go now. And do not fear for me – you heard what Mr Rayner promised?'

Ewen gazed at him with shining eyes. 'I know now that there is a God, and that you are going to Him! May He give me grace to follow you some day.'

Then Archie held out his hands as far as he could, they kissed each other, and Ewen turned away.

Yet on the narrow steps leading from the cart he all but stumbled. And above him he heard the sound of his cousin's voice for the last time. It still held the same extraordinary and unfeigned composure, even cheerfulness, in its tones.

'Take care how you go. I think you don't know the way as well as I do!'

The press was now so enormous that though Ewen was able to reach the carriage again it was found impossible to drive away. So he was there, on his knees, when Archibald Cameron died, though he saw nothing of it. Afterwards he was glad that he had been so near him at his passing, even glad that the long groan of the multitude round the scaffold told him the very moment. And before, at last, a way could be made for the coach, he knew by the length of time itself that Mr Rayner had kept his word, and that the brave and gentle heart cast into the fire had been taken from no living breast.

EPILOGUE

'KEITHIE wants to swim too!'

'Keithie cannot, and let us have no greeting over it, now,' said the handsome elderly lady who, coming at the end of the long, fine day to take the air by the side of Loch na h-Iolaire before sunset, had just been annexed by her younger great-nephew. Little Keith, in Morag's guardianship, had been enviously watching his brother's progress through the clear, very still water, but Donald was back now, and dressed, in the boat wherein Angus MacMartin, his instructor, had rowed him out a little way from shore.

'When Donald putched Keithie into the loch,' proceeded the small speaker, looking up earnestly at Miss Cameron, 'Keithie swimmed and swimmed till Father came. Donald couldn't swim then. Didn't Keithie swim when you putched him in, Donald?' he inquired, raising his voice to carry to the boat. Nine months older than on the disastrous day to which he so uncompromisingly referred, Keith no longer used the possessive case of the personal pronoun to designate himself.

Donald, preferring to ignore this query entirely, cupped his hands together and shouted with all the strength of his healthy young lungs, 'Angus says that you can come into the boat now, Keithie, if Aunt Margaret will allow it, and sail your wee ship. Will you come too, Aunt Margaret?'

'No thank you, Donald, I will not,' replied his great-aunt with much firmness and in her ordinary voice. 'I prefer something stable under my feet – Keithie!' she clutched at his impatient little form, 'bide still! Do you want to fall in again?'

'Keithie didn't fall in,' corrected the child, raising his eyes of velvet. 'Donald pu – '

'Now, don't say again that your brother pushed you,' admonished Miss Cameron. 'It may be true, but you'd do better to forget it. You know that Donald is very sorry for having done it; and you yourself were very naughty to throw in his claymore hilt.'

'Yes,' admitted small Keith, and his features took on an angelic expression of penitence. 'Keithie was very naughty.' He sighed. 'But good now,' he added with a more satisfied air.

'Come now,' interrupted Aunt Margaret, who was always direct, yet not the less esteemed by her great-nephews on that account, 'are you going with Angus or no, Keithie?'

'Wait, mem, if you please, till I make the boatie fast,' said the careful Angus. At three and twenty he was as reliable with his chieftain's children, or with anything that was his, as any veteran. He brought the boat into the bank and knelt to pass the rope round the root of a birch-tree.

'Preserve us, who's yonder!' broke in Miss Cameron, her eyes caught all at once by the figures of a man and a woman under the trees on the southern shore of the loch. They were standing very close together, looking at each other; very still, and very silent too, else in the windless calm their voices must have floated over the water. The westering sun smote upon an auburn head . . .

'It's Father – he's come home at last!' cried Donald, and was out of the boat like a flash and tearing along the path towards them.

The sunset had been angry; now it was smoothed to serenity – a sea of the palest chrysoprase, with little islands of gold which had once glowed fiery rose, and far-stretching harbours clasped between promontories of pearl.

'I shall never forget it,' said Ewen to the two women, the old and the young, who stood with him where the Loch of the Eagle reflected that dying glory. 'No one who was there will ever forget it: he went to his death as a man goes to a banquet. All London was talking of it, friends and foes alike – and now Scotland. See, when I came through Edinburgh this letter from London had already been published in a journal there.' He pulled out a newspaper and pointed, and the two ladies read:

'Doctor Cameron suffered last Thursday like a brave man, a

Christian and a gentleman. In short I cannot express what I have heard of his behaviour. It was reckoned by the thousands that saw him more than human, and has left such an impression on the minds of all as will not soon be forgot. His merit is confessed by all parties, and his death can hardly be called *untimely*, as his behaviour rendered his last day worth an age of common life.'

'We have had another Montrose in our kinsman,' said Miss Cameron proudly. 'But it does not surprise me. Did his body suffer the same fate as the great Marquis's?'

'No, Aunt Margaret. It was not quartered, and though his head was struck off, it was not exposed on Temple Bar, but buried in the coffin.'

And he was silent, thinking of that midnight scene in the vault of the Chapel of the Savoy, where, in the presence of a little half-clandestine gathering of mourners and sympathizers, the mangled body of the last Jacobite martyr had been laid to rest. Again, he saw the torchlight run glimmering over the inscription on the coffin-lid, heard Hector sobbing like a woman, and bowed his own head before the overwhelming conviction which possessed him, that the determination to have vengeance on the informer which flourished so greenly in his heart was but a mean, a shrivelled, a dishonouring wreath to lay upon the grave of one who died with such noble and unvindictive fortitude. Archie's life was too precious to be paid for in such coin. The traitor must go untouched by his hand; and the renunciation should be *his* tribute to the dear and honoured memory of Archibald Cameron.

Not that he forgave ... though Archie had forgiven ...

Ewen came back to the present. Miss Cameron was drying her eyes. Alison's face was hidden against his breast. He held her close, and laid his cheek for an instant on her head, for he could feel rather than hear her little sobbing breaths, and he guessed that she was saying to herself, 'Ewen, Ewen, what if it had been you!'

Then he saw Donald, preceded by Luath the deerhound, come bounding along the path under the birch-trees. In the boy's hand was the hilt of the broken claymore from Culloden Moor. 'I went to the house to fetch this, Father!' he cried, holding it aloft. 'I told you that Angus dived and brought it up again. And I've had a notion,' he went on fast and excitedly, 'that it could be mended, and have a new blade put to it ... Why is Mother crying?'

Holding Alison closer than ever, Ardroy took the broken blade and looked at it as if he were seeing more than what he held.

'No,' he said after a pause, 'I think it can never be mended now. It never could have been. . . . I do not know, Donald, but that you'll have to get you a new kind of sword when you are a man.'

He gazed over his wife's dark head at the sunset, fading, fading. . . . How Archie had loved this land of mist and wind and clear shining which he had left like a malefactor and a hero! And these lochs and hills would doubtless yet breed more of his temper, but never a one who united to his courage and loyalty so much simple goodness – never a one.

All the colour was gone from the sunset now, save the faintest opal tones, like the last cadence of a song. The four of them turned from the lochside, and began to go homewards under that June sky of the North which knows no real night and the child with the broken sword led the way.

About the author

D. K. Broster was born near Liverpool and educated at Cheltenham Ladies' College. She read History at St Hilda's, Oxford, and served during the First World War with a voluntary Franco-American hospital in France. She later returned to Oxford and was for several years secretary to the Regius Professor of History. Her other works include *Chantemerle* and *The Vision Splendid*. She died in 1950.

Some other Peacocks

THE FLIGHT OF THE HERON

D. K. Broster

A solitary heron flying over a Highland loch, a bright dirk, stained blood-red by the setting sun, a breathless messenger flinging himself at his chieftain's feet with the news: 'The Prince has landed in Scotland,' and charming young Ewen Cameron of Ardroy turns his back on his clan and his bride to follow the fortunes of the Young Adventurer.

This is not only an exciting account of the Jacobite Rebellion of 1745. It is also the story of how two fine men, sworn to be enemies, find deep and abiding friendship which ends only in death. And through all their adventures, their triumphs and defeats, blow the soft winds of the Highlands, the poetry and mysticism of its people and the beauty and hardships of its countryside.

WHEN THE LEGENDS DIE

Hal Borland

'Tom Black is back in the Garden with the rodeo, and the crowds are waiting for him to kill another horse. Black, a full-blooded Indian, is known to rodeo buffs as Killer Tom, Devil Tom, and an assortment of other grim nicknames. He has earned them all. A veteran Bronc rider, Tom Black has ridden nine horses to death in the rodeo arena, and at every performance the spectators expect him to kill another one.'

But Tom was once a gentle boy who talked with wild animals and had a grizzly-bear for his friend, and this is the story of how he was forced to leave his remote mountain home and give up the 'old ways' in preference for the white man's civilization. It is both an exciting adventure and a moving and absorbing account of the ways and beliefs of the Ute tribe to which Tom belonged.

LAST YEAR'S BROKEN TOYS

Barbara Ker Wilson

'Everything in Renchester is so conventional, so narrow. You meet the same little circle of people all the time. I feel as though I want to escape.' Pauline Stanford didn't know how soon all the young people there would be scattered by a war as wide as the world itself and how, for some of them, 'wanting to escape' could have a dreadful reality.

Barbara Ker Wilson ranges far from the High Street of Renchester to Germany, Czechoslovakia, and France, as she recreates the lives of a group of young people caught up in the nightmare of a total war.

THE WILD HEART

Helen Griffiths

This wonderful and sometimes alarming story is about the wild horses on the South American pampa, the gauchos who tried to capture them, and about one horse in particular – La Bruja, a cross between a thoroughbred and a wild pony, and the swiftest horse on the plain. She has need of this gift, for the lightning that struck and killed her mother left the little creature alone when only a few months old. Then, because she had to fight for herself to keep alive, she became an outcast even from her own kind. But her fleetness is also her greatest danger, for every gaucho longs to capture and tame this prize for his own . . .

SOME OTHER PEACOCKS

General

Especially for Girls

Louisa M. Alcott GOOD WIVES

Enid Bagnold NATIONAL VELVET

Beverly Cleary FIFTEEN

Esther Hautzig THE ENDLESS STEPPE

A. P. Herbert THE WATER GIPSIES

Janet Hitchman KING OF THE BARBAREENS

Grace Allen Hogarth AS A MAY MORNING

Irene Hunt UP A ROAD SLOWLY

Margaret Kennedy THE CONSTANT NYMPH

James Vance Marshall WALKABOUT

L. M. Montgomery ANNE OF GREEN GABLES

Dodie Smith I CAPTURE THE CASTLE

William Stevenson THE BUSHBABIES